IRON ORE BENEFICIATION

TACONITE BENEFICIATION PLANT

Reserve Mining Company plant at Silver Bay, Minn.

IRON ORE BENEFICIATION

by

Lawrence A. Roe

Manager of Process Engineering
International Minerals & Chemical Corp.
Chicago, Illinois

MINERALS PUBLISHING COMPANY
Box 85
Lake Bluff, Illinois
U.S.A.

IRON ORE BENEFICIATION

Copyright 1957 by Lawrence A. Roe

Library of Congress Catalog Card Number: 57-10891

Lithoprinted in U.S.A.

E D W A R D S B R O T H E R S , I N C .

Ann Arbor, Michigan

Dedicated to

The minerals beneficiation engineers
of the world who are continually
increasing man's standard of living
by their efforts to provide high
quality mineral products at minimum
cost.

PREFACE

Some excellent handbooks and textbooks on minerals beneficiation have been written during the past fifty years. Most of these publications cover a wide range of ores, equipment and processes. In recent years the field of minerals beneficiation, like many other fields of engineering, has been expanding rapidly and growing in complexity as well. The natural result of this has been specialization. Only a few books have attempted to cover specialized branches of the minerals beneficiation industry. This book covers, in some small way, the beneficiation of iron ores. It is of interest to note that Webster's unabridged dictionary defines beneficiation as follows: "to concentrate or otherwise prepare for smelting (esp. iron ore), as by drying, sintering, magnetic concentration etc." Thus the word "beneficiation" quite specifically covers iron ore processing.

The beneficiation of iron ores is an engineering field which is steadily increasing in scope and importance. Beneficiation methods used in processing gold, copper, tin, lead and other ores have been carefully studied and adapted for use in the iron ore beneficiation industry. On the other hand, some machines and processes originally developed by iron ore beneficiation engineers have found use in plants treating other types of ores. It is unfortunate that the findings of engineers concerned primarily with the processing of iron ores have been publicized so little. Until the advent of World War II, little attention was given the rapidly vanishing reserves of "shipping grade" domestic iron ores. The drain of iron ore caused by the war encouraged expansion and acceleration of studies related to the beneficiation of low-grade iron ores. Several new research laboratories devoted entirely to iron ore research were founded and hundreds of minerals

beneficiation engineers migrated to the iron ore
industry. Those engineers who relocated in this
special branch of the minerals industry soon
found that detailed information regarding iron
ore beneficiation was scattered and required much
literature searching to assemble background
information.

One important purpose of this book is to acc-
umulate in one place some of the many scattered
bits of information relating to iron ore beneficiation. It is hoped that this volume will serve
as a reference for those engineers devoting their
efforts to the study of iron ore beneficiation.

No attempt has been made to cover subjects or
processes common to the general field of minerals
beneficiation. The reader is referred to Taggart's
Handbook of Mineral Dressing for detailed information regarding unit operations such as crushing,
grinding, sizing and others.

The reader is cautioned that, unless otherwise
noted, all tonnage figures used in this book are
long tons (2240 pounds). This is in keeping with
iron ore trade practice.

The author wishes to express thanks to the
various companies who so generously provided
flowsheets, photographs and other information.
This book is intended to serve as an expression
of gratitude to the many minerals engineers the
author has had the good fortune to visit in plants
in most of the forty-eight states and Canada.
Their generosity and love for their work as expressed in their willingness to tour their plants
with visitors at any hour of the day or night is
a credit to this branch of the engineering pro-
fession. Another factor important in the undertaking of this book has been an understanding and
encouraging wife and family who gave up many
family activities in order that time could be
spent on this book.

                                Lawrence A. Roe

CONTENTS

CONTENTS

Chapter I

HISTORY

"Concentrating iron ores is beginning to attract the attention it deserves. Already the Lake Champlain District boasts of several works on a larger scale and with modern machinery; and now Lake Superior is to witness an experiment with a very extensive plant for dressing low-grade ores of the Jackson mine, the work being undertaken by the Negaunee Concentrating Company"---The Engineering & Mining Journal, vol 34, August 5, 1882, p 7.

The history of iron ore beneficiation is one of the most important chapters in the story of man's efforts to process low-grade ores and thus provide useful metal-bearing raw materials for the advancement of civilization. Many volumes have been written concerning the processing history of the more glamorous metals such as gold, silver, and copper. Little attention has been given iron ores. While premature starts have been made in the past, the beneficiation of iron ores will become increasingly important in the future. Just as new beneficiation methods for the porphyry copper deposits have added millions of tons of copper to man's useable resources, so will new and improved methods of iron ore beneficiation add enormous quantities of concentrates to the stockpiles of the great iron and steel industry.

In its broadest meaning, iron ore is any natural aggregate of minerals containing iron. As accepted in the mining industry, an iron ore is a natural aggregate of minerals containing iron in such physical and chemical state that it can be mined and sold at a profit. By accepting this definition of an iron ore it is easily understood

1

why a material containing 25 percent iron is not
an iron ore in Wyoming   or Canada but is good
ore in New York or Minnesota.   That is,   such
material can be mined, processed and sold at a
profit at the latter locations, but geographical
location and other factors cause the same grade
of iron-bearing material to be classed only as
rock or relatively worthless material in more
isolated locations.   Also, it is important to
realize that economic conditions alone can change
low-grade iron-bearing materials from worthless
rock to iron ore and vice versa.
     The date of the first ore beneficiation
operation cannot be given with any degree of
certainty. Perhaps the first record of any great
length is contained in Agricola's "De re metallica"
(1556). This valuable reference has been translated into English and is available in most
technical libraries. In moving from ores
generally to iron ores specifically we find even
less information as to specific dates and places
where iron-bearing materials were beneficiated
to produce materials of higher tenor for the
smelting furnaces. Forbes[1], in his book
"Metallurgy in Antiquity", mentions experimental
smelting of iron as far back as 3000 B.C., and
beneficiation of siderite ore by roasting as
early as 205 B.C. This roasting plant was at
the famous iron mines of Elba. Whether the ore
be gold, silver, or iron, the oldest beneficiation
method is undoubtedly "hand sorting".   This
involves the sorting of valuable pieces of ore
from waste material or material composed predom-
inantly of worthless rock. The basis for selection
or rejection is usually the weight, color or other
physical differences. Early operations were so
crude that only high-grade ore could be processed,
thus the operation usually resulted in production
of a good concentrate, however wasteful and inefficient the process may appear. Iron mines like
the Chinese Chin-ling-chen mine near the Chin-tao-
Chinan railroad were worked as far back as 500 B.C.

---

(1) Forbes, R.J., and E.J. Brill:Metallurgy in
     Antiquity, Leiden, Netherlands (1950), 489 pp.

and hand sorting was utilized to process marginal ores. It is interesting to note that this oldest of all beneficiation methods is still in use in many parts of the world today both to produce finished high-grade products and as a preliminary step in complicated processing operations.

The history of beneficiation is closely allied to the course of world history and promises to be of increasing importance in the future. Exploitation of mineral deposits has led to world power and their exhaustion to national decline and poverty. The present race for uranium ore is an example of how a once relatively unimportant mineral commodity suddenly became extremely important. The country which discovers and exploits large quantities of this material would now appear destined for power and wealth. History is being written today in the field of uranium ore beneficiation. Uranium ores long considered worthless are suddenly valuable and are being feverishly exploited. The efforts expended on uranium ore beneficiation are encouraging, and may very likely result in new developments which will be applicable to the beneficiation of other ores.

The first integrated ore beneficiation plant was completed at Clausthal, Germany in 1872. As reported by the construction engineer for the plant, "these new works were built to replace a series of very small works, very imperfectly equipped, in which the concentration losses were very large." The new plant, which processed a lead-zinc ore containing pyrite, had a capacity of 500 tons per 24 hours and was considered the largest ore dressing works in the world. Thus we see that ore processing on a large scale has been practiced for less than a hundred years.

Among the first integrated ore beneficiation plants was a large iron ore processing plant which was erected near the famous Jackson mine on the present Marquette Iron Range of northern Michigan. It is most interesting to read the Annual Reports of the Commissioner of Mineral Statistics of the State of Michigan for 1881, 1882, and 1885 to obtain at least part of the story of the first large-scale iron ore processing plant in the

United States,   if not the   world.   The following
excerpts from   the Commissioner's Reports   are
included for their historical value:
"A new enterprise has been inaugurated in
which the Jackson Company is directly
interested, and which promises to be of much
importance to the city of Negaunee and of
value to the   iron industry. This is the
undertaking to crush the rock in the waste
dumps, and obtained from the jasper walls
of the Jackson mine, and to separate out
and save the   ore   contained in the rock.
An immense building to contain the machinery for the necessary manipulations is
now constructing. The situation of this
mill is 600 feet north of the mine,in the
direct line of the railroad, which comes
out from the tunnel and is built against
the side of the bluff, which rises to the
north from the level of the small lake,
which lies to the west, from which the
necessary water is to be obtained. The
size of the buildings is 116 x 180 feet,
and from the level of the engine house
to the top is about 100 feet. There are
nine floors. The rock cars will be drawn
up into the top of the building on an
incline at the west end, and from the bins
into which it will be dumped, it will be
drawn out into the large 1,500 pound
crushers, of which there are five; from
thence the material will pass through the
separators; all but the finer portion,
which escapes, passes to the smaller break-
ers, placed upon the floor below; of them
there are 10; thence again through separators and to the floor below to the
rollers in which the rock is crushed to
the requisite fineness, and finally goes
into the washers, placed upon a succeeding
floor in which the work of separation is
completed. The company is called the
Negaunee Concentration Company. It ex-
pects to work up 1000 or 1200 tons of
rock per day, thus obtaining 300 or 400
tons of iron daily."---1881 Report, p 165.

"Negaunee Concentrating Company--April,
1883, The works of this company, which
are built on the Jackson company's
property, a short distance north of the
mine, have been partially in operation
during a portion of the past year, but
more or less difficulty has been met with,
necessitating changes and additions in
the machinery, etc; so that they are yet
not fully completed. One of the troubles,
which they have lately mastered, was in
the rollers; they were made in Chicago,
and speedily wore concave so that they
would not properly crush the rock; the
company having built a foundry for doing
their own work, have succeeded in making
a chilled face to their rollers, which
shows no signs of wear; the castings are
composed of a mixture of Lake superior,
Salisbury ores and steel.
Up to this time the average analyses
of the ore that they have obtained from
the rock gave a percentage of iron of 62
and 30/100%. They think of making two
grades, grinding over the refuse and getting a 57% ore from it. They get from
the rock so far 33-1/3% of ore."---1882
Report, p 223.

"The Negaunee Concentrating Works, erected
a few years ago near the Jackson mine for
the purpose of crushing the jasper and
saving the ore which it contains, have
proved a failure. They were operated a
short time and closed down two years ago
permanently."---1885 Report, p 29.

Available records show that the Negaunee plant
produced a total of 12,708 tons of concentrates
which were blended with coarser ores and used as
blast furnace feed. It now appears that this
plant was built about eighty years too soon. One
iron ore flotation plant has been in operation
at Humboldt, Michigan since 1954. This plant is
located a few miles west of the Negaunee plant.

Some significant dates in the history of iron ore beneficiation are listed in Table I. With the success of washing tests on Minnesota low-grade ore in 1908, beneficiation plants became important in the Lake Superior District. A simplified flow sheet of the first large-scale ore processing plant in Minnesota is given in Figure I.

It was not until the late nineteen thirties that iron ore beneficiation plants began to graduate from relatively simple washing plants to more complex operations. This does not imply that the beneficiation engineers of the iron ranges did not contribute to the art of mineral dressing during those early years. The greatest single contribution of the early iron ore plants to the art was their advancement of materials handling techniques. The necessity of moving large tonnages at the lowest possible cost resulted in many innovations in materials handling which have been adopted throughout the mineral industry.

The growth of the beneficiation industry in the Lake Superior District has not been rapid until recent years. The processing equipment in early plants usually included log washers, turbo washers, various classifiers, screens, and tables. During the period from 1924 to 1928 Butler Brothers introduced the jigging process at the Mary Ellen mine near Biwabik, Minnesota. They later installed jigs in their Harrison plant and shipped 530,000 tons of jig concentrates in 1930. The nineteen thirties were significant years in the history of iron ore beneficiation. It was during this period that the first Mesabi Range heavy-media plant was placed in operation. It is notable that the first use of ferrosilicon as a medium in a heavy-media plant occurred in 1939 at Cooley, Minnesota. Serious pilot attempts were made at Crosby, Minnesota in 1931 to process iron ores by froth flotation. A semi-commercial magnetic roasting plant operated several years at Cooley, Minnesota. The U.S. Bureau of Mines published many papers on iron ore beneficiation during this period. These served to stimulate much interest in the iron ore processing industry. Thus the 1930-1940 decade, in retrospect,

TABLE I

Significant Dates in the History
of Iron Ore Beneficiation

Year	Event
205 B.C.	Siderite ores roasted on island of Elba.
200 A.D.	Cast iron manufactured in China.
1645	The first article made in America from domestic iron ore was cast at Lynn, Mass. This was a small iron pot, holding about a quart.
1750	First coal mines to be worked in America were opened on the James river in Virginia.
1792	Patent awarded in England for a process of separating iron minerals by means of a magnet.
1806	Crushing rolls first used in Cornish tin mines.
1848	Continuous jigs introduced to mining industry.
1850	Iron ore found near Gunflint Lake, Minnesota.
1853	First attempts to utilize magnetic separation process on New York iron ores.
1854	First shipment of Lake Superior iron ore.
1858-69	Jaw crusher and gyratory crushers invented.
1868	"Hog-trough" classifier installed in Lake Superior copper mill.
1880	Ball and rod mills used in ore milling plants.
1882	First large-scale fully integrated iron ore beneficiation plant began operations at Negaunee, Mich.
1884	First shipment of Minnesota iron ore from Vermilion Range.
1887	Conkling jigs used at Lyon Mountain, N.Y. magnetite mine.
1892	Shipments of iron ore from great Mesabi began.
1893	Campbell bumping tables used in coal washing plant at Earlington, Kentucky. Wilfley table introduced in 1895. New era in gravity concentration begins. Tables used on iron ores by 1907.
1893	Beneficiation of low-grade Southern iron ores attempted by magnetic roasting experiments on a laboratory and a pilot plant scale at Ensley and Bessemer, Alabama. Ore grade raised from 44 to 61 percent iron.
1896	Plant for agglomeration of flue dust in use at the South works of the Illinois Steel Company.
1900	Hartz jigs used at the Pewabic Concentrating Works at Iron Mountain, Michigan.
1901	A car load of Minnesota iron ore was shipped to Cedartown, Georgia for testing in a log washer. These tests proved conclusively that a merchantable ore could be produced by a washing process.
1904	Development of first mechanical classifier by J.V.N. Dorr.
1906	Dwight-Lloyd system of roasting and sintering ores developed at Cananea, Mexico.

Table I continued

Year	Event
1907	Continuous slime thickening and counter-current decantation made possible by invention of Dorr thickener.
1907-08	Large-scale experiments on wash ores carried out in Oliver Iron Mining Company test plant at Coleraine, Minnesota.
1908	Initiation of tests by J.T. Jones for metallization of low-grade Michigan iron ores. A 120 x 8-foot kiln was used at Iron Mountain, Michigan for pilot tests. Similar to the Krupp-Renn process.
1910	World's first commercial magnetic taconite plant began operation at Sydvaranger, Norway.
1910	First commercial Minnesota iron ore washing plant in operation at Coleraine. Trommels, log washers, turbos, and tables used to eliminate fine silica.
1911	First iron ore sintering plant constructed at Birdsboro, Pennsylvania.
1912	Use of rheolaveur process initiated at the St. Nicholas coal mine near Liege, Belgium.
1915	Chance process introduced. Fore-runner of HMS process. Used on coal only.
1917	High-frequency induction heating invented by E.F. Northrup;first ingots cast from electric furnace, Illinois Steel Co., South works, Chicago, Illinois
1917	High-speed vibrating screen introduced.
1917	First shipment of iron ore concentrates from an underground Lake Superior mine;produced from ore mined at Hoadley and Pearson mines.
1924	Jigging of iron ores a commercial success at Biwabik, Minnesota.
1924	Soaps introduced to flotation process for collecting non-metallic minerals.
1925	Magnetic roasting by shaft furnace in commercial use in South Manchuria.
1933	Invention of cationic collectors for flotation of silicate minerals.
1934	Large-scale pilot plant using Krupp-Renn process for iron ore beneficiation operating at Borbeck, Germany.
1934-38	Semi-commercial magnetic roasting plant operated on low-grade iron ores at Cooley, Minnesota.
1938	First commercial installation of HMS process for iron ores made at Cooley, Minnesota.
1939	First HMS plant in the world using ferrosilicon medium put in operation at Cooley, Minnesota.
1948	First commercial use of Humphrey's spirals on iron ore at Hill-Trumbull plant on Mesabi Range.
1951	Buckeye plant of M.A. Hanna Co. operates first hydrocyclone plant for upgrading iron ores.
1954	Humboldt,Mich. iron ore flotation plant operates.
1955	E.W. Davis Works, large taconite plant, began operation at Silver Bay, Minnesota.

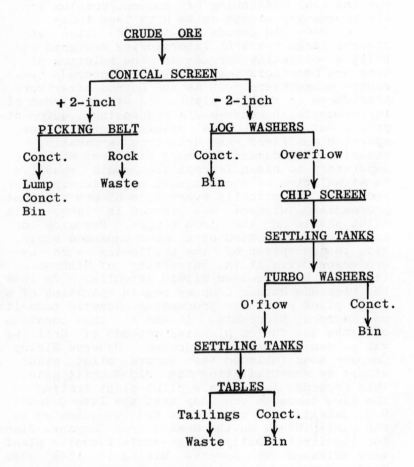

CRUDE ORE

CONICAL SCREEN

+ 2-inch   - 2-inch

PICKING BELT   LOG WASHERS

Conct.   Rock   Conct.   Overflow

Lump   Waste   Bin
Conct.
Bin   CHIP SCREEN

                                        SETTLING TANKS

                                        TURBO WASHERS

                              O'flow   Conct.

                                                  Bin

                    SETTLING TANKS

                    TABLES

            Tailings Conct.

              Waste   Bin

**Figure 1   Simplified Flow Sheet of Trout Lake
             Concentrating Plant in 1910**

was the real beginning of modern, complex iron
ore processing plants as we know them today.
The 1940-1950 decade saw the dedication of
several large research laboratories designed and
built specifically for use in the solution of
iron ore beneficiation problems. Improved hydraulic classifiers such as the Dorrco sizer were
introduced in washing plants. A steady stream of
improvements in heavy-media processing equipment-
poured out. Heavy-media plants tested cones,
spiral classifiers, and drum-type separating
vessels. The demand for more efficient magnetic
separators to clean ferrosilicon media resulted
in stimulation of the stagnant magnetic separator
industry. Practically every type of ore and coal
processing equipment was tested in large-scale
pilot plants on the iron ranges. Research on
taconites was resumed on a much expanded scale.
With the exception of the continuing work by
Professor Davis at the University of Minnesota,
taconites had received little attention. In 1948
the Pickands Mather Company begain operation of a
large pilot plant for processing magnetic taconite
near Aurora, Minnesota. It was at this location
that the new fusion piercing methods of drilling
was proven a commercial success. Reserve Mining
Company soon followed the Aurora pilot plant
effort by rehabilitating the old Babbitt plant.
This preceded large-scale pilot plant testing
the same taconite ore body that the late Colonel
D.C. Jackling and associates had investigated in
the early 1920's as the Mesabi Iron Company. Plans
for the first really large-scale taconite plant
were released by Reserve Mining in 1948 when
Martin revealed detailed plans for the proposed
Silver Bay plant on Lake Superior about 48 miles
from the Babbitt mine[2].

By 1950 the iron ore beneficiation industry
had completed a rapid study of all the common ore
processing methods. Then a move was made into
detailed studies of processing fundamentals in an

---

(2) Martin, H.K.:Proposed Flowsheet for Taconite
    Concentration at Babbitt, Proceedings Blast
    Furnace, Coke Oven & Raw Materials Committee
    AIME, vol 7, 1948, p 68-82.

effort to develop new methods of beneficiation
and to improve existing methods. A good example
of the progress made is the advancement of the
agglomeration art. All known agglomeration
methods were tested by laboratory and pilot-plant
experiments. These included briquetting, extrusion, pelletizing, nodulizing and sintering. The
pelletizing method had been known for many years,
but required much concerted effort to prove that
here was a satisfactory method of agglomerating
fine-sized iron concentrates. Ten years of
expensive large-scale experimentation established
pelletizing as a reasonably good method of agglomerating iron ores. Other new discoveries included
during the 1950-1955 period were the development
of the cyclone-heavy-media process for upgrading
iron ores, the construction and operation of the
first commercial iron ore flotation plant in
America and new developments in the art of
magnetic roasting.

New developments in the iron ore beneficiation
art are appearing regularly. The future will see
continued large expenditures on research efforts.
Larger portions of the research budget will be
expended on fundamental problems to promote
development of entirely new iron ore beneficiation
methods.

ADDITIONAL REFERENCES

Warhol, P, A.E. Matson, and L.J. Erck:Short History of Progress Used to Date on Intermediate Ores Skillings Mining Review, vol 35, Feb. 1, 1947, p 1,2,6,15.

Thoenen, J.R., A.H. Reed and B.H. Clemmons:The Future of Birmingham Red Iron Ore, Jefferson County, Alabama, U.S. Bur. Mines Rept. of Inv. 4988, July, 1953.

Anon:A Spark in Steel, Fortune, Dec. 1948, p 95-101, 174.

Haven, W.A.:Iron Ore Beneficiation Assumes a Major Role in the Manufacture of Pig Iron, Blast Furnace & Steel Plant, Jan. 1945, p 81-83,89.

Anon:Erie Mining Company's One and one-half Million Dollar Taconite Development, Range Facts (weekly newspaper) Virginia, Minn. Oct. 9, 1947, p 1.

Wiseley, A.J.:Making Low Grade Iron Ore Pay, Mining Congress Jnl., Aug. 1946, p 22-24, 64.

Pierce, J.C.:Iron from Taconites, Compressed Air Magazine, vol 57, Nov. 1952, p 300-303.

Anon:Mesabi Revival, Wall St. Jnl. Feb. 16, 1952, p 1,12.

Parsons, A.B.:Seventy-five Years of Progress in the Mineral Industry, 1871-1946. AIME Anniversary Volume, 1947, 817pp.

Chapter II

SOURCES & ECONOMICS

"As we look into past history we
find many instances indicating that
iron ore of and by itself cannot be
measured solely by so many million
tons in the ground at any one time.
It must take into consideration the
activities of human beings, their
work, their energy, and above all,
their brain power expressed in the
results of endless research in all
plases of the iron and steel industry."----Elton Hoyt, 2nd.

"Economics is the science (or perhaps the art) of measuring, quantitatively, the relative efficiencies
of alternative courses of action of
an industrial or similar nature."--
--George L. Parkhurst.

There are four major iron ore districts in the
United States. Thirty states have produced iron
ore but the bulk of the production has come from
ten -- Minnesota, Michigan, Wisconsin, New York,
New Jersey, Alabama, Texas, Wyoming, Utah, and
California. The most important area is the Lake
Superior District which has produced over 85 percent of the domestic iron ore. The remaining
important districts are the Southern, Northeastern,
and the Western districts.
Sources of iron ore are directly dependent upon
the relative economic positions of the ores in
question. One of the important reasons why taconite plant growth is not proceeding at a faster
rate is that some important discoveries of high-
grade foreign ores show promise of becoming low-
cost sources of raw material for the iron and
steel industry. This is especially true in the

13

case of ore supplies for steel plants located on
ocean waterways. Thus, low-cost foreign ores affect
the economics of domestic beneficiation plants.
     Two factors opposing excessive dependence on
foreign ores are, (1)unpredictable upheavals in
foreign governments which could disrupt or even
end ore shipments almost overnight in case of
internal revolutions, and (2)the insecure status
of overseas shipping in time of war. In the interest of the safety and well-being of the United
States it is imperative that a healthy domestic
iron ore industry be constantly maintained. J.D.
Morgan, Jr. [1] published a detailed study which
reviewed the domestic mining industry of the
United States in World War II. The vulnerability
of overseas ore shipments was emphatically pointed
out. The importance of the St. Lawrence Seaway
in the iron ore supply picture was also emphasized
in the Paley report [2] . The seaway will first be
used to bring in shipping-grade ores from Labrador,
South America and Africa. Later, large tonnages
of beneficiated ores will follow the same route
since large reserves of low-grade ores have been
discovered in Labrador and Quebec. The most
recent thinking in regard to wartime ore supplies
brings up a new mineral policy based on a very
short war. The overseas shipping factor then
assumes less importance. The inescapable fact is
that America cannot relax in technical effort.
This situation could develop if the steel industry
begins to depend largely upon foreign high-grade
ores. While we will always be dependent upon
foreign ores to some extent, we should never allow
ourselves to become completely dependent upon
foreign iron-ore technology.

(1) Morgan, J.D.,Jr.:The Domestic Mining Industry
     of the United States in World War II. Printed
     by the National Security Resources Board with
     the permission of the School of Mineral Indus-
     tries and the Graduate School of the Penn.
     State College, U.S. Govt. Printing Office,
     1949, 500 pp.
(2) Resources for Freedom, vol 1, Foundations for
     Growth and Security, June 1952, Chapt. 30,
     Preparing for Emergency Production, p 165-167.

The magnitude of the problem of finding replacement ores for the Lake Superior shipping-
grade ores is apparent when it is realized that
during the period from 1911 to 1949 this region
supplied, on the average, over 80 percent of the
total domestic shipments of iron ores. It has
been estimated that of all the iron ore mined in
this country since the discovery of America, one
third has been extracted in the short period that
has elapsed during and since World War II.   If
the rapid industrial and population growth which
followed the war continues in the future, iron
ore demands will skyrocket even more. According
to a U.S. Bureau of Mines Report[3] "the year 1953
marked the end of a long period of virtual self-
sufficiency in iron ore for the United States
although domestic sources could still supply all
requirements if necessary during an emergency."
Imported iron ores have increased from 1,193,514
tons in 1945 to over 26,000,000 tons in 1955.
Strassburger[4] points out an indication of the
economies possible when a 50 percent iron ore is
upgraded to 54 percent iron. He states:
"Until recently most blast furnace operators have been well satisfied with iron
ores which averaged about 50 per cent Fe,
10 to 11 per cent silica, and with other
elements in correct proportion. With the
advent of beneficiating processes for improving iron ore quality, together with
the use of these better ores has resulted
in a remarkable improvement in blast furnace operation with increased iron tonnage
and lowered costs due to reduction of coke
and limestone requirements. The following
shows the benefits of improving the quality
of iron ore burden. Starting with an iron
ore containing 50 percent Fe and 10.5 per
cent silica and by beneficiation processes
improving this ore so that it contains 54

(3) U.S. Bureau of Mines Mineral Market Report
    MMS No. 2327, Iron Ore in 1953.
(4) Strassburger, J.H.:Need for Iron Ore Benefi-
    ciation, Mining World, vol 18, March 1956,
    p 57.

per cent Fe and 8 silica, we estimate the
following savings on the basis that any
fines in the iron ore will be charged as
sintered or agglomerated material: Iron
production increased by about 13 per cent,
coke rate reduced 200 pounds per ton,
limestone reduced 250 pounds per ton .
Assuming a basis of $10.00 coke and $2.00
limestone, the estimated savings would
amount to approximately $0.75 per ton of
pig iron taking into account the savings
in coke, limestone, "cost above", and
allowing for the cost of producing sinter
from the ore fines. From the above analysis
it is our firm conviction that every effort
must be made by the iron ore mining industry
for research and development work so that
economic processes can be developed for the
beneficiation of the iron ores."
Blast furnace capacity has increased about 47
percent from 1940 to 1954. At the start of 1954
the steel capacity of the United States was over
124 million net tons of ingots and steel for
casting. By January, 1956 steel capacity had
grown to 128.4 million tons and another round of
expansion was announced for 1956. Provision of
adequate ore supplies for this giant industry will
continue to be a mammoth job.
In testimony before a U.S. Senate hearing,
N.B. Melcher of the U.S. Bureau of Mines provided
pertinent information as to the iron ore position
of the Western Hemisphere[5]. Excerpts are repeated
here:
"Essentially, the problem of supplying iron
ore for domestic consumption is one of balan-
cing costs, conservation of resources, and
preservation of national security, in reverse
order of importance."

(5) Special Subcommittee on Minerals, Materials
and Fuels Economics of the Committee on Interior and Insular Affairs, U.S. Senate, 83rd
Congress:Stockpile and Accessibility of
Strategic and Critical Materials to the U.S.
in Time of War, Part I. U.S. Dept. of Interior:
Bureau of Mines, 1953, p 66-72.

"It now appears that 30 to 40 percent of
United States iron-ore supply will come
from nondomestic sources by 1970. Canada
will supply an important share from deposits that will offset, to a substantial
degree, loss of strategic advantages due
to the diminishing expansibility of Lake
Superior open pits."
"Supplies from Venezuela will encourage
the migration of furnaces to coastal areas
of the United States, while Canadian ore,
with the St. Lawrence Seaway, will tend to
stabilize industry in place."
"Cuba's position is important when considered on a long-range basis." (lateritic
iron ore deposits).
"Imports from Chile will continue for
some years, but at a substantially reduced level."
"Reserves in Peru are relatively small
and the source appears unreliable for
long-range consideration."

Sources and Reserves of Iron Ore

The primary source of iron ore for American
steel plants for over half a century has been the
Lake Superior District. The first shipment of
ore via the Great Lakes was made in 1852. By
1873, this ore source was providing over a million
tons per year. The flow reached 10 million tons
in 1895 and jumped to over 40 million tons by
1907. Table I shows how domestic ore shipments
have compared with imported ore over a twenty-five
year period. From 1930 to 1942 Chile was the leading exporter to the United States; since 1942,
Canada, Venezuela, and Chile have been the three
major sources of foreign ore.
The periodically occurring estimates of iron
ore reserves in the Lake Superior District point
out that high-grade ore deposits are nearly ex-
hausted; also the ores being mined have steadily
decreased in iron content. The quantity of ore
being beneficiated has shown a steady increase.
Table II shows that the percentage of beneficiated
ore has grown from 12.5 percent in 1929 to 27.6

TABLE I

Domestic versus Imported Iron Ore Shipments, 1930-1955

Year	Gross Tons Domestic	Imported	%Imported
1930	55,201,221	2,775,124	5.0
1931	28,516,032	1,465,613	5.1
1932	5,331,201	582,498	10.9
1933	24,624,285	861,153	3.5
1934	25,792,606	1,427,521	5.5
1935	33,426,486	1,492,435	4.5
1936	51,465,648	2,232,229	4.3
1937	72,347,785	2,442,069	3.4
1938	26,430,910	2,122,455	8.0
1939	54,827,100	2,412,515	4.4
1940	75,198,084	2,479,326	3.3
1941	93,053,994	2,343,983	2.5
1942	105,313,653	731,325	0.7
1943	98,817,470	399,117	0.4
1944	94,544,635	463,532	0.5
1945	87,580,942	1,193,514	1.4
1946	69,494,052	2,754,216	4.0
1947	92,670,188	4,903,484	5.3
1948	100,821,714	6,091,677	6.0
1949	84,687,275	7,391,291	8.0
1950	97,764,410	8,281,237	8.7
1951	116,230,052	10,139,678	8.7
1952	97,972,584	9,760,625	10.0
1953	117,821,981	11,074,035	9.4
1954	76,998,000	15,768,771	20.5
1955	107,389,000	23,443,220	21.8

Source: U.S. Bureau of Mines

TABLE II

Percentage of U.S. Iron Ore Beneficiated, 1929 - 1952

Year	Tons Beneficiated	Percentage of Total Shipments Beneficiated
1929	9,424,445	12.5
1930	8,973,888	16.3
1931	4,676,364	16.4
1932	407,486	7.6
1933	3,555,892	14.4
1934	4,145,590	16.1
1935	6,066,601	18.1
1936	9,658,699	18.8
1937	12,350,136	17.1
1938	4,836,435	18.3
1939	9,425,809	17.2
1940	12,925,741	17.2
1941	19,376,120	20.8
1942	23,104,945	21.9
1943	20,117,685	20.4
1944	20,303,422	21.5
1945	19,586,782	22.4
1946	15,588,763	22.4
1947	21,407,760	23.1
1948	23,629,265	23.4
1949	20,658,232	24.4
1950	26,717,928	27.3
1951	30,664,648	26.4
1952	27,023,982	27.6

percent in 1952. Table III illustrates the fact
that, by 1950, five of the ten largest iron mines
in the United States used beneficiation to upgrade
their ore.
      Among the various estimates of domestic iron ore
reserves made during the past ten years are those
of Hewitt,[6] Gillies,[7] Pardee,[8] Fotheringham,[9]
DeMille,[10] and those given in the Cellar report.[11]
The latter reference makes the poignant statement,
"It should be noted, in advance of any discussion
of future supplies, that estimates of reserves are
a compound of precise measurements, less precise
measurements, and plain guesswork. Reflecting
these differences in knowledge, the United States
Department of the Interior has grouped reserves
into three classes; measured, indicated, and in-
ferred."

Marketing Iron Ores

      Domestic iron ores are marketed on the basis
of the long ton, 2240 pounds. Selling values are
quoted for ore delivered at the lower lake ports.
In 1925, the base chemical analysis of 51.5% iron
was arrived at. The important grades of ore and
the 1956 prices were:

----
(6) Hewitt, G.W.:Lake Superior Iron Ore Reserves
       for the Future Operation of the U.S. Iron and
       Steel Industry. Paper presented at the Eighth
       Annual Mining Symposium, Center for Continua-
       tion Study, Univ. of Minn., Jan. 1947, 29 pp.
(7) Gillies, D.B.:Future of Iron Resources, Mining
       Eng. vol 1, Dec. 1949, p 34-38.
(8) Pardee, F.G.:Iron Ore Reserves in Michigan,
       Mining and Met., vol 29, Nov. 1948,p613-614.
(9) Fotheringham, M.S.:Steep Rock's Huge Reserves
       an Ace for Canada's Future, Eng. and Mining
       Jnl. vol 153, April 1952, p 82-85.
(10)DeMille, J.B.:Canada's Future Brightens as
       Producer of Iron Ore, Eng. and Mining Jnl.
       vol 150, April 1949, p 90-91.
(11)Cellar, E. (chairman):Report of the Federal
       Trade Commission on the Control of Iron Ore,
       U.S. Govt. Printing Office, Washington, 1952,
       157 pp.

TABLE III

Largest Iron Ore Mines in the U. S. (a)
in 1950, in Order of Crude Output

Name of Mine	Nearest Town	Production, Gross Tons Ore	
		Crude	Usable
Sherman	Fraser, Minn.	5,830,710	5,819,277
Hull Rust	Hibbing "	5,792,852	5,640,151
Rouchleau	Virginia "	5,133,542	5,127,553
Mt. Iron	Mt. Iron "	3,557,961	2,857,477
Benson	Star Lake, N. Y.	2,913,157	1,018,679
Mahoning	Hibbing, Minn.	2,640,478	2,640,478
Monroe	Chisholm "	2,471,402	2,471,402
Lone Star	Daingerfield, Texas	2,242,196	893,550
Gross Marble	Marble, Minn.	2,181,847	1,155,958
Walker	Coleraine "	2,069,310	1,269,915

(a) Minerals Yearbook, 1950

Note: Underlined figures represent concentrates.

Grade	Gross Ton
Openhearth lump	$12.10
Old range, bessemer	11.25
Old range, non-bessemer	11.10
Mesabi, bessemer	11.00
Mesabi, non-bessemer	10.85
High phosphorus	10.85

Bessemer grade ore contains a maximum of 0.045% phosphorus, and when this element exceeds 0.18%, the ore is classed as high phosphorus ore. Non-bessemer has an intermediate phosphorus value. The bessemer grade ores command a premium because of their low phosphorus content. Also premiums in payment are included for ores containing more than 51.5% iron, high-grade lump ores, and ores containing more than 5% manganese.

When taconite pellets reach the market in volume and when more information regarding the value of highly beneficiated ores in furnace burdens is available, it seems reasonable to assume that a new pricing structure will be developed to fit the new situation.

Financing a Taconite Industry

The cost of financing a domestic taconite beneficiation industry is truly tremendous. Chemical Week, in January, 1952[12] described the large-scale financial transaction required when the financing of the first Minnesota taconite plant was announced: "Reserve Mining Company has sold $148 million of first mortgage $4\frac{1}{2}$% bonds, due 1980, to a group of life insurance companies. Names of all firms involved in the purchase have not been revealed, but Metropolitan Life Insurance Co. and Equitable Life Assurance Society have been mentioned among the leaders. The financing is reported as one of the biggest private placements in history." Since 1950, announced expenditures on taconite development have approached a total of about 3/4 of a billion dollars. This is approximately 3 percent of the total capital invested in

(12) Announcement in Chemical Week, vol 17, Jan. 17, 1952, p. 25.

property, plant, and equipment for the U.S. petroleum industry as of Dec. 31, 1950.[13] The petroleum industry is the fourth largest in the country --exceeded only by agriculture, railroads, and the combined divisions of the public utility field. In making this comparison with the petroleum industry reference should be made to capital expenditures of 30 leading companies comprising over 2/3 of this industry over the 17 year period 1934-1950. During this period these companies spend $17 billion for domestic facilities and $2.4 billion for foreign facilities. These figures indicate that the petroleum industry maintains by far a major portion of its facilities at home and in the past has minimized investment in foreign plants. It will be interesting to compare the trend of iron ore mine and processing plant expenditures with past history of the petroleum industry.

Thomas,[14] in reviewing the technology of iron ore in the Paley report in 1952, estimates that capital expenditures for beneficiating Lake Superior taconites, for mining and transportation developments for Quebec-Labrador ores, and for the transportation and development costs of foreign ores, principally Venezuelan, may total $5 billion in the next 25 years. Others feel that a $10 billion estimate is more realistic.

Early cost estimates for Mesabi magnetic taconite plants averaged about $25 per annual ton of finished product. According to figures made available late in 1954, actual costs for the first two large taconite plants will exceed this figure. However, when it is considered that whole towns, docks, powerhouses and railroads are being built for these first plants, it becomes apparent that pioneering plants may be more costly than later installations and additions.

---

(13) Coqueron, F.G. and J.E. Pogue:Capital Formation in the Petroleum Industry, Paper presented at the 1952 annual meeting of the Petroleum Branch of the AIME, New York, Feb. 1952.

(14) Thomas, B.D.:The Technology of Iron Ore, Resources for Freedom, vol IV--The Promise of Technology, p 40-44.

There are no published data indicating the
magnitude of profits expected from taconite plant
investments. According to Tielrooy,[15] an analysis
of the profits of eight large chemical companies
in 1954 showed an average net profit of 6-3/4
percent on total assets of $636,000,000. This is
probably in line with future profits of large taconite plants.

The Economics of Taconites

Since failure of the early venture at
Babbitt, Minnesota by the Mesabi Iron Company in
1924, analyses of the economics of processing taconite iron ores have been extremely pessimistic
except for the reports by E.W. Davis of the University of Minnesota. Taconite studies during the
1940-1950 decade included careful examination of
two important low-grade iron ore plants which had
a backlog of good processing data. The first of
these was the famous Sydvaranger mine in Norway.
This plant began processing a difficult low-grade
magnetite ore in 1910 and has offered much technical information to those willing to study this operation. More recently, and in our own country,
the Benson Mines operation of Jones and Laughlin
Steel Corporation in upstate New York was revived
on a much enlarged scale in 1944. With the exception of a considerably coarser liberation size, its
problems approach those of a magnetic taconite operation. The Benson operation has provided valuable information for studies of taconite plant
economics. Sydvaranger reached a production rate
of 1,340,408 metric tons of concentrates in 1939
while Benson reached 1,018,679 long tons of concentrates in 1950 according to the U.S. Bureau of
Mines.[16] Total shipments from three operating
pilot magnetic taconite plants on the Mesabi Range,
including the 1954 season were: Erie, 704,531 tons;

(15) Tielrooy, Jack:The Importance of Complete and
     Accurate Capital Cost Estimates in Economic
     Evaluations, Paper presented at Los Angeles
     Meeting of Amer. Inst. of Chemical Engineers,
     Feb. 28, 1956.
(16) U.S. Bureau of Mines Minerals Yearbooks

Reserve, 694,631 tons; Pilotac, 464,827 tons.[17]
The most-quoted disadvantages of taconite as
a source of iron are high capital investment costs
for mining and upgrading and the high cost of
agglomeration. There is no escaping the first
objection, but a point often overlooked regarding
the latter is the increased value of an agglomerated product. A report in January, 1955, showed
that introduction of iron-ore pellets from Minnesota pilot plants increased blast furnace production 15 percent. This seems quite logical when
pellets are compared to direct shipping Lake Superior ore. The pellets may contain up to 65 percent iron as compared to 50 percent iron in direct
shipping ores. Good size characterisitics, good
porosity and general uniformity of product results
in more rapid reduction of pellets in furnaces.
    Further support to possible savings by use of
high-grade pellets is given in a 1950 report.[18]
"During the years 1935-1939 one ton of pig iron
required an average of 0.357 tons of limestone
and 0.887 tons of coke. By 1948 these two tonnages
had increased to 0.44 and 0.954 respectively." The
quantity of iron ore required for each ton of pig
iron also increased. More fuel was required because of the lower quality of the iron ore and
coal used in the burden. Coal quality is being
adversely affected due to the rapid increase in
mechanized mining. Coke made from this coal contains more ash and sulphur which require additional limestone. This situation is now recognized by
the steel industry and accounts for the steady
increase in the number of coal washing plants.
By the end of 1955 about 60 percent of all coal
mined in the United States was processed in coal
preparation plants.
    The grade of iron ore which can be profitably
beneficiated is steadily dropping. While it is
difficult to illustrate this trend with statistics,
a generalization here may be appropriate. Table IV
shows the economic history of several low-grade

(17) Anon:Newsitem, Eng. & Mining Jnl. vol 156,
         April 1955, p 143.
(18) Anon:Poorer Raw Materials Increase Cost of
         Steel, Industrial Heating, Sept. 1950, p
         1564.

TABLE IV

Economic History of Domestic Magnetite Ores

Year	Mine	% Fe in Ore	Grind	Plant Size-- Tons/24hrs	Commercial success or failure of enterprise
1888	Benson, N.Y.	30	20mesh	1050	Produced first concts. ever used in a blast furnace; plant failed.
1890	Ogden, N.J.	12 to 20	60mesh	4000	Failed because of Mesabi discovery;also ore lower grade than anticipated.
1913	Mt.Hope, N.J. remodeled in 1943	48		1440	One of the first successful plants. sale of aggregates aids operations
1917	Scrub Oak, N.J. remodeled in 1930 & 1936	33	8mesh	2160	Successful operation.
1901	Mineville N.Y.	30	10mesh	1600	Attempt made to use mag. sep. in 1853;plant successful in 1901.
1917	Cornwall, Pa. remodeled in 1952 to 3000 tons/24 hrs.	42	20mesh	600	Recovers copper as well as iron
1944	Benson, N.Y.	24	28mesh	10,000	Largest magnetite plant in the world for several years.

magnetite ores over a 60 year period. The crude
ores tabulated range from 30 to 48 percent iron.
These plants processed ores which required grinding to somewhere in the range of 8 to 20 mesh.
This is a "coarse" grind when we consider the
present 80 to 90 percent minus 325-mesh grind required for taconites. From this analysis it appears that the grade of magnetite ore (coarse liberation) which can be profitably beneficiated has
been halved during the past fifty years.

The Benson Mines plant of today could probably
process ores as low as 15 percent iron at a profit
as long as a plus 1,000,000 ton per year concentrate rate is maintained. At Sydvaranger, Norway,
where a much finer grind is required, a crude ore
of at least 25 percent iron may be required for
profitable operation at the 1,000,000 ton annual
rate.

As early as 1917 Norton and Lefevre pointed
out important facts regarding the economics of
processing low-grade magnetite ores.[19] They
stated, "The concentration of low-grade magnetic
iron ores is a field of work in which the lessons
taught by the development of the porphyry coppers
can be studied to advantage." In discussing this
same paper, G.C. Foote of Port Henry, N.Y. stated
"25 percent iron ore can be mined at a profit and
an even break can be made at present prices on a
20 percent iron ore."

The economics of the iron ore industry can be
compared to the lime industry in many respects.
Only a few years ago an investment of $50,000
would finance a profitable lime plant. Now a
$1,000,000 unit is generally considered a minimum
plant under normal conditions. This trend is
emphasized by the fact that 1073 lime plants in
the year 1910 produced an average of 3260 tons per
year. By 1950, with only 168 plants in existence,
an average output of 44,600 tons per year was reported. Iron ore may well follow a similar pattern.

(19) Norton, S. and S. Lefevre:The Magnetic
       Concentration of Low Grade Ores, Trans.
       AIME, vol 56, 1917, p 892-916.

Taxes

As in every other industrial enterprise, taxes have an important bearing on iron ore beneficiation developments. Little information is available regarding this vital aspect of the mining industry. A book often used as a text on the subject by some universities is that of Roberts[20] which was published in 1944. In this reference almost a hundred pages are devoted to a critical review of iron ore tax history in Alabama, Michigan, and Minnesota. A liberal constructive tax policy will be an important prerequisite in all future low-grade iron ore mining developments.

Power

Any analysis of the future of iron ore beneficiation should include a survey of power costs. Johnson[21] at the 1955 annual meeting of the AIME gave an excellent paper regarding the use of coal as a source of power for production of aluminum. While, in comparison, iron ore processing plants consume much less power per ton of output, they are still large consumers of power. At this time accurate figures for taconite power costs are not available. The power cost per ton of finished iron ore agglomerate from magnetic taconites may range from 5 to 7 percent of the total cost per ton of product. Johnson points out that coal mines integrated with power plants and with industrial plants are the key to low cost power. Moreover he states that "Considering both investment costs and operating costs, it is estimated that power from coal can be made for as little as 3.5 mils per kilowatt hour in plants of 300,000 kilowatt capacity or more when made firm 365 days per year by interconnection with a public utility system." According to the Federal Power Commission fuel costs generally range from 60 to 80 percent of the total production costs of steam-electric

(20) Roberts, W.A.:State Taxation of Metallic
        Deposits, Harvard University Press,
        Cambridge Mass., 1944, 400 pp.
(21) Johnson, A.F.:Coal As a Source of Power for
        Production of Aluminum,Paper presented at
        annual AIME meeting, Chicago, Feb. 1955.

power.[22] Coal is the principal fuel, accounting
for about 66 percent of the total fuel requirements followed in order by natural gas and oil.
In 1938 the electric utility industry required
1.40 pounds of coal per kilowatt hour, as compared
to 3.00 pounds of coal in 1920. During the period
following World War II coal requirements have
shown a steady decline until a figure of 0.99
pounds was reached in 1954.

In his 1950 estimate of taconite concentrate
costs, E.W. Davis gives 70 kilowatt hours per
gross ton of pellets as the total power cost.
Scaling this up to 10 million tons of yearly capacity the power requirement rockets to 700 million
kilowatts per year or a demand of 80,000 kilowatts
per hour. Thus it is clear that taconite plants
will favor the erection of large power plants.

Since shipping charges for Eastern coal to the
North Central ore plants is costly, there is a
strong possibility that lignite fields of the
Dakotas will soon be used for power generation.
The Alcoa plant at Rockdale, Texas uses lignite
as fuel. An early report on this plant ventured
a prediction that an eventual cost of 2.5 mils
per kilowatt hour was possible.[23]

The impact of power from lignite has not yet
been fully analyzed. Miller,[24] in 1952, reported
this observation: "The development of processes
which will make all types of coal as well as lig-
nites and other low grade fuels suitable for iron
and steel production may have a marked effect on
steel plant location, both in this country and
abroad. Finally, the availability of low-cost
electric power will become an increasingly important determinant in the geography of steel. This
will result from the increase in the use of electric furnaces as compared to open-hearth practice.
Fifty years ago the open-hearth furnace replaced
the Bessemer converter, and in those years has been

(22) Steam-Electric Plant Construction Cost and
      Annual Production Expenses (Seventh Annual
      Supplement), 1954, 135 pp, Fed. Power Comm.
(23) O'Conner, J.A.:Alcoa Turns to Lignite, Chem.
      Eng. vol 58, Sept. 1951, p 107.
(24) Miller, J.R.:Letter to Editors, Scientific
      American, vol 186, March 1952, p 3-4.

developed to a point where steelmakers are getting
from it nearly as much as is technically possible.
With rising costs, a new process capable of more
efficient and cheaper operation, and requiring
smaller capital investment, must inevitably replace
the open hearth. Some of us who have been closely
allied with the industry during the past decade
and longer believe that this will be the large-
diameter, high-powered electric furnace, operated
with high hot-metal (molten pig iron) charges.
Such a development will cut the tie which has
hitherto bound steel plants to locations within
economic distance from coking-coal sources. The
availability of low-cost electric power, however,
will then become a major consideration."
    While it is still early to predict the ultimate
commercial success of electricity from nuclear
reactors, it may require less than a decade to
show that electric power from this source may be
competitive with coal-fired power plants in areas
remote from low-cost coal or petroleum fuels.
Capital costs of nuclear plants are high. One
report[25] by experts in the field gives a cost of
$250 per kilowatt of installed electrical capacity.
This compares with an average of $160 per kilowatt
for coal or oil fueled power plants.

Process Water

    An accessory raw material which must be avail-
able in great quantities for large taconite plants
is that valuable liquid--water. Considerable survey work regarding water supplies and uses has been
carried out by the government agencies during the
past ten years. One report by the U.S. Geological
Survey[26] contains the following notes regarding the
important Minnesota iron ranges: (under "Current
Situation")--"Iron Range, Area bounded by Mississippi and South Kawishi Rivers; lies on divide and

(25) Cotton, C.M.Cost of Nuclear Power Heads Lower,
        Wall St. Jnl., March 7, 1955, p 1,8.
(26) McGuinness, C.L.:The Water Situation in the
        United States With Special Reference to
        Ground Water, U.S. Geol. Survey Circular 114,
        June 1951, 127 pp.

streams within area are small. Ground water
scanty except in iron-ore bodies, water drained
from which is used for such cities as Virginia
and Hibbing. Concentration of low-grade ore will
require large amounts of water for processing
and increased domestic use." (under "Deficiencies
in Information")--"Comprehensive water-resources
study to determine most economical sources of
water, including wells, mines (research needed on
drainage design), and streams." (under Corrective
Measures")--"Formation of a conservancy district
is a possibility. Water available from Mississippi
and South Kawishi Rivers if sources within area
shown by careful study to be inadequate."
    It is interesting to compare the estimated
1534 pounds of yearly steelmaking capacity per
person[27] in the United States with the estimated
1100 gallons of water per day used for each man,
woman, and child.[28] This amounts to slightly
over $4\frac{1}{2}$ short tons of water per day per person.
Water is a natural resource used in enormous
quantities in all ore processing plants. Future
large-scale iron ore beneficiation plants will
require serious study of water supplies

Transportation

Newton[29] in his early discourse at an AIME
meeting stated, "It requires no argument to show
that England's position, as one of the highest
civilized countries, arises mainly from the extent
of her manufactures and her commercial intercourse
with the rest of the world, which are due almost
exclusively to the great magnitude of her iron
industries. Thus in 1871, of the total of
13,315,000 tons of pig iron made in the world,

(27) Steelways, Feb. 1956, p 5.
(28) MacKichan, K.A.:Estimated Use of Water in the
      United States-1950, U.S. Geol. Survey
      Circular 115, May 1951, 13 pp.
(29) Newton, H.:The Ores of Iron; Their Geograph-
      ical Distribution & Relation to the Great
      Centres of the World's Iron Industries,Trans.
      AIME vol 3, 1875, p 360-391.

England produced about one half, or 6,500,000 tons.
Her facilities for iron manufactures are almost un-
surpassed, for all the materials necessary, the
iron ore, coal, etc., may be drawn from very limited areas, and often from the same mine, thus being
in marked contrast with the condition in the United
States where such long and expensive transportation
is necessary." These observations made 80 years
ago are still applicable in the economic analyses
of taconite and foreign iron ore developments.

In order to compare the cost of domestic iron
ore concentrates with that of imported high-grade
foreign ore it is necessary to have first-hand
knowledge of transportation costs for each product.
Unfortunately there is little published information
regarding transportation costs for the important
foreign iron ore sources. An excellent reference
on transportation costs of foreign bauxite is given
by A.F. Johnson.[30] In his paper, Johnson mentions
a cost of 6 to 7 dollars per long ton for hauling
bauxite from British or Dutch Guiana via Trinidad
to the United States. He also states that shipping
costs vary considerably according to the supply of
ships. A comparison of the rates of crews under
their respective flags gives emphasis to high wages
paid U.S. crews. In his summary Johnson states,
"From the long range viewpoint foreign bauxite cost
will rise gradually with increasing wage rates and
taxes excepting where producers are able to count-
eract such increases by improved handling methods.
Domestic bauxitic clays and anorthosites may ulti-
mately replace foreign bauxites as a source of
aluminum. Although treatment costs are greater on
domestic ores, transportation costs between plants
are greatly reduced." A similar conclusion may be
eventually developed by importers of foreign iron
ores.

Wright,[31] in 1950, estimated that an amortiza-
tion figure of between 1 and 3 dollars per ton of

(30) Johnson, A.F.:Cost Factors in the Utilization
       of Foreign Bauxite to Make Aluminum, Mining
       Eng. vol 6, June 1954, p 598-603.
(31) Wright, E.C.:The Economics of Raw Material
       Supplies in the Birmingham District, Mining
       Eng. vol 187, Dec. 1950, p 1214-1220.

iron ore will have to be faced in supplying the mining plant, port facilities and ships needed for foreign ore development. Thus, in many situations domestic taconite concentrates will have more than an even chance of competing with high-grade foreign ores.

New Steelmaking Processes

Another old process now undergoing serious experimentation which may affect the economics of iron-ore beneficiation and future steel plants is the continuous casting process. The first work on this process is usually credited to Sir Henry Bessemer who cast iron between moving rolls in 1858. Other references attribute the first work to J. Laing who as early as 1843 continuously cast soft metal tubes. The success of the non-ferrous industry in applying continuous casting has been a constant inspiration to the steel industry. The higher temperatures involved and the lower heat conductivity of steel has introduced many problems when the process was applied to steel. As of December, 1954 there were only two commercial installations of the process—one at the Atlas Steels Ltd. plant in Welland, Ontario Canada and another at Barrows, England. In addition, there was a pilot plant at Watervliet, N.Y. operated by Allegheny Ludlum Steel Corp. One enthusiastic supporter of the process is Norman Goss who claims,[32] "Projected studies indicate that continuous casting with electric or oxygen steelmaking can make profitable the operation of an integrated mill of no more than 50,000 tons per year." Using conventional equipment and techniques, it is generally conceded that 300,000 tons is the minimum figure for profitable operation of ingot breakdown equipment. A new corporation, Continuous Metalcast Corp. of New York, has been organized to take title to the American and Canadian rights to the Junghans and Dunross continuous-casting patents owned by Irving Rossi of New York.[33]

(32) Hruby, T.F.:Fewer Steps to Finished Steel, Steel vol 135, No. 19, Nov. 8, 1954, p 88-89.
(33) Cellar, E.:Op. cit.

Coupled with atomic power plants and low cost
electric furnaces, continuous casting may stimulate development of small isolated iron ore
deposits which are now considered uneconomical.

New Era in Beneficiation Machines

One of the first magnetic taconite plants is
the largest ore processing plant ever built as a
unit. It now appears that a whole new era is
beginning in the beneficiation equipment field.
This is necessary if minimum processing costs are
to be obtained. Most of the jumbo-sized machines
in the past were special installations and, for
the most part, not profitable items for the manufacturing companies. Now with the prospect of
several large taconite installations in a relatively short space of time, equipment manufacturers
can afford to invest in considerable engineering
and research on the design of bigger and better
ore beneficiation machines.

One of the primary crushers in a Minnesota
plant was the world's largest gyratory crusher at
the time of its installation. One of the new
features of the crusher was its dual drive. Two
500 horsepower wound-rotor motors, located 180
degrees apart furnish a smoother drive with the
possibility of less maintenance. Also included
is a pushbutton-controlled hydraulic mechanism
for raising or lowering the mainshaft assembly
to change the open side setting. Thus compensa-
tion for concave wear or change in product size
can be accomplished with a minimum of effort.

Larger, improved magnetic separators, flotation
machines, furnaces, sintering machines, pelletizers
and materials handling equipment are rapidly appearing on the scene. All will aid in decreasing
iron-ore processing costs.

Future Sources of Iron Ores

A study of current trends in the iron ore industry results in the following list of future iron
ore sources for America's iron and steel industry:
1) Lake Superior intermediate and high-grade
ore (declining tonnages).

2) High-grade ore from Labrador, Steep Rock and other Canadian ore fields; also from Brazil, Venezuela, Peru and other Latin and South American deposits.

3) Concentrates from domestic and Canadian magnetic and nonmagnetic taconites; recent estimates predict shipment of 12 million tons by 1958 and 23 million tons by 1963.

4) Concentrates from Cuban, Philippine and other laterite deposits.

5) Increased production of concentrates from pyrite, pyrrhotite and other iron sulphides.

6) Concentrates from industrial wastes. For example, ferrous sulphate from steel mill wastes and recovery of iron from plating and steel fabrication wastes; coal ashes.

7) Concentrates from undersea deposits of glauconite.

8) Iron-bearing concentrates recovered as by-products from ilmenite ores.

ADDITIONAL REFERENCES

Retty, J.A.:Labrador--North America's Newest
Great Iron Ore Field, Mining & Met. vol 29,
Sept, 1948, p 480-483.
Retty, J.A.:Surface Work Indicates Possibility of
a Major Iron Ore Field in Central Labrador,
Mining & Met. vol 26, May 1945, p 255-256.
Anon:Iron Ore Discoveries Give Labrador New
Importance, Eng. & Mining Jnl. vol 146, June
1945, p 88-89.
Lee, Oscar:Birmingham's Future Depends on Con-
centration, Eng. & Mining Jnl. vol 145, Oct. 1944,
p 104-106.
Benitez, L.A.T.:Cerro de Mercado--Mexico's Iron
Mountain, Eng. & Mining Jnl. vol 145, Sept. 1944,
p 88-89.
Davis, E.W.:When Will We Mine Taconite?, Eng. &
Mining Jnl. vol 145, April 1944, p 82-85.
Anon:New York State's Iron Ores Draw New Attention,
Eng. & Mining Jnl. vol 144, May 1943, p 67-69.
Bockman, K.L.:Mining Flourishes in Norway, Eng.
& Mining Jnl. vol 141, March 1940, p 41-42.
Malozemoff, A.:The United Nation's Newest Source
of Iron, Eng. & Mining Jnl. vol 143, Dec. 1942,
p 55-59; vol 144, Jan. 1943, p 56-59.
Hagar, I.D.:The MacIntyre Development--New Source
of Titanium, Eng. & Mining Jnl. vol 143, Dec.
1942, p 47-49.
Lasky, S.G.:The Concept of Ore Reserves, Mining &
Met. vol 26, Oct. 1945, p 471-474.
Huttl, J.B.:Eagle Mountain, New Source of Iron
Ore for Fontana, Eng. & Mining Jnl. vol 150, May
1949, p 92-93.
Hubbell, A.H.:The Problem of Iron Ore--and How It
Will Be Solved, Eng. & Mining Jnl. vol 150, July
1949, p 84-91.
Hughlett, L.J.:Getting at Itabira's Iron, Eng. &
Mining Jnl. vol 150, Oct. 1949, p 76-79.
Durrell, W.H.:Labrador Iron Ore and the St. Law-
rence Seaway, Eng. & Mining Jnl. vol 151, May
1950, p 92-93.

Gillies, D.B.:Adirondack Iron Ore Field   Still
Offers Many Challenges, Eng. & Mining Jnl. vol
151, June 1950, p 84-87.
Lake, M.C.:Cerro Bolivar--U.S. Steel's New   Iron
Ore Bonanza, Eng. & Mining Jnl. vol 151, Aug.
1950, p 72-83.
Jensen, Homer:Aeromagnetic Survey Helps Find New
Pennsylvania Iron Orebody, Eng. & Mining Jnl.
vol 152, Aug. 1951, p 56-59.
Anon:Full-Scale Taconite Beneficiation Nearer,
Eng. & Mining Jnl. vol 152, Nov. 1951, p 102-103
Anon:Rich Titanium Strike Enters Development Sta-
ge, Mining & Met. vol 29, Nov. 1948, p 615-617.
Lippert, T.W.:Cerro Bolivar--Saga of an Iron Ore
Crisis Averted, Mining Eng. vol 187, Feb. 1950,
p178-192.
Hubbell, A.H.:Work on Taconite Now Heads Toward
Commercial Goal, Eng. & Mining Jnl. vol 153,
July 1952, p 72-75.
Anon:Reserve Mining Co. Starts Taconite Plant at
Babbitt, Eng. & Mining Jnl. vol 153, Nov. 1952,
p 72-79.
Kemp, J.F.:The Titaniferous Iron Ores of the
Adirondacks, U.S. Geol. Survey 19th Annual Report,
Part III Economic Geology, p 1897-98, Govern-
ment Printing Office, 1899.
Mein, W.W. Jr.:The Calaveras Cement Co. Dust Suit,
Mining Eng. vol 190, June 1951, p 534-536.
Mitchell, Will, Jr., C.L. Sollenberger, and F.F.
Miskell:Factors in the Economics of Heat-Treated
Taconites, Mining Eng. vol 4, Oct. 1952, p 962-
967.
Gardner, P.S., Jr.:Hydraulic Hoist Pumps Ore in
Full-Scale Trial Run, Eng. & Mining Jnl. vol 153,
Jan. 1952, p 95.
Anon:Industrial Waste--An Important Factor in
Process Planning, Chem. & Met. Eng. vol 52, Aug.
1945, p 117-124.
Welch, H.V.:The Fume and Dust Problem in Industry,
Jnl. of Metals, vol 1, Dec. 1949, p 934-947.
Thoeman, J.R., A.H. Reed and B.H. Clemmons:The
Future of Birmingham Red Ore, Jefferson County,
Ala. U.S. Bureau Mines Rept. of Inv. 4988, July,
1953.
Adirondack Iron Mining Issue, Mining & Met. vol
24, Nov. 1943.

Park, C.F.,Jr.:What to Do About Our Iron Ore
Reserves, Mining & Met. vol 28, April 1947,
p 192-196.
Jenkins, O.P.:Iron Resources of California, Div-
ision of Mines, State of California, Bulletin
129, 1948.
Kihlstedt, P.G.:Aspects of Swedish Iron Ore Con-
centration, Jnl. of the Iron & Steel Inst.
(London), vol 177, Part 1, May 1954, p 63-75.
Selvig, W.A. and F.H. Gibson:Analyses of Ash from
Coals of The United States, U.S. Bur. Mines Tech.
Paper 679, 1945, 20 pp.
Anon:Water Supply, Chem. Eng. vol 55, Jan. 1948,
p 137-144.
Anon:The Water Problem, Chem. Eng. vol 56, July
1949, p 119-126.
Anon:Pollution Control, Chem. Eng. vol 58, May
1951, p 111-158.
Anon:What Price Process Plants, Chem. Eng. vol 58,
May 1951, p 164-165.
Paxton, R.R.:Establishing Responsibility for Dust,
Rock Prods. vol 54, June, 1951, p 127-128, 144.
Forbes, J.J., S.J. Davenport and G.G. Morgis:Re-
view of Literature on Dusts, U.S. Bur. Mines
Bulletin 478, 1950.
Anon:Steel--Acquisitions, Mergers, and Expansion
of 12 Major Companies, 1900 to 1950, Hearings
Before the Select Committee on Small Business,
House of Representatives, Eighty-First Congress,
March 10, 1950, 80 pp.
Paulsen, C.G.:Quality of Surface Waters of the
United States, 1945, U.S. Geol. Survey Water
Supply Paper 1030, 1949.
Dean, R.S. and R.E. Swain:Report Submitted to the
Trail Smelter Arbitral Tribunal, U.S. Bur. Mines
Bulletin 453, 1944.
Kelley, V.C.:Geology and Economics of New Mexico
Iron-Ore Deposits, University of New Mexico
Press, Publications in Geology No. 2, 1950.
Agnew, C.E.:Postwar Importance of Beneficiated
Iron-Bearing Materials, Steel, vol 115, Sept. 4,
1944, p 98-100, Sept. 11, 1944, p 112.
Davis, E.W.:Iron Ore Concentration and the Lake
Erie Price, AIME Tech. Pub. 1202, 1940, 13 pp.
Davis, E.W.:When Will We Mine Taconite, Eng. &
Mining Jnl. vol 145, April 1944, p 82-85.

Yaworski, N. et al:Technology, Employment, and Output per Man in Iron Mining, W.P.A. National Research Project in Cooperation with U.S. Bureau of Mines, Report No. E-13, Philadelphia, Pa. June 1940, 264pp.

U.S. Dept. of Agriculture:Water, The Yearbook of Agriculture, 1955, U.S. Govt. Printing Office Washington 25, D.C., 751pp.

Johnson, V.D.:An Expert Looks at Iron Ore Sources, Eng. & Mining Jnl. vol 156, Dec. 1955, p 86-89.

O'Donnell, A.J.:Geneva---The World and Our Nuclear Future, Stanford Research Institute Report, 1955, 43pp.

Hoyt,2nd, E.:Iron Ore In An Expanding Industry, Address given before General Meeting of American Iron and Steel Institute, New York, May 24, 1951.

Davis, E.W.:A Report on Taconite, Eng. & Mining Jnl. vol 151, Nov. 1950, p 84-85.

Beall, J.V.:Stream Pollution-A Mineral Industry Problem, Mining & Met. vol 29, Dec. 1948, p 650-652.

Richards, L.C,:Effect of Freight Rates on Marketing Northwest Industrial Minerals, Mining Eng. vol 187, Feb. 1950, p 285-288.

Hoffert, J.R.:Abating Stream Pollution, Mining Eng. vol 187, March 1950, p 340-343.

Specht, R.C.:Effect of Waste Disposal of the Pebble Phosphate Rock Industry in Florida on Condition of Receiving Streams, Mining Eng. vol 187 , July 1950, p 779-784.

McCabe, L.C.:Air Pollution by Industrial Fumes, Gases, and Dusts, Mining Eng. vol 187, Sept., 1950, p 971-973.

Cuscoleca, O.:Development of Oxygen Steelmaking, Trans. AIME vol 200, 1954; Jnl. of Metals, July, 1954, p 817-827.

King, C.D.:Steelmaking Processes-Some Future Prospects, Trans. AIME vol 200, 1954; Jnl. of Metals, April 1954, p 455-465.

Davis, V.C.:Taconite Fragmentation, U.S. Bur. of Mines Rept. of Inv. 4918, June 1953.

Zimmerman, J.H.:Jet-Piercing Process for Blast-holes, Mining & Met. vol 29, May 1948, p 289-290.

Trauffer, W.E.:Oxy-Acetylene Drilling Expedites
Production of Flint Grinding Pebbles, Pit &
Quarry, April 1944.
Knoerr, A.W.:Hard Iron Ore Yields to Fusion Pier-
cing, Eng. & Mining Jnl. vol 147, Nov. 1946,
p 66-69.
Lutjen, G.P.:Another Step in Jet-Piercing, Eng. &
Mining Jnl. vol 150, Aug. 1949, p 64-65.
Anon:Tough Taconite Yields to New Technology,
Life, Jan. 4, 1954, p 63-65.
Fleming, D.H. and J.J. Calaman:Production Jet-
Piercing of Blastholes in Magnetic Taconite,
Mining Eng. vol 190, July 1951, p 585-591.
Olson, K.C.:Primary Blast Hole Drilling at The
Humboldt Mine, Mining Congress Jnl. vol 42,
April 1956, p 70-73, 119.
Anon:Materials Survey - Iron Ore, Compiled by U.
S. Bureau Mines and the Geological Survey, May,
1956.
Luttrell, G.W.:Bibliography of Iron Ore Resources
of the World (To January 1955), U.S. Geological
Survey Bulletin 1019-D, U.S. Govt. Printing Off-
ice, Washington 25, D.C.

Chapter III

IRON ORE MINERALS

"Iron seemeth a simple metal but
in its nature are many mysteries
---and men who bend to them their
minds, shall, in arriving days,
gather therefrom great profit not
to themselves alone but to all
mankind."---Joseph Glanvill, 1650.

The beneficiation of iron ores begins with a
study of the crude ore. In the past, for the
most part, this has involved only a macro-
examination, a few chemical analyses, and perhaps
a cursory examination of the iron bearing materials under the microscope. The low-grade   iron
ores are really "high-grade ores" if we compare
the metal content to other metallic ores such as
copper, zinc, or lead. However, such examination
tions sufficed for the crude washing or other
relatively simple processing methods in use.
Now, as we begin to process lower grade and more
complex iron ores requiring more complex beneficiation methods, it becomes necessary to
utilize more detailed and exacting methods of
examination. Fortunately, the common iron
minerals are easily identified by a variety of
chemical and microscopical tests.
Iron is the second most abundant metallic
element in the earth's crust. It is exceeded
only by aluminum. The pioneer work of H.S.
Washington and F.W. Clarke [1] has provided some
remarkably accurate figures on the composition
of the lithosphere. Their last published data
(1924) has remained remarkably accurate despite
the accumulation of new data since then. Their
data gave 3.08% Fe_2O_3 and 3.80% FeO . Aluminum
is present to the extent of 15.34% Al_2O_3.

---

(1) U.S. Geological Survey Bulletin 770, 1924.

41

Expressed as elements, the contents are 5.11% iron
and 8.11% aluminum. Recent estimates [2,3] change
these to 5.00% iron and 8.13% aluminum. Iron
occurs in nature in an extremely wide variety of
combinations with other elements. In fact, nearly
every rock exposed at the surface of the earth
contains some iron. The iron oxides are by far
the most important sources of iron. The carbon-
ates and sulphides are secondary in importance.
Table I lists some of the important iron ore
minerals. Table II lists some of the less well
known properties of iron ore minerals.

The iron-containing minerals not considered
important ore sources today but due for steadily
increasing attention in the future are those
associated with the laterites, beach sand deposits,
and by-product iron sulphides. The laterites
provide one of the largest known reserves of iron
ores. In addition, they contain a bonus of nickel,
cobalt, aluminum, and chromium. The Nicaro plant
in Cuba is a successful laterite processing plant
which produces nickel and cobalt. The iron oxide
tailings still contain some nickel and considerable
chromium which forces a "waste" classification on
this potential ore source. Chromium and nickel
are very undesirable constituents since even small
amounts have adverse effects upon iron and steelmaking processes. When chromium and nickel removal methods are further improved enormous
quantities of good grade iron ore and alumina
for aluminum production will become available.
Table III lists the chemical analyses of several
important laterite deposits.

The quest for radioactive minerals, titanium,
and zirconium minerals has given impetus to the
mining and processing of beach sands in all parts
of the world. A logical conclusion is that it
will soon be practical to utilize the large
quantities of magnetite contained in these sands.
Of course this will carry the processing over

(2) Mason, Brian:Principles of Geochemistry,
       John Wiley & Sons, N.Y., 1952, 276 pp.
(3) Fleischer, M.:Recent Estimates of the Earth's
       Crust, U.S. Geological Survey Circular 285,
       1953, 7 pp.

TABLE I

Iron Ore Minerals

Name	Chemical Comp.	% Iron & Sp. Gr.	Crystal System & Color
Goethite	$Fe_2O_3.H_2O$	62.9 4.3	rhombohedral, yellow, red, brown, black
Hematite	Fe_2O_3	70.0 4.9-5.3	hexagonal-rhombohedral red, black, steel gray
Martite	Fe_2O_3	70.0 4.8-5.3	cubic, iron black, often tarnished
Magnetite	$FeO.Fe_2O_3$	72.4 5.16- 5.18	cubic, iron black, many associations, strongly magnetic
Siderite	$FeCO_3$	48.2 3.83- 3.88	hexagonal-rhombohedral, gray, brown, white, yellow
Pyrite	FeS_2	46.5 4.95- 5.10	cubic, brass yellow

Remarks;
Goethite is often called limonite;modern mineralogists do not recognize limonite as a mineral. Goethite has a yellowish streak, hematite a reddish-brown streak. Martite is pseudomorphic after magnetite.

Pyrrhotite, $Fe_{11}S_{12}$ contains 61.6% Fe and 38.4% S; sp.gr.of 4.5 to 4.6, is brittle, fractures unevenly and is magnetic.

TABLE II

Miscellaneous Properties of Iron Ore Minerals

Name	Electro-(a) static Conduct-ivity	Avg. (b) Value Dielect. Constant	Perme-(c) ability	(d) Attract-ive force. iron equ-als 100
Goethite	-----	11.70		---
Hematite	6,240	over 81	1.008 to 1.024	1.32
Magnetite	7,800	over 33.7 under 81	1.47	40.18
Siderite	7,176	6.78	1.022	1.82
Pyrite	7,800	over 33.7 under 81	1.0007 to 1.0064	0.23

(a) after Johnson
(b) Rosenholtz, J.L. and D.T. Smith:The
    Dielectric Constant of Mineral Powders,
    Amer. Mineralogist, vol 21, 1926, p 115-
    120.
(c) after Crane
(d) after Davis

TABLE III

Chemical Analyses of Laterites

Location	%Fe	%SiO$_2$	%Cr	%Ni	%S	%Al$_2$O$_3$
Surigao Deposits Phillipine Republic	44.77	1.33	4.19	0.78	0.17	7.93
Manicani Island Phillipines	48.41	1.86	2.99	1.06	0.185	9.88
Sungei Duwa Deposits, SE Borneo	48.0	4.50	0.95	0.67	0.23	10.42
Larona Deposits SE Celebes:						
Lump Ore	49.60	2.04	1.70	0.31	0.096	5.04
Clay Ore	48.99	1.53	3.28	0.73	0.196	7.45
Mayari Ore, Cuba	54.98	3.45	2.03	1.00	0.110	14.00
Nicaro Ore, Cuba	50.0	6.00	1.50	1.25	--	3.50
Conakry Ore, French Guinea	52.9	1.90	0.50	0.30	0.07	7.60
Red Flats, Oregon	38.5	7.58	2.12	0.92	--	10.76
Dominican Republic, W.I., Aluminous lateritic soil	14.13	1.72	0.07	0.007	--	48.18

Note: CaO and MgO content is less than one percent
in all deposits. Surigao analysis is average
of 2000 samples (U.S. Bureau of Mines). Manganese ranges from 0.27 to 0.85%;phosphorus
from 0.005 to 0.083% and ignition loss from
11.50 to 25.85%.

into the titanium minerals beneficiation area
since practically all beach sand magnetites contain appreciable titanium. The titanium is often
intimately associated with magnetite.

Iron sulphides have long been a source of iron
and once accounted for a large proportion of the
total iron production as well as the major source
of sulphur. These minerals will be utilized in
increasing quantities and the tailings piles of
many mining operations will be reworked for the
iron and sulphur content.

The most common gangue mineral associated with
iron ores is quartz which is often present as the
chert variety. Other gangue minerals found with
iron ores are listed in Table IV.

Goethite, $Fe_2O_3.H_2O$

Goethite contains 62.9% iron but the mineral
is rarely found pure in nature. Its color ranges
from brown to red and it crystallizes in the
rhombohedral system. It often occurs as euhedral
crystals or in a fibrous form. Other common forms
are massive, botryoidal and reniform. Chemically
it is a ferric oxide monohydrate. Common impurities in the mineral are silica, phosphorus,
alumina, manganese, chromium, and titanium. This
mineral is often wrongly referred to as "limonite"
which is in reality goethite with varying amounts
of water. A mineral closely similar to goethite
is lepidocrocite. Uytenbogaardt[4] adopts the
classification alpha-$Fe_2O_3.H_2O$ for goethite and
gamma-$Fe_2O_3.H_2O$ for lepidocrocite. This appears
reasonable since it is well known that dehydration of the latter will produce gamma hematite
while dehydration of geothite results in the
non-magnetic alpha hematite.[5,6] Albrecht gives

(4) Uytenbogaardt, W.:Tables For Microscopic
      Identification of Ore Minerals, Princeton
      University Press, 1951, 242 pp.
(5) Herroun, E.F., and E. Wilson:Ferromagnetic
      Ferric Oxide, Proc. Phys. Soc. (London),
      vol 41, 1928, p 100-111.
(6) Davis, C.W.:Magnetic Properties of Mineral
      Powders and Their Significance, U.S. Bur.
      Mines Rept. of Inv. 3268, 1935, p 91-100

TABLE IV

Gangue Minerals

Name	Chemical Comp.	Remarks
Quartz Chert	SiO_2	Chert is microcrystalline quartz. These two are very common gangue minerals.
Greenalite	$FeO.SiO_2$ $n\ H_2O$	Green, yellow, brown; sol. in HCl.
Grunerite	Magnesium, iron silicate	Grayish brown or brown; fibrous or lamellar.
Glauconite	SiO_2, Al_2O_3, Fe_2O_3, FeO, MgO, K_2O, H_2O	Green, granular, earthy.
Serpentine	SiO_2, MgO, Al_2O_3, Fe_2O_3, H_2O, etc.	Variable comp., light to dark green, yellow, nearly white and variegated.
Stilpnomelane	$2(Fe,Mg)O.$ $(Fe,Al)_2O_3.$ $5SiO_2.3H_2O$	Black; decomposed by HCl.
Minnesotaite	Complex Fe silicate, molecular structure similar to talc.	Chemically similar to greenalite and stilpnomelane.
Calcite	$CaCO_3$	Colorless or white; characteristic rhombohedral cleavage.
Clays	Complex Al-silicates	Staining aids in microexamination.
Apatite	$9CaO.3P_2O_5$ $Ca(Fe,(OH)_2$ $CO_3,Cl_2)$	Sol. in acid; dark green; often source of P in iron ores.
Chlorite	Hyd. silicates .. of Al, Fe & Mg.	Dark to grass green; massive material feels slightly soapy.
Garnet group	Complex Fe, Al,Ca,Mg,Mn silicates	Red, brown, yellow; often easily separated by electrostatic or hi-intensity magnetic separators.

detailed instructions on how to prepare both the
alpha- and the gamma-ferric oxide monohydrate.[7]
Goethite is the most common mineral in many
of the oolitic iron ores. It is also a major
constituent of the laterite ores. In the laterites goethite rarely approaches any high degree
of purity. It is usually contaminated with
silica, alumina, chromium-mineral residues and
other compounds.

Hematite, Fe_2O_3, alpha form (non-magnetic)

Hematite contains 70.0% iron when pure, is
red, gray, or black in color, and crystallizes
in the hexagonal-rhombohedral system. Hematite
is ferric oxide and has been found quite pure
in nature. The crystal habit is varied and the
mineral may occur in a variety of forms. The
common forms are specular hematite or specularite
micaceous hematite, cryptocrystalline hematite,
and fibrous hematite. The term martite is often
given the variety of hematite which results from
the oxidation of magnetite. The oxidation process is referred to as "martitization." The
simplest field test for detecting the presence
of martite in magnetite ore is the reddish-brown
streak given by the martite; magnetite has a
black streak. Magnetite ores which have under-
gone martitization are often quite friable. This
is easily explained by the expansion feature
brought out by Gruner.[8] Martitization is accompanied by expansion of 5.2% by volume. This
causes the individual crystal grains of altering
magnetite to separate. The martite formed on
magnetite crystal faces is often lathlike and
very brittle. Martite sometimes contains various
amounts of residual magnetite allowing magnetic
recovery of some of the martite in plants processing magnetite ores.

(7) Albrecht, W.H.:Magnetic and Crystallographic
     Researches:Hydrated Ferric Oxide, Ber. 62B,
     1929, p 1475-82. (Chem. Abs. vol 23, Oct. 20,
     1929, p 4858.)
(8) Gruner, J.W.:Magnetite-Martite-Hematite,
     Economic Geology, vol 21, 1926, p 375-393.

Hematite often hydrates to form goethite.
Cooke[9] says that incipient hydration of hematite
is readily recognized in polished sections. The
grains assume a dull color and at a very high
magnification appear finely mottled. This mott-
ling may be consistent with the theory of Posnjak
and Merwin[10] that there are transition types
between hematite and goethite. In most discussions regarding the hydration of hematite, the
term "limonite" invariably appears. It has been
quite definitely proven that limonite is goethite.
Holser[11] reiterates this in stating, "Since the
earliest days of X-ray diffraction it has been
known that most mineral specimens labeled 'limonite' are goethite, some are lepidocrocite, and
a few are hematite." W. Uytenbogaardt, in his
excellent book on ore minerals,[12] lists limonite
in the appendix titled "Superfluous Ore Mineral
Names." Concerning limonite, he says,"Limonite.
A mixture of oxides of iron, usually hematite,
Fe_2O_3 and goethite, $Fe_2O_3.H_2O$. The greater part
is commonly goethite."
The reduction of hematite to magnetite in
nature is very rare, but may have taken place in
a few instances. Gruner[13] and Cooke have reported
apparent reduction of specularite to magnetite by
natural processes.
The magnetic susceptibility of hematite is not
great enough to allow beneficiation by commercial
wet magnetic separators. However the susceptibility is high enough to allow deflection in high

(9) Cooke, S.R.B.:Microscopic Structure and
     Concentratability of the Important Iron Ores
     of the United States. U.S. Bur. Mines
     Bulletin 391, 1936, 121pp.
(10)Posnjak,E., and Merwin, H.E.:The Hydrated
     Ferric Oxides. Am. Jnl. Science, vol 47, 1919,
     p 311-358.
(11)Holser, W.T.:Limonite is Goethite, Acta. Cryst.
     vol 6, 1953, p 563 (in English).
(12)Op.cit.
(13)Gruner, J.W.:Paragenesis of the Martite Ore
     Bodies and Magnetites of the Mesabi Range,
     Economic Geology, vol 17, 1922, p 1-14.

intensity induced roll magnetic separators. Also
laboratory alternating current separators based
on coercive force and remanence have made good
recovery of hematite from low-grade iron ores.
Hayes, in his much quoted report[14] on the ferromagnetic properties of hematite, drew the following
conclusions;

1. The use of the Gouy-type magnetic balance has been extended so that it is
possible to measure the hysteretic
constants of weakly ferromagnetic
materials.

2. Alpha hematite has been shown to be
distinctly ferromagnetic because:
a) Its X_g vs H curve shows a maximum.
b) It exhibits residual magnetism.
c) A definite coercive force is required to reduce its remanent
magnetism to zero.
d) It has a Curie point.

3. The hysteresis phenomena can be attrib-
uted only to hematite and not to other
ferromagnetic impurities because of the
large coercive-force values and because
of the maximum X_g that occurs at high
fields.

4. Hematite approaches saturation in fields
of 10,000 oersteds.

5. The slight repulsion of hematite from
an alternating-current field after
magnetization in high direct-current
fields is insufficient for practical
concentration by such means. The
remanence is so low and the hematite is
so near saturation in fields of 10,000
oersteds that "activating" the hematite
in fields of 25,000 to 30,000 oersteds
would not help very much.

6. The fact that hematite is ferromagnetic
even though the susceptibility values
are only those of a strongly paramagne-
tic substance suggests a definition of
ferromagnetism based upon hysteretic
phenomena."

(14) Hayes, E.T.:Ferromagnetic Properties of Hematite, U.S. Bur.Mines Rept Inv.3570, June
1941, 29pp.

There are several investigators who still question whether or not alpha hematite has ferromagnetic properties. Among these are Neel[15] and
Chevallier.[16] Both these scientists believe
that the essential magnetic properties of alpha
hematite are due to a fundamental paramagnetism,
upon which is superimposed a ferromagnetism of
varying intensity. Neel concludes that the
ferromagnetic properties can be explained by the
presence of minute crystalline precipitates of
magnetite.

The composition of some typical hematite-
goethite ores are listed in Table V. Those
listed are, for the most part, direct shipping
ores which have supplied much of the blast
furnace burden for America's iron and steel
industry in the past. A steadily increasing
quantity of iron ore for this great industry will
be won from low-grade ores. A detailed tabulation
of the analyses of low-grade Mesabi taconite
samples was prepared by Scott and Wesner. These
data are reproduced in Table VI. Most of the
taconite samples analyzed fall into the nonmagnetic class. "Taconite" was the name given by
early geologists to the iron formation of the
Mesabi Range. The word is derived from a Greek
word meaning to melt. Legally, taconite is now
defined in the laws of Minnesota as follows:
"ferruginous chert or ferruginous slate in the
form of compact, siliceous rock, in which the
iron oxide is so finely disseminated that substantially all of the iron-bearing particles of
merchantable grade are smaller than 20 mesh.
Taconite may be further defined as ore-bearing rock
which is not merchantable as iron ore in its natural state, and which cannot be made merchantable
by simple methods of beneficiation involving only
crushing, screening, washing, jigging, drying, or
any combination thereof."

(15) Neel, L:Magnetic Properties of the Rhombo-
     hedral Sesquioxide of Iron, Chem. Abstracts
     vol 43, August 1949, p 5685.
(16) Chevallier, R:Magnetic Properties of the
     Rhombohedral Ferric Oxide, alpha Fe_2O_3,
     Chem. Abstracts vol 46, April 1952, p 3345.

IRON ORE BENEFICIATION

TABLE V

Chemical Analyses of Hematite - Goethite Ores

Location	Percent						
	Fe	SiO$_2$	Al$_2$O$_3$	P	Mn	MgO	CaO
Mesabi Range[a] Group 2 Bess.	56.50	4.21	1.02	0.030	0.28	0.04	0.05
Mesabi Range[a] Group 3 NonBess.	50.81	5.97	1.89	0.055	0.64	0.18	0.32
Mesabi Range[a] Group 7 Conc. Non Bessemer	49.45	15.56	0.58	0.048	0.13	0.14	0.27
Birmingham,[a] Sized Red Ore	45.70	15.83	3.15	0.310	0.12	0.45	14.59
Birmingham,Ala.[b] Basin Ore Reserves;average analysis	31.0	35.0	--	0.210	--	--	9.0
Marquette Rng. Michigan[c] Cliffs Shaft Lump Ore	59.18	9.82	1.91	0.115	0.33	0.69	0.73
Cuyuna Rng.[c] Minn. Alstead Ore	43.28	12.89	2.43	0.177	4.20	0.17	0.35
Humboldt Mining Co. Mich. Flotation Concentrate	62.39	8.99	--	--	--	--	--

(a) Hogberg, C.G.:The Iron Blast Furnace Process, Metals
    Handbook, Amer. Soc. for Metals, 1948 Edition, p 318.
(b) Thoenen, J.R., A.H. Reed and B.H. Clemmons:The Future
    of Birmingham Red Iron Ore, Jefferson County, Alabama,
    U.S. Bur. Mines Rept. of Inv. 4988, July 1953, 71 pp.
(c) Ess, T.J.:Jones & Laughlin--Pittsburgh Works, Iron &
    Steel Engineer, Nov. 1954.

CHEMICAL ANALYSIS OF MESABI TACONITE SAMPLES *

Sample No.	Total Fe(1)	Ferrous Fe	Acid-Soluble Fe	Mag. Fe(2)	Nonmag. Fe(2)	SiO_2	P	CaO	MgO	Al_2O_3	MnO	Carbonate, CO_2	L.O.I.(3)
1	32.9	3.0	32.3	11.0	21.3	51.5	0.016	0.01	0.01	0.15	0.24	0.05	1.78
2	25.4	12.8	25.3	5.9	19.4	46.1	0.029	0.34	1.97	2.00	2.18	9.4	9.40
3	27.7	13.1	26.8	5.4	21.4	50.0	0.027	0.01	0.05	0.19	0.74	5.6	7.97
4	33.1	7.4	32.7	19.7	13.0	49.7	0.026	0.03	0.05	0.14	0.52	1.16	1.63
5	34.1	7.6	33.8	17.6	16.2	47.6	0.022	0.02	0.11	0.24	0.49	1.79	1.79
6	32.4	7.7	32.3	18.2	14.1	48.4	0.033	0.15	2.49	0.70	0.18	0.3	0.13
7	32.9	12.8	32.7	27.7	5.0	47.3	0.013	0.03	2.32	0.40	0.14	1.8	0.94
8	36.7	1.8	36.3	1.8	34.5	46.5	0.016	0.22	0.01	0.14	0.08	0.10	0.64
9	44.2	1.8	43.4	8.4	35.0	35.1	0.027	0.08	0.04	0.41	0.10	0.11	1.31
10	34.1	2.8	34.0	12.3	21.7	49.1	0.025	0.23	0.04	0.22	0.04	0.13	1.57
11	30.0	9.4	29.2	16.0	7.1	48.9	0.025	0.34	0.98	1.00	0.72	4.81	5.9
12	28.5	14.4	28.0	11.1	5.4	45.6	0.038	0.55	1.57	1.20	1.16	9.04	9.1
13	27.9	14.7	27.8	5.9	8.8	44.1	0.043	0.50	1.24	1.42	0.97	10.30	11.0
14	28.7	4.8	28.5	9.5	18.5	56.1	0.046	0.01	0.09	1.03	0.08	0.42	1.2
15	31.4	3.6	31.1	4.7	26.0	53.5	0.039	0.01	0.03	0.29	0.11	0.30	1.7
16	36.5	3.2	36.0	3.6	30.4	45.0	0.017	0.01	0.16	0.42	0.52	1.56	2.1
17	34.1	2.9	34.0	11.6	22.4	50.3	0.020	0.01	0.06	0.10	0.21	0.43	1.09
18	33.3	1.5	33.2	6.1	27.1	51.3	0.015	0.01	0.07	0.13	0.06	0.31	1.52
19	32.5	1.9	32.4	12.2	20.2	52.6	0.020	0.01	0.10	0.17	0.12	0.19	1.53
20	33.5	13.3	32.7	25.2	6.5	43.8	0.025	1.04	1.84	0.26	0.80	3.95	3.2
21	28.8	15.6	27.4	17.6	9.8	46.6	0.056	1.07	3.12	0.36	0.44	5.43	4.9
22	29.2	9.9	27.8	18.4	9.4	47.1	0.022	1.52	3.08	0.33	0.37	2.77	2.6
23	26.7	11.9	25.9	11.3	14.6	47.3	0.031	2.17	2.53	0.79	1.17	7.40	7.0

(1) Determined by fusion, includes acid insoluble silicates.

(2) Magnetic and nonmagnetic assays were determined by Davis-tube tests on 270-mesh head samples. The results reported are calculated as proportional parts of the total acid-soluble iron assays.

(3) All results for samples dried at 110 C; moisture loss was under 0.5 per cent.

*Scott, D.W., and A.L. Wesner:Properties of Nonmagnetic Taconites Affecting Concentration, Mining Engineering, vol 6, June 1954, p 635-641.

Magnetic Iron Ore Minerals

The magnetic iron ore minerals which are important in magnetic beneficiation processes are natural magnetite, artificial magnetite, and gamma hematite. Published studies on these materials include a great volume of effort on natural magnetite, considerable information on artificial magnetite, and very little on gamma hematite. In fact, until a market for gamma hematite was found in the tape recording industry, this magnetic form of hematite was little more than a laboratory curiosity. Recent studies of processes utilizing the exothermic reaction which takes place when magnetite is oxidized to gamma hematite has also stirred more interest in this unusual iron oxide. The beneficiation of magnetic iron ore minerals requires one of the most simple and yet very efficient processing methods--magnetic separation. Because of the low cost of this processing method, the magnetic taconites were the first really low-grade iron ores to be successfully processed. Table VII lists the chemical analyses of several magnetite ores.

Natural Magnetite, Fe_3O_4 or $FeO.Fe_2O_3$

Natural magnetite is rarely found with any high degree of purity in nature. Common impurities found intimately associated with magnetite are titanium, sulphur, phosphorus, magnesium, aluminum, nickel, chromium, vanadium, and manganese. Pure magnetite contains 72.36 percent iron, crystallizes in the isometric system, and is black in color. The mineral is very magnetic and sometimes exhibits polarity. Magnetite is a conductor of electricity and provides good shielding for radioactive materials. The coercive force of magnetite increases as the grain size decreases. It forms solid solutions with ilmenite at high temperatures; by rapid cooling homogeneous titaniferous magnetite is formed with properties intermediate between magnetite and ilmenite. With slow cooling fine intergrowths or blades of ilmenite may form

TABLE VII

Chemical Analyses of Magnetite Ores

Location	Percent						
	Fe	SiO$_2$	Al$_2$O$_3$	P	Mn	MgO	CaO
Port Henry, N.Y. Sintered Concentrate [1]	67.13	2.88	0.96	0.165	0.41	0.24	1.80
Mesabi Range[2] Mag. Taconite Concentrate, Pelletized	63.23	8.30	0.37	0.025	0.18	0.69	0.46
Kirkenes, [3] Norway, Sydvaranger Conct.	66.0	7.00	0.60	0.010	0.13	--	0.40
Geneva, Utah[4] Ore, primarily magnetite	54.3	7.2	1.75	0.10	0.10	1.50	3.0
Benson Mines, N.Y. Ore	25.7	40.0	--	0.20	0.10	--	--
Benson Mines[5] magnetite sinter	61.38	7.59	3.52	0.030	0.31	0.37	0.21
Richard Mine[6] N.J.	55.75	12.02	1.91	0.449	0.07	2.01	2.90
Yeno-Kovdar, Russia Ore	33.0	--	--	2.7	--	--	--
Yeno-Kovdar, concentrate	63.0	--	--	0.5	--	--	--

(1) Hogberg, C.G.:The Iron Blast Furnace Process, Metals Handbook, Amer. Soc. for Metals, 1948 Edition, p 318.
(2) Anon:Beneficiation of Magnetic Taconite - An Explanation to Accompany a Demonstration at the Mines Expt. Station , Univ. of Minn., Oct. 27, 1950, 14 pp.
(3) Lund, W.:Sydvaranger's Agglomerates, Mining World vol 10, Oct. 1948, p 38-42.
(4) Lewis, J.R.:Rate of Reduction of Geneva Ore, Trans. AIME vol 172, 1947, p 27-45.
(5) Ess, J.T.:Jones & Laughlin--Pittsburgh Works, Iron & Steel Engr. November 1954.
(6) National Bureau of Standards Analysis.

parallel to the octahedral planes of the magnetite. Polished specimens then show the true Widmanstatten structure. Ilmenite precipitated in magnetite may be easily mistaken for martite due to very similar appearances. A microchemical test with hydrochloric acid and stannous chloride solution will differentiate these minerals; martite is etched, but ilmenite is negative to these reagents.
Magnetite alters to martite and, if natural processes continue, to goethite. Magnetite is one of the most stable oxides of iron and occurs in many terrestrial rocks and in meteorites.

Hematite, Fe_2O_3, gamma form (very magnetic)

Gamma hematite is only rarely found in nature. The hydrated variety carries one molecule of water and is often called "lepidocrocite." The anhydrous variety is usually called "maghemite." It crystallizes in the isometric system and ranges in color from bluish gray to dark reddish brown. Gamma hematite can be formed in nature by three methods:
1. Precipitation and oxidation of a solution containing ferrous iron and ferric iron as in the gossan of a copper ore body.[17]
2. Dehydration of the mineral lepidocrocite.[17,19,20]
3. Oxidation of magnetite.[18,20]
The mineral occurs as fine network type structures or spongy formations. If ilmenite is present in

(17) Sosman, R.B. and Posnjak, E.:Ferromagnetic Fe_2O_3,Artificial and Natural, Jnl. Washington Acad. Science, 1925, vol 15, p 329-342.
(18) Uytenbogaardt, W.:Op.Cit.
(19) Gheith, M.A.:Stability Relations of Ferric Oxides and Their Hydrates, Congr. Geol. Intern. Compt. Rend. 19th Session, Algiers, 1952, No. 10, 1953 (In French).
(20) Ralston, O.C.:Iron Oxide Reduction Equilibria: A Critique from the Standpoint of the Phase Rule and Thermodynamics, U.S. Bur. Mines, Bulletin 296, 1929, 326 pp.

the magnetite from which maghemite is formed, then the ilmenite lamellae will appear unaltered in the maghemite.

A detailed discussion of gamma hematite in this review of iron ore minerals is justified by the importance of this artificial mineral in beneficiation methods which are built around the magnetite to gamma hematite oxidation reaction. This exothermic reaction is an important source of heat units in at least one proposed magnetic roasting process for low-grade iron ores.

There are several "chemical" methods of producing gamma hematite, but these are relatively unimportant in beneficiation processes at the present time. They are important in the magnetic recording industry which uses magnetic powders on recording discs, tapes and on film. Marvin Camras, a pioneer in the magnetic recording field, has summarized some of the chemical methods for preparing gamma hematite in a recent U.S. patent.[21]

In considering iron ore beneficiation, the most important method of producing gamma hematite is by controlled oxidation of artificial magnetite. The earliest recorded observation of the properties of gamma hematite were noted in 1859 by Robbins.[22] Abraham and Planiol rediscovered the oxide and reported[23] "reduction of red nonmagnetic Fe_2O_3 with hydrogen or carbon monoxide at 500 degrees Centigrade gives magnetic Fe_3O_4 quantitatively. Rapid reoxidation at high temperature gives nonmagnetic Fe_2O_3. Slow reoxidation in air at 200-250 degrees Centigrade gives yellowish brown, strongly magnetic Fe_2O_3, stable at atmospheric temperature and converted to the nonmagnetic variety by heating at or above 650 degrees Centigrade." The first U.S. patent on the use of the reduction-oxidation process was

(21) Camras, M.:Magnetic Impulse Record Member, Magnetic Material and Method of Making Magnetic Material, U.S. Pat. 2,694,656, Nov. 16, 1954.

(22) Robbins, J.:Magnetic Peroxide of Iron, Chemical News, vol 1, 1859, p 11-12.

(23) Abraham, H. and Planiol, R.:Magnetic Iron Sesquioxide, Compt. rend., vol 180, 1925, p 1328-1329.

issued to W. Luyken in 1932. Luyken specified[24]
oxidation temperatures of 220-500 degrees Centigrade and a magnetic separation step to recover
the gamma hematite. The Battelle process, first
publicized in 1953, specifies low reduction temperatures (about 400 degrees C.) and oxidation
temperatures as high as 500 degrees.[25] The
Battelle report covers pilot plant operations on
several low-grade ore samples and claims recoveries of 92 to 96 percent of the iron. At Battelle
the reduction-oxidation process was accomplished
in shaft furnaces, while a similar British process specifies a rotary kiln.[26] In the latter
the crude ore is heated to 500 degrees Centigrade
in a "slightly" reducing atmosphere to convert
the Fe_2O_3 to Fe_3O_4. The artificial magnetite is
cooled in air for the oxidation step. The oxidation temperature may be as high as 750 degrees
without imparing the magnetic properties. If the
ore contains lime in the form of $CaCO_3$ it is first
roasted in an oxidizing atmosphere above about 900
degrees and below 1050 degrees in order to prevent combination of the lime with the iron.
   The reason for the high magnetic susceptibility
of gamma hematite is the subject of much current
research. Fortunately this information is of
interest outside the minerals field and much effort is being expended in the electronics and
ceramics industries. Proponents of the so-called
"defect structure" of magnetic hematite claim
that the difference in crystal structure causes the

(24) Luyken, W.:Reducing and Magnetic Treatment
       of Iron Ores, U.S. Patent 1,865,869, July 5,
       1932.
(25) Stephens, F.M., B. Langston and A.C. Richard-
       son:The Reduction-Oxidation Process for the
       Treatment of Taconites, Jnl. of Metals, June
       1953, p 780-785:U.S. Patent 2,693,409, Nov.
       2, 1954.
(26) United Steel Companies Ltd. and Lewis Reeve:
       Concentration of Iron Ore, British Patent
       657,518, Sept. 19, 1951.

change in magnetic properties.[27,28,29.] Gamma
hematite has the same chemical composition as
that of alpha hematite, but has a cubic crystalline structure as compared to the rhombohedral
structure of alpha hematite. Thus, it seems
plausible to suggest that the difference in the
magnetic susceptibility of the two minerals is
related to this difference in crystal structure.
The importance of trace elements which are often
present as an integral part of the space lattice
of hematite is a relatively unknown quantity at
present. Thermal history and other genetic
features could also have a pronounced effect on
magnetic properties.

An investigation at the Imperial College,
London by David and Welch[30] has offered a new explanation for the magnetic properties of gamma
hematite. They report, "Specimens of magnetite
which gave gamma ferric oxide on oxidation invariably contained appreciable percentages of
combined water, while specimens prepared under
dry conditions oxidized with great difficulty,
never yielding the gamma oxide. It has also been
found that the gamma oxide itself contains a small
percentage of water, which apparently cannot be
removed without destroying the characteristic
spinel structure. It is suggested that current
views on the 'defect' structure of gamma ferric
oxide are inadequate, and that the structure is
stabilized by the presence of hydroxyl ions which
replace some of the oxygen ions of the spinel

(27) Stephens, F.M., B. Langston and A.C. Rich-
     ardson: Op. Cit.
(28) Osmond, W.P.:An Interpretation of the Mag-
     netic Properties of Some Iron Oxide Powders,
     Proc. Phys. Society (London) vol 66B, 1953,
     p 265-272.
(29) Sveshnikov, G.B.:Ferromagnetic Properties of
     Minerals, Vesnik Leningrad Univ. vol 5,
     1950, p 83-87.
(30) David, I., and A.J.E. Welch:Oxidation of
     Magnetite and Related Spinels. Constitution
     of "Gamma" ferric Oxide, Abstracts of
     Papers--XII International Congress of Pure
     and Applied Chemistry, New York, Sept.
     10-13, 1951.

lattice." Another European investigator, E.
Herrmann[31,32] has published considerable data
supporting the view that the water content of
artificial magnetite and gamma hematite greatly
influences ultimate magnetic properties. Herrmann
also reported that artificial magnetite and
gamma hematite have very similar magnetic properties. Other tests showed that the magnetic permeability of gamma hematite can be changed by
varying the cooling time. Gheith[33] points out
the importance of water in the transformation of
gamma hematite to alpha hematite. In the absence
of water vapor Gheith obtained transformation of
gamma hematite to the alpha form at 400-550
degrees Centigrade. Traces of water catalyzed
the change at temperatures as low as 95 degrees.

Gamma hematite is bluish gray to dark reddish
brown in color and very magnetic. In finely
pulverized samples these properties alone suffice
to differentiate gamma hematite from magnetite
after standardized test procedures are set up.
Magnetite, artificial or natural, is always black
in color.

Artificial Magnetite, Fe_3O_4

Artificial magnetite is chemically the same as
natural magnetite and contains 72.36 percent iron
when pure. It is included in this discussion of
iron minerals because of its increasing importance
in iron ore beneficiation processes. Artificial
magnetite has been produced in various pyrometallurgical processes for several hundred years. Its
physical properties are somewhat different than
those of the natural mineral. This is especially

(31) Herrmann, E.:Magnetic Properties of Gamma
      Ferric Oxide, Arhiv. Kem. vol 22, 1950,
      p 85-100 (in German); Chemical Abstracts,
      vol 46, Nov. 1952, p 9910-9912 (English).
(32) Herrmann, E.:Variations of Magnetic Proper-
      ties of Gamma Ferric Oxide, Arhiv. Kem. vol
      23, 1951, p 22-29; Chemical Abstracts, vol
      46, Nov. 1952, p 9912-9913 (English).
(33) Gheith, M.A.:Op. Cit.

true of its magnetic properties. Few quantitative
measurements have been made of the magnetic properties of artificial magnetite. Gottschalk and
Davis[34] reported on the difficulty of demagnetizing artificial magnetite as early as 1933. More
recently Hartig, Onstad, and Foot[35] have thoroughly studied this phenomenon and made definite
recommendations for the design and use of demagnetizing coils for artificial magnetite. The
intensity of magnetization of artificial magnetite
may be affected by several factors. Okamura[36]
reports that the concentration of oxygen in magnetite influenced the intensity of magnetization
and the conductivity of the product. Substitution
of aluminum or manganese for some of the iron in
the space lattice also affects magnetic properties.[37] Heat treatment and thermal history are
also claimed to be important factors influencing
magnetic properties of artificial magnetite.
Artificial magnetite can be made by either chemical or pyrometallurgical methods. Chemical reduction methods find use in the preparation of
extremely pure magnetite used in the study of
ferrites and similar research work. Magnetic
powders for use in the magnetic recording industry
are often made from chemically prepared magnetite.
At present, only the pyro-methods are important in
iron ore beneficiation. Usually artificial magnetite is made by the reduction of hematite or

(34) Gottschalk, V.H. and C.W. Davis:A Magnetic
      Material of High Coercive Force, Nature,
      vol 132, 1933, p 513.
(35) Hartig, H.E., N.I. Onstad and N.J. Foot:
      Demagnetization of Magnetite, Univ. of Minn.
      Mines Expt. Station Inf. Circ. No. 7, May
      1951, 22 pp.
(36) Okamura, T., Y. Torizuka and Z. Shimoizaka:
      The Magnetic Property of Artificial Magnet-
      ite and Its Related Phenomena, Science Repts.
      Research Insts. Tohuku Univ. Ser. A. vol 1,
      1949, p 327-333.
(37) Guilland, C. and A. Michel:Magnetic Proper-
      ties of Magnetites Substituted by Trivalent
      Aluminum Ions in Relation to Their Structure
      J. Phys. Radium, vol 12, 1951, p 65.

goethite with hydrogen, carbon monoxide or mixtures of these gases. Commercial plants in Manchuria, Canada and Cuba produce large daily
tonnages of artificial magnetite by roasting
processes.

Siderite, $FeCO_3$

Iron ores containing siderite as the major
ore mineral are often called "spathic iron ores."
Siderite is ferrous carbonate and contains 48.2
percent iron when pure. Due to its isomorphism
with the minerals calcite, magnesite, and rhodochrosite, it is often contaminated with calcium,
magnesium and manganese. It crystallizes in the
hexagonal-rhombohedral system and commonly occurs
as rhombohedra. Siderite is the only iron ore
mineral with significant properties in transmitted
light under the microscope. Its very high index
of refraction renders its identification very
simple by use of immersion media.

Iron carbonate deposits are in general low
grade and rarely contain more than 40 percent
iron. This is due to the relatively low iron
content of siderite and to the presence of impurities such as organic matter, clay, sand, chert,
and calcite. Some experts claim that Precambrian
iron formations of the Lake Superior region were
originally composed of alternate laminae of chert,
siderite, greenalite and hematite. Subsequent
oxidation of siderite and greenalite has produced
the ferruginous cherts and jaspers, which consist
of alternate beds of iron oxide and chert. Table
VIII lists chemical analyses of some important
siderite ores. The two largest siderite mining
operations in America are the Algoma, Canada and
the East Texas siderite mines. The latter mine
is operated by the Lone Star Steel Company.

Titaniferous Iron Ores

Most of the known deposits of magnetite, both
lode and placer types, contain titanium. In most
cases this titanium is so intimately associated
with magnetite that it cannot be removed by ore
dressing methods even when ground to minus 325

TABLE VIII

Chemical Analyses of Siderite Ores

Location	Percent				
	Fe	SiO$_2$	Al$_2$O$_3$	Mn	P
Algoma, Canada, Ore	34.70	7.88	1.01	2.09	0.013
Above ore after sintering	50.64	11.74	1.60	3.08	0.014
Siegerland [a] ore, Germany. Roasted concentrate	46.0	--	--	8 to 10	low
Texas washed [b] siderite ore	41.0	12.0	--	--	--
Texas calcined siderite ore	55.0	16.0	--	--	--

(a) Luyken, W.:Lean Ores - German Experience in
      Their Preparation, Iron & Steel (London)
      Oct. 1947, p 471-475.
(b) Longenecker, C.:Lone Star Steel Rapidly Inc-
      reasing Service in the Southwest, Blast
      Furnace & Steel Plant, vol 38, Sept. 1950,
      p 1042-1049.
Note:Algoma ore had 2.42% sulphur before sinter-
      ing and 0.051% after sintering.

mesh in size. Singewald,[38] in his excellent publication on titaniferous iron ores classifies
those magnetic ores of iron that carry more than
2 or 3 percent of titanium as "titaniferous magnetites." Today, over 40 years after Singewald's
book appeared, this volume is still one of the
best references available on the subject. In its
preface, J.A. Holmes covers the problem of beneficiating these ores in two succinct sentences,
"The problem of utilizing titaniferous magnetites
involves the application of chemical rather than
physical methods. In short, the problem is not
one of eliminating the titanium by milling but
of reducing the ores directly by some smelting
process." Table IX lists the average composition
of various titaniferous magnetites.

Emmons and Grout[39] note some interesting
features of titaniferous magnetite deposits in
or near the large intrusive mass known as the
Duluth gabbro in northeastern Minnesota. The
most important deposits occur as banded segrega-
tions in the gabbro. In most of these the chief
gangue mineral is feldspar, but in some there is
olivine. Many of the lenses are thin and lean,
others are as much as 15 feet thick. Several
carry more than 20 percent titanium oxide and
over 50 percent iron. Old and perhaps question-
able assays of selected samples of these magnetites showed as much as 2.74 percent vanadium
oxide. A study by the U.S. Geological Survey
indicated that titaniferous magnetites commonly
carry more vanadium than magnetites low in titanium content. In case of magnetic concentration,
the vanadium tends to concentrate with the magnetite fraction of the ore, not with the ilmenite
or titaniferous fraction.

Although titaniferous magnetites are more
widespread and receive more attention, the titaniferous hematites and martites should also be

(38) Singewald, J.T. Jr.:The Titaniferous Iron
        Ores in the United States, Their Composition
        and Economic Value, U.S. Bur. of Mines
        Bulletin 64, 1913, 145 pp.
(39) Emmons, W.H., and F.F. Grout:Mineral Resources
        of Minnesota, Univ. of Minn. Geol. Survey
        Bulletin 30, 1943, 149 pp.

TABLE IX

Chemical Analyses of Titaniferous Magnetites

Location	Percent				
	Fe	SiO_2	TiO_2	P	S
Tahawus, N.Y., magnetite ore	55.8	--	10.1	--	--
concts.	57.95	3.6	9.8	0.002	0.19
Duluth gabbro, Minnesota	49.11	--	7.94	0.006	0.126
Iron Mt., Wyoming	49.89	--	15.96	trace	0.87
Taberg, Sweden	32.0	--	6 - 7	0.1	--
Luan-Ping Mine Jehol, China	53.2	2.2	12.3	0.04	0.09
Chi-chia-tzu area, Jehol, China	48.0	5.5	11.2	--	0.047
Misawa, Iwate Prefecture beach sands, Japan	35.0	--	12.0	--	--

Note: Tahawus ore and concentrates contain
about 0.40 percent vanadium.

recognized. Examples of these ores are found at
Benson Mines, New York and at Tsukumoushi, Iwate
Prefecture, Japan. Comparative analyses show:

	Percent				
	Fe	TiO$_2$	Mn	SiO$_2$	MgO
Benson Mines (selected sample)	62.77	12.20	0.38	4.56	0.22
Tsukumoushi, Japan	66.60	18.12	0.42	1.40	0.16

Uytenbogaardt[40] mentions "titanhematite" or
"white ilmenite" to designate hematite which
contains a maximum of 10 percent TiO$_2$ in solid
solution. If the TiO$_2$ content exceeds 10 percent
oriented exsolution intergrowths of ilmenite and
Ti-hematite may be formed.

Hartman[41] describes titaniferous hematite among
the heavy minerals occurring in Jamaican bauxite.
He states, "Titaniferous hematite forms partly,
perhaps entirely, by oxidation of the iron of
titaniferous magnetite. When a grain of titaniferous magnetite is confined in the limestone,
it has little chance of becoming altered. Once
the titaniferous magnetite grain has been liberated from the limestone, however, oxidizing solutions can readily attack it and convert magnetite
to martite. If the process is carried to comple-
tion magnetite is completely replaced by martite;
ilmenite commonly is little affected and the result is a grain of hematite with ilmenite laths
oriented as in titaniferous magnetite."

While iron ores are generally classified as
"titaniferous" only if they contain over 2 or 3
percent titanium, it should be pointed out that
it is the titanium content of the "end product"
that really counts. For example, it is quite
common to find that a low-grade magnetite ore
containing somewhat less than 2 percent titanium

---

(40) Uytenbogaardt, W.:Op. Cit.
(41) Hartman, J.A.:Origin of Heavy Minerals in
        Jamaican Bauxite, Economic Geology, vol 50,
        Nov. 1955, p 738-747.

will produce concentrates containing 4 or 5 percent titanium. Edwards[42] uses titaniferous iron
ores as an example to illustrate the importance
of mineral textures in relation to metallurgical
problems. He gives three examples of texture:
"Where the ore consists of granular magnetite and
ilmenite or a coarse-grained ex-solution intergrowth of these minerals, a considerable degree
of concentration may be achieved, but there is
generally a residuum of finely intergrown ilmenite in magnetite that cannot be liberated, even
with fine grinding. Where the ore consists of a
uniformly fine intergrowth of ilmenite and magnetite, little or no reduction of titanium content can be achieved, even with fine grinding.
Most titaniferous magnetite ores lie between these
extremes, but some Norwegian ores which are coar-
ser-grained than most North American ores are distinctly more amenable to magnetic concentration."
Another occurrence of the rare coarse-grained
titaniferous magnetite is reported by Holman.[43]
This Egyptian ore was crushed to only minus 80
mesh for good separation of the ilmenite from the
magnetite. Ramdohr[44] describes the existence of
ulvospinel (Fe_2TiO_4) in titaniferous iron ores.
The magnetic properties are such that it will
follow magnetite rather than ilmenite in magnetic
separations. Again, quoting Singewald,[45] "In
conclusion, it may be stated that the characteristics of the chemical composition of the titaniferous iron ores of the United States are the
same as those that mark these ores the world over.
As regards iron content most of them must be
classed as medium to low grade ores. Fortunately,
however, the deposits with the greatest economic
possibilities are the richest and their ores are

(42) Edwards, A.B.:Textures of the Ore Minerals
     and Their Significance, Australasian Inst. of
     Mining & Met. (book)
(43) Holman, B.W.:Ilmenite in Egypt, Mining Maga-
     zine (London) vol 89, 1953, p 212-216.
(44) Ramdohr, P:Ulvospinel and its Significance in
     Titaniferous Iron Ores, Economic Geology,
     vol 48, 1953, p 677-688.
(45) Singewald, J.T. Jr.:Op. Cit.

high grade. Phosphorus and sulphur are present in
objectionable quantities in only rare instances."
    With interest in titanium metal running high it
seems safe to predict   that the   titaniferous magnetite deposits of the world   are due for another
reappraisal. Many small deposits of beach sands
containing ilmenite can be worked with a minimum
of plant investment. In cases where the freight
rate is favorable, market should be found for the
by-product magnetite. It also seems that steel
mills should be blending more of the titaniferous
magnetites with low- or non-titaniferous ores.
This is being done on a small scale in the United
States where magnetite from the Tahawus, New York
ilmenite-magnetite mine containing 9.8 percent
TiO_2 is shipped to blast furnaces for blending with
low-titanium hematite ore. Le Visuer[46] reported
on use of a mixture of 1/3 Tahawus titaniferous
magnetite, 1/3 Warren flue dust, and 1/3 New York
magnetite concentrate to produce a sinter containing 2.5 percent TiO_2. When furnaces were burdened
to about 1 percent TiO_2 in the ore mix, iron was
produced which contained 0.15 to 0.2 percent titanium and a slag containing about 0.5 to 1.0 percent TiO_2.
    The so-called "black sands" which often cause
difficulties in gold placers are composed primarily of magnetite. This magnetite is very often
titaniferous, and   only rarely can   be processed
to give iron concentrates which contain less than
1 or 2 percent titanium. Singewald[47] describes
magnetic separation tests made on several important deposits of magnetite sands. A sand from
Lofoten Islands, Norway contained 13.20 percent
TiO_2 and 56.55 percent iron. The sand was
processed in a magnetic separator in three
conditions: (1)as mined, (2)crushed to less than
1/6 mm., and (3) powdered." The concentrates
contained: (1)67.70% Fe, 5.03% TiO_2, (2)69.24% Fe,
3.14% TiO_2 and (3)70.33% Fe, 2.5% TiO_2. Sands
from the famous lower St. Lawrence river deposits

————————————————————————————
(46) Le Visuer, V.G.:Use of Magnetic Ores from
         New York State, Blast Furnace & Steel Plant,
         vol 39, Feb. 1951, p 200-202,222.
(47) Singewald, J.T. Jr.,:Op. Cit.

were also magnetically processed. With only one
exception, the high grade magnetite concentrates
from these sands contained over 2% TiO_2. Large
quantities of titaniferous magnetite sands occur
in Argentina, S.A.; some of these contain from
0.3 to 1.0% TiO_2. Again, the intimate association of the titanium prevents separation by ore
dressing procedures.[48]

Pyrite, FeS_2 and other iron sulphides

Pyrite contains 46.5 percent iron, crystallizes
in the isometric system and is brass yellow in
color. Impurities may include copper, arsenic,
gold, selenium, nickel, cobalt, and tin. The
mineral will strike fire with steel: this property
allowed it to be used instead of flint in the old
wheel lock firearm. Pyrite occurrences are widespread throughout the world and before the discovery of the Frasch process for sulphur, supplied
most of the world supply of sulphur. Future demands for sulphur will again eventually force increased use of pyritic sulphur. One Canadian
plant is now recovering high-grade iron oxide
sinter and elemental sulphur from pyrites.
International Nickel Co. has completed a large
plant which is recovering magnetic iron oxide
from pyrrhotite which is sintered into a high-
grade iron ore.
By-product iron sulphide minerals will steadily
increase in importance as sources of iron ore.

(48) Mochulsky, M.:Studies in the Extraction of
Titanium Dioxide Contained in Titaniferous
Sands, Industria y Quimica (Buenos Aires),
vol 9, 1947, p 162-169.

ADDITIONAL REFERENCES

Egleston, T.:Analysis of Rocks, Trans. AIME vol 3, May 1874 to Feb. 1875, p 94-98.

Winchell, A.N.:Elements of Optical Mineralogy, Part I, Principles & Methods, Part II Descriptions of Minerals, Part III Determinative Tables, John Wiley & Sons, New York, 1937.

Anon:Photomicrography--An Introduction to Photography With the Microscope, Eastman Kodak Co., Rochester, New York, 1935.

Murata, K.J.:The Significance of Internal Structure in Gelatinizing Silicate Minerals, U.S. Geol. Survey Bulletin 950, 1946, p 25-33.

Shell, H.R.:Chemical Analysis of Clay, U.S. Bur. Mines Rept. of Inv. 4420, August, 1949.

Ross, C.S. and S.B. Hendricks:Minerals of the Montmorillonite Group, Their Origin and Relation to Soils and Clays, U.S. Geol. Survey Professional Paper 205-B, 1945.

Ross, C.S. and P.F. Kerr:The Kaolin Minerals, U.S. Geol. Survey Professional Paper 165-E, 1948.

Rogers, A.F. and P.F. Kerr:Optical Mineralogy, McGraw-Hill, New York, 1942.

Wilson, H.:Iron Oxide Mineral Pigments of The United States, U.S. Bur. Mines Bulletin 370, 1933, 198 pp.

Domenicali, C.A.:Magnetic and Electric Properties of Natural and Synthetic Single Crystals of Magnetite, Physical Review, vol 78, No. 4, May 15, 1950, p 458-467.

Mackenzie, R.C.:Investigations on Cold-Precipitated Hydrated Ferric Oxide and Its Origin in Clays, Problems of Clay and Laterite Genesis, AIME Special Volume, 1952, p 65-75.

Timm, W.B.:Summary of Experimental Tests on the Beneficiation of Canadian Iron Ores, Investigations In Ore Dressing and Metallurgy, Publication No. 617, Canada Dept. of Mines, 1923, p 123-131.

Moore, Jr. C.H. and H. Sigurdson:Petrology of High Titanium Slags, Jnl. of Metals vol 1, Dec. 1949, p 914-919.

Bozorth, R.M.:Magnetic Materials, Scientific American, vol 192, Jan. 1955, p 68-73.

Tyler, S.A.:Sedimentary Iron Deposits, Chapt. 28,
Applied Sedimentation, John Wiley & Sons, 1950.
Tyler, S.A.:Development of Lake Superior Soft
Iron Ores from Metamorphosed Iron Formation,
Bulletin of the Geological Society of America,
vol 60, July, 1949, p 1101-1124.
Wienert, F.:Formation of Martite and Other Iron
Oxides in Sideritic Ore of the Marquette Dist-
rict, Michigan, Economic Geology, vol 28, 1933,
p68-74.
Allen, R.C. and L.P. Barrett:Contributions to
the Precambrian Geology of Northern Michigan and
Wisconsin, Mich. Geol. Survey, Pub. 18, p 47-72.
Gruner, J.W.:The Composition and Structure of
Minnesotaite, a Common Iron Silicate in Iron
Formations, Amer. Mineralogist, vol 29, 1944,
p 363-372.
Spurr, J.E.:The Iron-Bearing Rocks of the Mesabi
Range in Minnesota, Geol. Nat. Hist. Survey Minn.
Bulletin No. 10, 1894, p 259.
Allen, E.T., J.L. Crenshaw and J. Johnston:The
Mineral Sulphides of Iron, Amer. Jnl. of Science,
vol 33, 1912, p 169-236.
Hendricks, S.B., and C.S. Ross:Chemical Composi-
tion and Genesis of Glauconite and Celadonite,
Amer. Mineralogist, vol 26, 1941, p 683-708.
Kemp, J.F.:The Mayari Iron Ore Deposits, Cuba,
AIME Bulletin 98, 1915, p 129-154.
Leith, C.K. and E.C. Harder:The Hematite Ores of
Brazil and a Comparison With Hematite Ores of
Lake Superior, Economic Geology vol 6, 1911,
p 670-686.
Barnett, C.E. and G.R. Durland:Luminescence of
Minerals and Synthetic Compositions, Min. & Met.
vol 29, Nov. 1948, p 603-605.
Stewart, E.W., et al:Influence of Additives in
the Production of High Coercivity Ultra-Fine
Iron Powder, Jnl. of Metals, vol 7, Trans. Sec-
tion, Jan. 1955, p 152-157.
Dean, R.S. and C.W. Davis:Magnetic Separation of
Ores, U.S. Bur. Mines Bulletin 425, 1941, 417 pp.
Members of British Intelligence Objectives Sub-
committee:Iron Ore Preparation in Germany, B.I.
O.S. Trip No. 1234, Nov. 1945, (London).
Doan, D.J.:Effect of Lattice Discontinuities on
the Magnetic Properties of Magnetite, U.S. Bur.
Mines Rept. of Inv. 3400, 1938, p 65-86.

Humphrey, G.L., E.G. King and K.K. Kelley:Some
Thermodynamic Values for Ferrous Oxide, U.S. Bur.
of Mines Rept. of Inv. 4870, June, 1952, 16 pp.

Barrett, E.P. and C.E. Wood:Relative Reducibility
of Some Iron Oxide Materials, U.S. Bur. Mines
Rept of Inv. 4569, October, 1949, 17 pp.

Laurila, E., O. Jantti, and R.T. Hukki:Magnetic
and Chemical Analyses of Ores and Mill Products
Containing Magnetite and Ilmenite, Mining Eng.
vol 190, Sept. 1951, p 797-802.

Davis, E.W.:Magnetic Concentration of Iron Ore
Univ. of Minn. Mines Experiment Station Bulletin
No. 9, Dec. 21, 1921, 138 pp.

Tobelmann, H.A. and H.J. Morgan:Review of the
Nicaro Nickel Project, Oriente, Cuba, Office of
the Production Board, Dept. of Commerce, Washington, D.C. Plancor 690, Jan. 15, 1948, 151 pp.

Sosman, R.B. and J.C. Hostetter:The Ferrous Iron
Content and Magnetic Susceptibility of Some
Artificial and Natural Oxides of Iron, Trans.
AIME vol 58, 1918, p 409-433.

Herroun, E.F.:A Comparison of the Magnetic Properties of Solid and Powdered Magnetites With
Observations on Coercive Force, Proc. Phys. Society (London), vol 55, 1943, p 338-343.

Zetterstrom, J.D.:Oxidation of Magnetite Concentrates, U.S. Bur. Mines Rept. of Inv. 4728,
Sept. 1950, 8 pp.

Rowland, R.A. and E.C. Jonas:Variations in Differential Thermal Analysis Curves of Siderite, Amer.
Mineralogist, vol 34, July-August, 1949, p 550-
558.

Gheith, M.A.:Differential Thermal Analysis of
Certain Iron Oxides and Oxide Hydrates, Am. Jnl.
of Science, vol 250, 1952, p 677-695;cf. Kulp
and Trites, Amer. Mineralogist, vol 36, 1951,
p 23-44.

Chapter IV

WASHING AND JIGGING

"Wash me thoroughly from mine
iniquity, and cleanse me from
my sin."---Psalms 51:2

Beneficiation of iron ores by "washing" is an
application of gravity concentration and is usually accompanied by a scrubbing step. Jigging is
a mechanical process which utilizes an induced
stratification of a mass of ore particles in a
liquid to effect separation of heavier from
lighter weight particles.

According to Phillips[1] washing operations in
the states of Alabama, Georgia, Tennessee and Virginia produced the greater portion of 13 million
tons of iron ore concentrates during the six year
period 1907-1912. Washing, as applied to iron
ores, usually involves the removal of fine clay
and sand by suspension of these unwanted materials
in water followed by removal in a flowing stream.
The heavier and often larger particles of iron
ore sink to the bottom of the separating vessel
and are subsequently removed as a concentrate.
Taggart, in his 1927 Handbook of Ore Dressing ,
lists three classes of washers. These are: Screening washers, classifying washers and streaming
washers. The first two, which have been applied
to iron ores, are further subdivided as follows:

A) Screening Washers
    1. Wash trommels
B) Classifying Washers
    1. Drum washers
    2. Puddling
    3. Log washers
    4. Vertical-current washers

---

(1) Phillips, W.B.:Concentration by the Goltra
    Process, Iron Age vol 94, Nov. 12, 1914,
    p 1148-1150

5. Tank washers
6. Heavy-fluid washers

The most common machines used in washing iron
ores have been log washers and rake or spiral
classifiers. The log washer is simply an inclined
steel tank provided with paddle-type agitators
extending the full length of the tank. The paddles stir the ore and cause the coarser, sunken
material to move up the incline to a concentrate
outlet. The fine-sized waste particles and some
fine-sized ore particles overflow at a weir on the
lower end of the machine. The thick shaft that
carries the blades is called the log, hence the
name "log washer." The length and slope of the
tank are such that the upper third portion of the
log is not submerged. Usually two logs are used
per trough; logs are usually 20 to 30 feet long.
A 25-foot long by 6-foot wide double-log washer
will handle up to 5000 tons of easily washed iron
ore per 24 hours. Difficult clay-containing ores
may lower capacity of this size washer to only
150 tons of feed per 24 hours.

Rake or spiral classifiers are often used in
a secondary processing step following log washers.
Spiral classifiers as large as 84 inches in diameter are now in use in washing plants. In some
of the Mesabi washing plants built in recent years,
log washers are omitted altogether and either one
or two stages of spiral classification are used.
This practice is permissable only where a minimum
of sticky clay gangue is present.

Various types of hindered settling classifiers
have been used in washing iron ores. None app-
roached the simplicity of log washers or spiral
classifiers, but they can be used on finer sized
feeds. Some Mesabi Range washing plants have included various versions of the Fahrenwald sizer
which is a vertical-current washer. The Dorrco
sizer uses automatic controls to modernize the
hindered settling classification process. It was
introduced on the Mesabi Range in 1944 and several
installations have operated continuously since
that time. Application of the Dorrco sizer to
iron ore beneficiation was described in detail

by Johnson[2] at Duluth in 1947. Figure 1 is a typical flow sheet for a Mesabi Range washing plant which utilizes a Dorrco sizer for recovery of fine-sized ore particles.

Turbo washers have also been used in Mesabi Range washing plants. They are log washers with perforated false bottoms through which water is forced. Turbos were used in the first large washer in the Lake Superior District. A flow sheet of this plant is given in Chapter I.

Typical metallurgical results from Mesabi washing plants are:

	Percent	
	Fe	SiO_2
Crude Ore	40 - 45	38 - 28
Concentrate	49 - 59	18 - 8
Tailing	15 - 20	65 and up

The importance of washing plants in the domestic iron ore beneficiation industry cannot be denied, yet, it now appears that continued large-scale use of this method of ore processing is limited. Unless more ore deposits similar to the Mesabi Range are discovered, a decline in use of the washing method can be expected to follow depletion of the so-called intermediate type of iron ores. An analysis of methods of beneficiation used to produce the total shipments of concentrates from the Mesabi Range from 1907 to 1950 is covered by Table I. Washing and jigging produced 87 percent of all Minnesota concentrates during this period. These data point out the importance of washing and jigging during the years prior to 1950. During the 1950-1960 decade washing will probably lose its first place position.

Iron ores that do not respond to simple washing methods can often be upgraded by the more complex jigging method of beneficiation. Jigging of iron ore involves the stratification of a mass of ore particles in alternating upward and downward pulsations of water. The upper layers eventually

---

(2) Johnson, R.A.:The Dorrco Sizer, Eighth Annual Mining Symposium, Center for Continuation Study, Univ. of Minn., 1947, p 87-98.

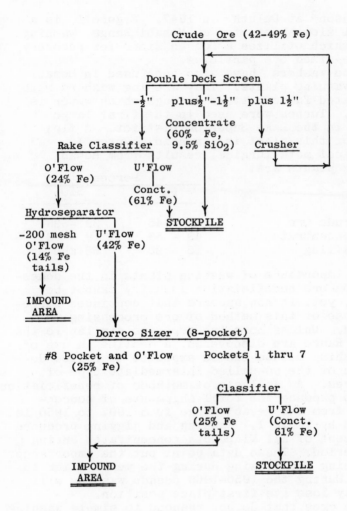

Figure 1. Flowsheet for Mesabi Range Washing Plant Using Dorrco Sizer

TABLE I

Methods of Beneficiation Used to Process
Minnesota Ores from 1907 to 1950 (a)

Method of Processing	Tonnage of Concentrates	Percentage
Washing & Jigging	266,754,722	87.0
All other Methods	39,193,808	13.0

Total Shipments of Concentrates from the
Mesabi Range Prior to Jan. 1, 1940
Summarized as to Method of Beneficiation (b)

Method of Processing	Tonnage of Concentrates	Percentage of Total Concts.
Washing	117,601,000	92.4
Jigging	6,543,000	5.1
Drying	2,282,000	1.8
Sintering	375,000	0.3
Magnetic	219,000	0.2
Heavy Density	185,000	0.2
	127,205,000	100.0

(a) Wade, H.H.:Mining Directory of Minnesota 1951
    Univ. of Minn. Mines Expt. Station, May 1,
    1951, 259 pp.
(b) Craig, J.J.:Statistical Data on the Mesabi
    Iron Range, Minn. Mines Expt. Station Tech.
    Inf. Circ. No. 2, December, 1940.

overflow as tailings while the concentrates are
periodically or sometimes continuously withdrawn
as an underflow product. Jigs have the advantage
of being able to produce a middling product in
many cases. Bird[3] has pointed out that the
distinction between the classifier and the jig
lies mainly in the fact that the jig uses downward as well as upward currents. The range of
sizes effectively treated is increased many times
over that of a simple classifier. Jigging is
useful in separation of coarse tailing from an
ore. Although jigs have been developed for recovery of iron ore particles finer than 150 mesh,
capacity is low and no commercial installations
are known. From 65 mesh to one-half inch particles are considered good jig feed. With an ore
containing 40 percent iron, capacity ranges from
0.5 to 3.0 tons per square foot of jig screen
area per hour.

Conkling jigs were used at Lyon Mountain, N.Y.
to process magnetite ores in 1887. A concentrate
containing 66.90 percent iron was obtained from a
feed containing 43.56 percent iron. The recovery
was low--about 47 percent.[4] The use of jigs on
the Gogebic Range in 1900 actually predates the
introduction of washing to the Mesabi Range.[5]

Jigging accounted for 5.1 percent of the total
concentrates produced on the Mesabi Range up to
1940. Jigging has been and will continue to be
commercially feasible in special situations. Application of modern automatic controls to jigs shows
promise of improved performance. In Germany good
results have been obtained using iron ore slimes
as the liquid medium in a conventional jig. It
appears that jigging will continue as an iron ore
beneficiation method of minor importance.

(3) Bird, B.M.:Mechanical Concentration Methods,
      Chem. & Met. Eng. vol 45, May, 1938.
(4) Ruttman, F.S.:Concentrating Magnetite With
      The Conkling Jig at Lyon Mountain, N.Y.,
      Trans. AIME vol 16, 1888, p 609-623.
(5) Hardenburgh, L.M.:The Pewabic Concentrating
      Works, Proc. of the Lake Superior Mining
      Institute (Sixth Meeting), Feb. 1900.

ADDITIONAL REFERENCES

Grondal, G.:Concentration of Iron Ores, British Patent 18,826, Aug. 16, 1909.

Newton, H.W.:Changes in Treatment of Wash Ores, Mining Cong. Jnl. vol 12, April 1926, p 273-275.

Bolthouse, H.C.:Beneficiation of Hill-Trumbull Mine Ores, Mining Cong. Jnl. vol 15, Oct. 1929, p 752-756.

Morgan, C.:Prospecting, Mining, and Washing the Brown Ores of Alabama, AIME Tech. Pub. 860, 1937, 12 pp.

Anon:The Growth of an Independent Iron Ore Operator, Eng. & Mining Jnl. vol 144, July 1943, p 74-77.

Bird, B.M.:The Baum Jig, Paper presented at the Eighth Annual Mining Symposium, Center for Continuation Study, Univ. of Minn., Jan. 1947.

Bird, B.M.:Jigs, Coal Preparation, AIME, 1950, Chapter 12, 830 pp.

Keehn, R.W.:Charleson Lean-Ore Plant to Treat Old Stockpile, Eng. & Mining Jnl. vol 150, April 1949 p 80-81.

Taggart, A.F.:The Mechanism of Jigging, Trans. AIME vol 153, 1943, p 442-452.

Counselman, T.B.:Developments in the Concentrating of Minnesota Iron Ores, Trans. AIME vol 153, 1943, p 645-654.

Remer, C. and M.P.J. Walle:Virginia Jig Plant of the Charleson Mining Company, Paper presented at the Eleventh Annual Mining Symposium, Center for Continuation Study, Univ. of Minn., Jan. 1950.

Thomas, B.D.:Principles of Gravity Concentration, AIME Coal Preparation, 1943, p 249-273.

Finkey, E.M.:The Scientific Fundamentals of Gravity Concentration, Bulletin Missouri School of Mines vol 11, Nov. 1927, 295 pp. Translated from German by C.O. Anderson and M.H. Griffitts.

Coghill, W.H. and G.D. Coe:Mineral Dressing Characteristics of the Red Iron Ores of Birmingham Alabama, U.S. Bur. Mines Bulletin 464, 1946, 99 pp.

Wendt, A.F.:The Concentration of Iron Ores, Trans AIME vol 13, 1885, p 35-39.

DeVaney, F.D. and W.H. Coghill:Concentration Tests on Tailings from the Washing Plants of the Mesabi Range, Minnesota, U.S. Bur. Mines Rept. of Inv. 3052, Nov. 1930.

White, E.D.:Brown Iron Ore Mining Active in Georgia-Alabama Field, Eng. & Mining Jnl. vol 152, May 1951, p 98-99.

Rockwood, N.C.:Trends in Fine Aggregate Processing, Rock Products vol 52, Jan. 1949, p 91-95, 120-121.

Anon:New West Hill Plant Points Way to Mining of Leaner Mesabi Iron Ores, Mining World vol 16, March 1954, p 46-50.

Chapter V

HEAVY-MEDIA SEPARATION PROCESSES

"The idea of using a magnetic
metallic medium was conceived
during the period mentioned
(1936-1937) and definite tests
as to suspension qualities
were made on crushed steel and
ferrosilicon in the early fall
of 1937 by the staff of Butler
Brothers in conjunction with
Henry Wade of the Mines Experiment Station."---Grover J. Holt,
Eng. & Mining Jnl. vol 141, Sept.
1940, p 33.

It has often been stated that the biggest single advance in the field of ore dressing since the
discovery of froth flotation is the heavy-media
separation process. Certainly no other ore dressing process of recent vintage can claim more simplicity or efficiency of operation. The range of
materials now processed by this method includes
gravel to diamonds. Various heavy-liquid or "sink-
and-float" processes have been utilized in laboratory test procedures for at least a hundred years.
The simple principle involved is the sinking and
floating of mineral particles in liquids having a
specific gravity intermediate between the specific
gravities of the minerals to be separated. For
example, quartz with a specific gravity of 2.65
will float in a medium having a specific gravity
of 3.00 while hematite with a specific gravity of
5.00 will sink.

One of the early heavy-liquid separation patents was issued to Sir Henry Bessemer in 1858. The
liquids used included solutions of iron, manganese,
barium, and calcium chlorides. On the basis of
this patent, one large coal processing plant was
installed in Germany. The plant utilized a

calcium chloride medium, but was soon abandoned.
In 1902 the DuPont Company began research on
heavy-liquid separatory methods. Laboratory tests
with brown iron ores from Virginia showed good
results; the expensive separatory liquids, tin
bromide and antimony bromide precluded any
commercial application. U.S. Patent 994,950 was
issued to DuPont in 1911 on a process using carbon tetrachloride (sp. gr. 1.595 @ 20 degrees
Centigrade). Later work with other organic liquids resulted in installation of a commercial
plant at the Weston Coal Company plant at Shennan-
doah, Pennsylvania in 1936. Metallurgical results
were excellent but excessive losses of medium and
toxicity problems forced the plant to discontinue
operations.[1] With the failure of this plant,
efforts were concentrated on those processes based
on use of "heavy suspensions" as separatory media.

The Chance process, based on use of a medium
consisting of a mixture of sand and water, was
patented in 1917 (U.S. Patent 1,224,138). The
sand must be uniformly sized; particles about 40
to 60 mesh in size are preferred. The process
has been used in a number of coal plants but is
unsuited for iron ore since the specific gravity
of the medium is too low. The Barvoys process
based on a suspension of clay and fine-sized
barite has been used on coal in Holland. The
Conklin process was used by the Hudson Coal
Company in 1922 for cleaning anthracite. Minus
200 mesh magnetite was used as medium.

C. Erb Wuensch obtained the first patents
granted in the United States on a sink-float
method of mineral processing based on the principle of stable or semi-stable media of controllable
gravity. The basic U.S. Patents covering his work
were issued during the period 1933 to 1939.
Wuensch introduced his new process to operators
of the Tri-State lead-zinc district during the
early nineteen thirties. Since his pioneering
work is considered the real beginning of the

---

(1) Foulke, W.B.:Heavy Organic Liquids Used for
    Separation in Sink and Float Process, Coal
    Age, vol 43, May 1938, p 74-79.

modern heavy-media separation process, Wuensch's early patents are listed here:

U.S. Patent No.			
1,895,504	January	31,	1933
1,895,505	January	31,	1933
2,113,609	April	12,	1938
2,125,663	August	2,	1938
2,135,957	November	8,	1938
2,139,789	December	13,	1938
2,151,175	March	21,	1939
2,373,635	April	10,	1945

The first large successful plant using galena medium, pioneered by Wuensch, was built by American Zinc, Lead and Smelting Company at Mascot, Tennessee in 1936. A 10-ft-diameter cone-type vessel successfully processed up to 160 tons of zinc ore per hour. This heavy-media plant replaced a jig plant with the net result of a 4 percent increase in recovery and a much simplified flow sheet. The Mascot plant was followed by a much larger installation at the Central Mill of Eagle-Picher Mining & Smelting Company near Cardin, Oklahoma in 1939. This plant handled 10,000 tons of low-grade lead-zinc ores per day and was later enlarged to handle 12,000 tons per day.

In 1937 a test unit was operated at the Merritt plant of Butler Brothers on the Cuyuna Range to determine the efficiency of the process on iron ores. The galena medium proved unsuccessful and the plant was shut down. Further experimentation by Henry Wade of the University of Minnesota and the Butler Brothers research group led to successful development of ferrosilicon as a medium for heavy-media separation processes. In 1939 the first plant in the world to use ferrosilicon medium was successfully operated at Cooley, Minnesota. This revolutionary development led to rapid adoption of the heavy-media process all over the world.[2]

(2) Hyer, J.W.Jr.:Heavy-Density Separation--A Review of Its Literature, Colorado School of Mines Quarterly, vol 43, Jan. 1948, 94 pp.

Basic Components of Heavy-Media Plants

Heavy-media separation plants for iron ore beneficiation consist of three basic components. These are:

1) Medium handling and processing equipment
2) Feed preparation and product handling equipment
3) Separatory vessels

The preparation, control, continuous cleaning and re-introduction of medium into a heavy-media circuit is the most complex phase of plant operation. However, even this phase is simple as compared to many other beneficiation methods. All iron ore heavy-media plants use magnetic media. The favored medium for iron ore processing is ferrosilicon. The grade used is usually 85 percent iron and 15 percent silicon. Table I lists various properties of ferrosilicon and magnetite media used in iron ore plants. The processing and control of magnetic media is considerably more simple than the steps involved when non-magnetic media are used. It is significant that basic flow sheets for the latest 1956 plants are very similar to the flow sheet used in the first plant which pioneered magnetic media. Figure 1 is a simplified standard flow sheet for heavy-media plants using magnetic media. There has been a steady trend towards simplification of flow sheets in heavy-media plants. This trend has been assisted by the design and manufacture of equipment specifically for the heavy-media process.

The main requirement of the medium handling section of a heavy-media plant is to continuously provide clean, well-dispersed medium to the separatory vessel. This is accomplished by use of magnetizing blocks, thickeners, magnetic separators, densifiers and demagnetizing coils. The magnetizing blocks speed up the thickening operation; the separators clean the medium; densifiers increase the density of pulps discharged from the magnetic separators; demagnetizing coils disperse the magnetic particles before they are fed to the separatory vessel. Ferrosilicon medium will provide the following specific gravities for various pulp densities:

TABLE I

Properties of Ferrosilicon & Magnetite Media

Size Analyses of Media

Mesh	New FeSi, % Wt.		Magnetite, %Wt.	
	65 mesh	100 mesh	Taconite Conct.	Eastern Conct.
plus 65	5.5	0.0		11.0
" 100	11.0	0.6		7.0
" 150	11.5	8.8	5-8	10.0
" 200	10.5	21.0	7-10	13.0
" 325	11.0	18.0	17-24	14.0
" 400	24.5	16.3	(65-75)*	(45.0)*
- 400	26.0	35.3		

( )*weight percent minus 325 mesh.

Chemical Analysis of Ferrosilicon

Iron	84-85%
Silicon	15%
Carbon, max.	0.15%
Sulphur, max.	0.04%
Phos., max.	0.05%

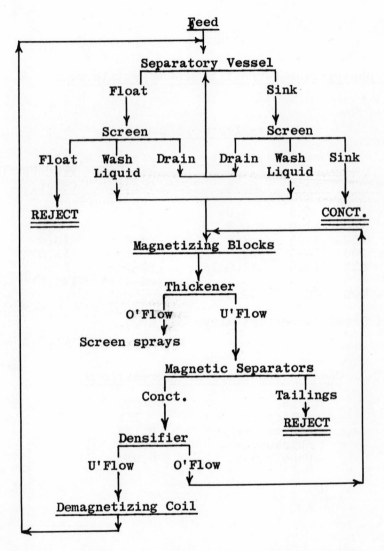

Figure 1.   Simplified Flowsheet for
Heavy-Media Plant (Magnetic)

% Solids	Specific Gravity
64	2.20
73	2.60
79	3.00
83	3.40
85	3.60

The specific gravity of the medium can be controlled by adjusting the speed of the densifier
spiral (the densifier is usually a simple spiral-
type classifier). As the speed of the spiral is
increased, the density of the underflow discharge
decreases. The amount of moisture entering the
circuit with feed ore is held as constant as possible; the return medium is held at a density high
enough to compensate for water entering the system
with the feed.

Ordinarily a considerable excess tonnage of
medium is held in the circuit or is readily available in a wetted condition. New ferrosilicon
should be agitated for a few hours, cleaned, and
then soaked for a few days before placing in service. This treatment serves to remove some of the
sharp corners, produce more fine particles and re-
moves carbon and other extraneous materials present
in new medium. Chemicals sometimes used with magnetic media are trisodium phosphate for slime control; lime to inhibit decomposition of ferrosilicon
and to prevent formation of bicarbonate when carbonate ores are processed; chromium compounds help
prevent caking of media as well as aid in preven-
tion of rust and oxidation.

Both drum- and belt-type magnetic separators
are used in processing magnetic media. Rapid
growth in use of the heavy-media process has stimulated improved design and efficiency of wet magnetic separators. Medium reclamation involves the
drainage of both sink and float products followed
by thorough washing of the products on screens.
The large bulk of returned medium is drained off
the drainage screens and is sent to the separatory
vessel without further treatment. The medium obtained by washing of the separated products is
processed by steps mentioned previously. Presence
of an appreciable amount of magnetite in hematite
ores being processed by heavy-media methods some-

times complicates the medium reclamation phase of
the process. Dalhammar[3] has reported on problems
of removing magnetite which entered the ferrosilicon medium via the primarily hematitic feed ore
of a Swedish plant. Fine-sized magnetite gave
difficulty since it lowered the specific gravity
of the ferrosilicon medium. Froth flotation,
cyclones and shaking tables were tested as methods
for removing excess magnetite from the medium.
Froth flotation with sulphonate collectors was
unsuccessful due to the small tonnages handled and
the effect of flotation reagents on the medium.
The cyclone method was based on the fact that hard
ferrosilicon abraded the softer magnetite to a
much finer particle size. Cyclones, operated as
deslimers, removed the magnetite as an overflow
product. The flotation and cyclone methods were
finally discarded in favor of a shaking table which
effectively removed the slimed magnetite.
    Feed preparation for heavy-media processing of
iron ores consists of sizing, wetting and desliming of the ore. The average feed size of iron
ores processed is in the range of minus $1\frac{1}{2}$ inch
to plus $\frac{1}{4}$ inch. The material is sized by heavy
duty shaking screens. Water sprays are used to
remove fines and to provide moistened ore surfaces
which are more amenable to processing.
    Separatory vessels used on iron ores have in-
cluded cones, spiral and other types of classifiers, and a variety of drum-type vessels. Drum and
spiral classifier-type vessels are often preferred
in iron ore heavy-media plants. The function of
the vessel is extremely simple; it provides continuous removal of the sunken iron ore particles
at one point and continuous removal of floating
waste mineral at another.
    Some typical operating results of iron ore
heavy-media plants are given in Table II. It is
significant that the heavy-media tailing product
from most iron ore plants is not a low-grade
clean tailing as is customary in most non-ferrous

---

(3) Dalhammer, S. and P.H. Son Fahlstrom: The
    Heavy-Media Plant at Stripa Mine, Sweden,
    Recent Developments in Mineral Dressing
    (London) 1953, p 627-632.

TABLE II

Typical Operating Results for
Heavy-Media Plants

Plant	%Wt.	Fe,%	SiO$_2$,%	Dist. % Fe
Minnesota plant "A"				
Feed	--	41.82	35.58	--
Conct.	--	55.42	13.03	--
Tails	--	21.56	65.86	--
Alabama plant				
Feed	100.0	40.94	27.09	100.0
Conct.	74.5	51.24	9.46	93.3
Tails	25.5	10.83	78.60	6.7
Minnesota plant "B"				
Feed	100.0	54.23	16.20	100.0
Conct.	82.93	57.32	11.83	87.7
Tails	17.07	39.22	38.46	12.3
Canadian siderite				
Feed	--	31-33	11-16	--
Conct.	--	35.0	6-8	--

plants. The primary objective of the iron ore
plant is to make a finished iron ore concentrate
whereas the non-ferrous plant usually operates
the heavy-media step as a preconcentration step.

Heavy-Media Processing in Cyclones

Development of the hydrocyclone as a separatory
vessel for the heavy-media process has greatly
extended the utility of this process in the iron
ore beneficiation industry. Iron ore particles
in the "awkward" size range of minus $\frac{1}{4}$ inch to
plus 65 mesh have been processed by jigging and
other gravity separation methods. In most cases
unsatisfactory results were obtained and in cases
where ores were amenable to gravity methods, plant
costs were high. The heavy-media cyclone has
found wide application in the processing of these
sized fractions of iron ores.

The basic equipment used in a cyclone plant is
similar to that used in a conventional heavy-media
plant; only the separatory vessel is different and
the densifier is omitted. The hydrocyclone
"vessel" has had a very successful record in
thickening and classification operations. The
first test work on adaption of the cyclone to the
heavy-media process for iron ores was done by the
American Cyanamid Company at their laboratory in
Stamford, Connecticut. This work was a logical
sequence to work publicized by M.G. Driessen in
1937 relating to beneficiation of coal in a cyclone in the Netherlands. Driessen noticed that the
cyclone concentrated fine coal when the cyclone
was being used as a thickener in a sink-and-float
plant which used loess medium. Erickson and
Herkenhoff[4] released detailed results of the
first successful pilot cyclone plant on the
Mesabi Range in 1950. This pilot plant used six-
inch diameter cyclones with good results. Data
from this installation led to rapid adoption of
the method by several plants in the area.

(4) Erickson, S.E. and E.C. Herkenhoff:Cyclone
    Separator May Be Solution For Fine Ore
    Problem, Eng. & Mining Jnl., vol 151, June
    1950, p 71-73.

The cyclone used in heavy-media cyclone plants is not basically different from cyclones used as classifiers. Figure 2 is a sketch of a cyclone showing its main features. Most of the Mesabi Range heavy-media cyclone plants have standardized on the 10-inch diameter cyclone which gives a sharp separation for ores processed in that area. Earlier plants used cyclones ranging from 6 to 15 inches in diameter.

A basic difference which becomes evident in any comparison of a cyclone plant with a conventional heavy-media plant is that magnetite medium is favored. Also the medium employed has a lower specific gravity range (2.1 to 2.5). This gravity makes a separation in the cyclone which is equivalent to that obtained with heavy liquids ranging from 2.8 to 3.0. Centrifugal and centripetal forces involved in the cyclone raise the effective specific gravity to this extent. All cyclone plants on the Mesabi Range use magnetic taconite concentrates as media. Table I gives the screen analysis of taconite concentrate.

When excessive natural magnetite is present in hematite ores the coarser particles sometimes present problems in cyclone plants by "build-up" in the circulating medium. This is corrected by use of screens to remove tramp magnetite from the medium circuit.

Cyclones used in heavy-media plants generally utilize feed pressures of 12 to 35 psi. Higher pressures will increase capacity, but also greatly increase maintenance due to increased abrasion. Typical performance data from Mesabi Range heavy-media cyclone plants are given below:

	Percent	
	Fe	SiO_2
Feed	48-56	18-13
Concentrate	53-58	11-9
Tailing	33-42	65-51

The separation in a cyclone plant is controlled by changing the specific gravity of the medium just as is done in a conventional heavy-media plant. Residence time of a given particle in the cyclone is measured in fractions of a second and a large volume of medium is circulated with each

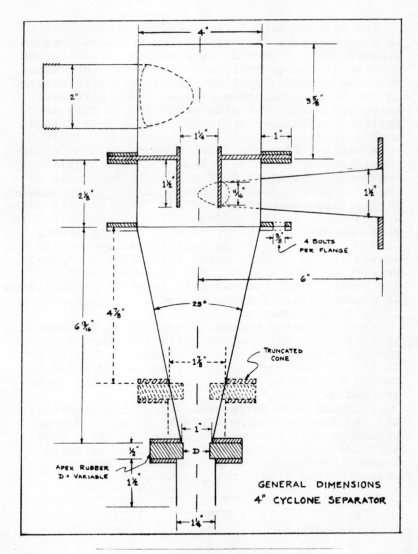

Figure 2.   General Dimensions for
a 4" Diameter Cyclone

ton of feed to the cyclone. Loss of medium in cyclone plants is generally higher than loss of medium in the conventional heavy-media plant. Manpower requirements are low and plant operating efficiency is high. Two 10-inch diameter cyclones can handle over 100 tons of minus $\frac{1}{4}$ inch feed per hour. The successful application of heavy-media cyclones to iron ores has led to use of this new beneficiation tool in the processing of several non-ferrous ores.

ADDITIONAL REFERENCES

Wuensch, C.E.:Pipeline Ore Transport May Lower
Mining Cost, Eng. & Mining Jnl., vol 145, April
1944, p 91-93.
Cronk, A.H.:Heavy-Media Cuts Costs At a Fluorspar
Mill, Eng. & Mining Jnl, vol 146, Jan. 1945,
p 66-68.
Metallurgical Staff of American Zinc, Lead and
Smelting Company:Differential Density Separation
at Mascot, Tennessee, Eng. & Mining Jnl., vol 141,
July 1940, p 35-39.
Anon:How the Cyclone Works on Mineral Separations,
Eng. & Mining Jnl., vol 148, Dec. 1947, p 74-75.
Vogel, H.H. and E.C. Bitzer:Shift to New Separator
Cuts Garnet Milling Costs, Eng. & Mining Jnl.,
vol 150, August 1949, p 62-63.
Britton, S.A.:Heavy-Density Separation Cuts Brown
Ore Treatment Cost, Eng. & Mining Jnl, vol 151,
July 1950, p 68-70.
Anon:New West Hill Plant Points Way to Mining of
Leaner Mesabi Iron Ores, Mining World, vol 16,
March 1954, p 46-50.
Shook, A.M.:Blackburn Heavy-Density Plant Opens
New Brown Iron-Ore Reserves, Eng. & Mining Jnl.,
vol 151, Sept. 1950, p 78-81.
Erickson, S.E.:How to Simplify Testing For Sink-
Float Separation, Eng. & Mining Jnl., vol 152,
June 1951, p 88-89.
Anon:How New Units, New Uses Widen Scope of Sink-
Float, Eng. & Mining Jnl., vol 152, July 1951,
p 130-133.
Banks, H.R.:It Pays to Use Scale Models for Sink-
Float Plant Installations, Eng. & Mining Jnl.,
vol 152, Sept. 1951, p 91.
Bitzer, E.C.:Finding A Way to Handle the HMS
Middlings Problem, Eng. & Mining Jnl., vol 152,
Nov. 1951, p 91-95.
Falconer, S.A.:Some Recent Investigations with
the Dutch State Mines Cyclone Separator on Fine
Coal Slurries, Mining Eng., vol 187, July 1950,
p 790-800.
Bitzer, E.C.:A New Separating Vessel for Sink-
Float Concentration, Trans. AIME vol 183, 1949,
p 257-275.

Grove, D.B., R.B. Brackin, and J.H. Polhemus:
Comparative Results with Galena and Ferrosilicon
at Mascot, Mining Eng., vol 190, August 1951,
p 691-698.
Bitzer, E.C.:Recent Developments in Heavy-Media
Concentration on the Mesabi Range, Paper pres-
ented at the Eighth Annual Mining Symposium,
Center for Continuation Study, Univ. of Minnes-
ota, Jan. 1947.
Foulke, W.B.:Sink and Float Separation Commands
New Attention, Eng. & Mining Jnl., vol 139, May
1938, p 33-39,48.
Crabtree, E.H. and T.C. King:Wet Grinding of Ferro-
silicon for Heavy Media, Trans. AIME vol 183,
1949, p 361,366.
Holt, G.J.:Development of Sink-and-Float Concen-
tration on the Iron Ranges of Minnesota, Trans.
AIME vol 169, 1946, p 209-214.
Van Slyke, W.:Hardinge Heavy-Media Separator, Paper
presented at the Eleventh Annual Mining Symposium,
Center for Continuation Study, Univ. of Minnesota,
Jan. 1950.
Erickson, S.E. and E.C. Herkenhoff:A Study of the
Application of the D.S.M. Cyclone Separator
Process to the Problem of Concentrating Fine
Iron Ores, ibid.
Meerman, P.G. and H.J. Odekerken:Sedimentation
Analysis of Magnetite, Fuel (London) vol 32,
Jan. 1953, p 62-66.
Beals, R. and L.A. Roe:A New Method for Quantita-
tive Determination of Magnetite in Magnetite-
Ferrosilicon Mixtures, Unpublished Paper.
DeVaney, F.D. and S.M. Shelton:Properties of Sus-
pension Mediums for Float-and-Sink Concentration,
U.S. Bur. Mines Rept. of Inv. 3469-R, May 1940.
Clemmons, B.H., R.H. Stacy, and B.G. Saunders:
Concentratability of Birmingham, Ala. Red Iron
Ores by Separation in Heavy Media, U.S. Bur. Mines
Rept. of Inv. 4249, May 1948.
Kenworthy, W.A., W.A. Calhoun and M.M. Fine:In-
vestigation of Concentration Sections at the
Central Mill of the Eagle-Picher Mining & Smelt-
ing Co., Cardin, Okla., U.S. Bur. Mines Rept. of
Inv. 4511, May 1949, 37 pp.
Gaudin, A.M.:Principles of Mineral Dressing,
McGraw-Hill Book Co. N.Y., 1939, p 239-249.

Geer, M.R. and H.F. Yancey:Preliminary American Tests of a Cyclone Coal Washer Developed in the Netherlands, Trans. AIME vol 177, 1948, p 220-239.

Driessen, M.G.:The Use of Hydraulic Cyclones as Thickeners and Washers in Modern Coal Preparation, ibid, p 240-261.

Yancey, H.F. and M.R. Geer:The Cyclone as a Thickener of Coal Slurry, ibid, p 262-291.

Kelsall, D.F.:A Study of the Motion of Solid Particles in a Hydraulic Cyclone, Recent Developments In Mineral Dressing, The Institution of Mining & Met. (London), 1953, p 209-227.

Fontein, F.J. and Ir. C. Dijksman:The Hydrocyclone, Its Application and Its Explanation, ibid, p 229-257.

Michell, F.B.:Recent Developments in Gravity Concentration, ibid, p 261-269.

Fern, K.A.:Major Alterations in Heavy Media Separation During Recent Years, ibid, p 271-278.

Trotter, F.J.:Recent Developments in Plant Design for Dense Medium Processes, ibid, p 279-296.

Palowitch, E.R., T.R. Jolley, and M. Sokaski:Use of Pulverized Rock as Dense Medium for Salvaging Coal from Pittsburgh-Bed Refuse, U.S. Bur. Mines Rept of Inv. 5184, Dec. 1955, 33 pp.

Brown, R.L. and W.H. Ode:Annual Report of Research and Technologic Work on Coal and Related Investigations, Fiscal Year 1952, U.S. Bur. Mines Inf. Circular 7663, 1953, 67 pp.

Hidnert, P. and E.L. Peffer:Density of Solids and Liquids, Natl. Bur. of Standards Circular 487, March 15, 1950, 29 pp.

Crabtree, E.H.:Comparison of Galena and Ferrosilicon in Heavy-Media Separation, AIME Tech. Pub. 2181, March, 1947, 5 pp.

Van Slyke, W.R. and R.A. Derby:Pilot Cyclone Plant Paves Way for Two Full-Scale Operations, Eng. & Mining Jnl., vol 154, April 1953, p 88-94.

Chapter VI

TABLING & SPIRAL TREATMENT

"The theory of the prospector's
pan is undoubtedly to be derived from the laws of centrifugal
force, which has been shown to
be the most powerful agent applied in the treatment of ores
by water. "---J.A. Church, Trans.
AIME vol. 8, 1880, p 146.

Tables and Humphreys spirals can both be considered examples of flowing-film concentrators.
In both machines, the velocity of the water varies
at different depths of the film. The velocity
approaches zero at the bottom of the film and
reaches its maximum just below the water surface.
Spirals also utilize centrifugal and centripetal
forces not used by tables.

Shaking Tables

The shaking table consists of a plane surface,
inclined slightly from the horizontal;this surface is jerked or shaken in the direction of the
long axis and washed at right angles to the direction of motion by a film of water. Riffles or
cleats are usually provided on the deck surface
to provide quiescent zones and to guide the heavier particles to the concentrate removal area.
Figure 1 illustrates the action of a typical concentrating table . The reciprocating motion of a
table is such that the deck moves relatively slowly away from the head motion or power source and
returns quickly toward it. This action causes
intermittent travel of the ore particles along
the deck as they are exposed to the transverse
film of water. The ore fed to the table flows to
the deck at the upper corner near the head motion.
The higher gravity particles separate according
to their specific gravity and deposit between

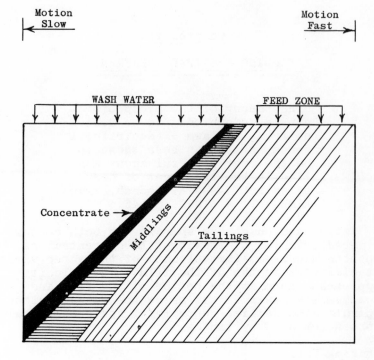

Figure 1.   Diagram Illustrating Action of
an Ore Concentrating Table

the riffles. The low-gravity gangue minerals
flow across the riffles as they are exposed to
repeated washing. The shaking action transports
the heavy particles parallel to the long axis of
the deck and discharges them as concentrate and
middling products.

According to Gaudin [1] the famous silver mines
of Attica utilized stationary stone tables   for
concentration of argentiferous lead ores.   This
was the beginning of the tabling process;a long
successful career followed until the advent   of
froth flotation early in the twentieth century.
As the flotation process proved its   efficiency,
tables were replaced by flotation cells in   most
plants processing non-ferrous ores.   In the coal
preparation field flotation was much less competitive and large table installations are still in
use.

Several of the early eastern United States iron
ore processing plants used tables to recover non-
magnetic iron ore minerals from magnetic separator
tailings.   The Scrub Oak mine was reopened in 1917
by the Wharton Steel Company to obtain Bessemer
ore for its furnaces.   The mill included dry Ball-
Norton magnetic separators, wet pulsator jigs,
and tables to recover martite.   In 1929 this mill
was rebuilt and again used tables for recovery of
the nonmagnetic iron minerals.   Roche and Crockett[2] described the improved plant in 1933.   A
summary of metallurgical results of the tabling
section follows:

	% Fe	Tons/hour
Table feed	10.17	54.2
Concentrate	60.03	5.3
Tailing	4.75	48.9

Ratio of Concn.	10.2:1
Iron Recovery	58 percent.

Other eastern iron ore beneficiation plants
which have used tables to concentrate the nonmag-

---

(1) Gaudin, A.M.:Principles of Mineral Dressing,
    McGraw-Hill Book Co. New York, 1939, 554 pp.
(2) Roche, H.M., and R.E. Crockett:Iron-Ore Mill-
    ing at Scrub Oak, Eng. & Mining Jnl., vol
    134, 1933, p 161.

netic fraction of their ores are the Ringwood Mill
in New Jersey and the Cornwall Mill at Lebanon,
Pennsylvania. The historic Trout Lake plant of
the Oliver Iron Mining Company at Coleraine,
Minnesota at one time included twenty Overstrom
tables in its flowsheet. These tables produced
about 350 pounds of concentrate per table per
hour from a low-grade feed. DeVaney and Coghill[3]
reported that use of these tables had been discontinued by 1930. In this same report a review
was given of work by the U.S. Bureau of Mines on
concentration tests on tailings from the washing
plants of the Mesabi Range. The effectiveness of
the tabling method of concentration was summarized
as follows:"Provided the feed is first classified,
tabling is also effective. Concentrates were
made with a tenor of 61 percent iron, 0.0343 percent phosphorus, and 8.85 percent silica, and
contained 82 percent of the total iron". Details
of these tests are reproduced in Table I.

In spite of the favorable results reported by
the U.S. Bureau of Mines and others, the use of
tables never reached any large scale commercial
use in the Lake Superior District. However one
large plant was placed in operation in the Birmingham, Alabama area in 1940. This was the
Spaulding plant of Republic Steel Corporation[4].
The plant was designed as a 1000-ton per day pilot
plant, but wartime demands for increased iron ore
production forced expansion of the plant to 3000
tons. An all-gravity method of concentration was
employed. The flowsheet involved crushing to 3/8-
inch, grinding to 8 mesh, desliming, hydraulic
classification, tabling, filtering and sintering.
Eight-cell hydraulic classifiers were used in
preparation of the table feed. Eighty-eight dia-
gonal deck, rubber-covered tables produced concentrate, middling, and tailing products. The middling product was rescuffed in rod mills before
retreatment on tables. The ore contained 32-36%
Fe, 20-30% SiO_2, 3-4% Al_2O_3, 7-12% CaO, and 0.25-

(3) DeVaney, F.D. and W.H. Coghill:Concentration
     Tests on Tailings from the Washing Plants of
     the Mesabi Range, Minn., U.S. Bur. Mines Rept.
     of Inv. 3052, Nov. 1930, 23 pp.
(4) Lee, O:Birmingham's Future Depends on Concen-
     tration, E & M J vol 145, Oct 1944, p104-106.

TABLE   I

Results of Table Tests on Mesabi Range Washing Plant Tailings *

Product	%Fe	%Insol.	% of total Fe	Insol
Head sample	50.89	24.20	100.00	100.00
Spigot 1 Conc.	60.21	10.30	17.96	6.45
Spigot 2 Conc.	62.89	7.68	12.02	3.08
Spigot 3 "	63.69	6.60	12.56	2.73
Spigot 4 "	64.18	6.60	6.74	1.45
Spigot 5 "	64.58	6.40	2.06	.43
Spigot 6 "	61.40	11.40	1.54	.60
Middling	58.73	12.80	14.55	6.66
Plus 8 mesh	56.94	13.20	14.71	7.15
Total Concts.	61.03	9.48	82.14	28.55
Total Tails	29.70	53.11	17.86	71.45

*Data from U.S. Bureau of Mines Rept. of
  Investigations 3052, Nov. 1930 p 21.

0.38% P. Manganese averaged about 0.2%. The
table concentrates contained 46-48% Fe, 9-11%
SiO_2, 3-3.8% Al_2O_3, and 6-8% CaO. Iron recovery
ranged from 50 to 63 percent, depending on the
iron content of the crude ore.

The Humphreys Spiral Concentrator

The successful introduction of the Humphreys
Spiral Concentrator in 1943 provided a new gravity concentration machine for use on iron ores .
This device was first used at an Oregon plant
which processed beach sands containing chromite.
An earlier table plant had proven uneconomical
but spirals were immediately successful. Huttl[5]
described this early plant which used 56 spiral
concentrators.
The Humphreys Spiral Concentrator is a spiral
channel with a modified semi-circular cross-section. The standard spiral has five complete
turns but three-turn units are used in some instances. As the water and solids flow down the
channel grains with the highest specific gravity
move in toward the inside of the channel. The
lighter weight particles move to the outside and
are carried away by the faster running water.
Simple disc-splitters direct the flow of heavy,
fine grains into concentrate ports set at 120
degree intervals in the bottom of the channel.
Wash water is added at the inner edge of the
stream and flows outwardly across the concentrate
band. There are fifteen ports in a five-turn unit
but usually some are blocked off and do not remove
concentrate. The material drawn off from ports
in the final turn is usually returned as a middling product. The spiral has no moving parts,
requires very little floor space, and has a low
operating cost. Figure 2 is a photograph of a
Humphreys Spiral Concentrator.

(5) Huttl, J.B.:New Type Concentrator Cuts
     Chromite Dressing Costs, Eng. & Mining Jnl.,
     vol 144, Oct. 1943, p 68-70.

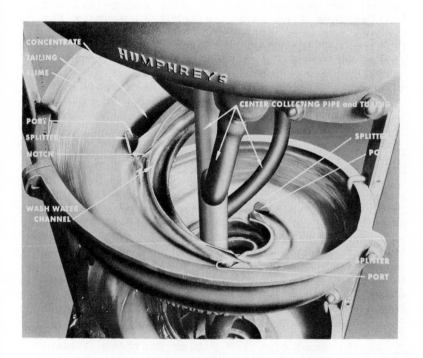

Figure 2. Humphreys Spiral Concentrator
(Photo courtesy The Humphreys
Investment Company)

In 1947 Erck [6] reported on the first application of Humphreys spirals to iron ore concentration. Tests were made by the Humphreys Investment Company on Minnesota iron ore in Denver in 1943. The results were encouraging enough to have a spiral sent to the University of Minnesota Mines Experiment Station for further tests. Following these tests, the spiral was shipped to a Mesabi Range plant where various washing plant products were tested for amenability. It soon became evident that maximum feed size was about 10 mesh or the same as for many non-ferrous ores. This meant that one of the most suitable applications for the spiral would be further processing of classifier overflows which contained a minimum of plus 10-mesh material. Early in 1947 Butler Brothers installed a spiral pilot plant at their Patrick Washer near Cooley, Minnesota. The plant had a capacity of about 20 tons per hour.

The first commercial spiral plant for beneficiation of iron ores was completed in 1948 at the Hill-Trumbull plant of the Cleveland - Cliffs Iron Company on the Mesabi Range. Plant operations and results were described in detail by Brown and Erck [7] . In this plant two stages of spirals were used to process minus 1/8-inch material from a heavy-media plant. A total of 84 spirals processed 120 tons of feed per hour with good results. The spiral concentrate produced during one month averaged 56.10 percent iron and 13.26 percent silica. About 78 tons of concentrate were recovered per hour from 120 tons of feed material. A flowsheet of the Hill-Trumbull spiral plant is given in Figure 3.

At the same time the Butler Brothers Company was experimenting with Mesabi ores, the Jones & Laughlin Steel Corporation was operating a five-spiral plant at Benson Mines, New York. This

(6)   Erck, L.J.:Humphreys Spiral Concentrator, Eighth Annual Mining Symposium, Center for Continuation Study, Univ. of Minn., Jan. 1947, p 52-59.

(7)   Brown, W.E. and L.J. Erck:Humphreys Spiral Concentration on Mesabi Range Ores, AIME Trans., vol 184, 1949, Mining Eng. June, 1949, p 187-193,405.

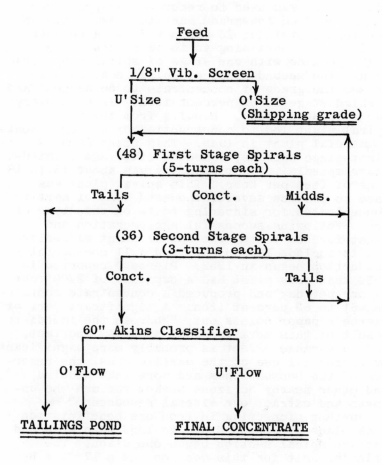

Figure 3. Flowsheet of Hill-Trumbull
           Spiral Plant (Minnesota)

Note: Flowsheet from page 188, Trans.
      AIME vol 184, 1949.

pilot plant was used to recover high-grade concentrates from low-grade martite ores. With an
ore feed containing 25 percent iron, a rougher
concentrate containing 45 to 48 percent iron
could be made with one stage of spiral concentration. The second stage of spiral concentration
raised the grade of concentrate to 56 percent and
a third stage to 62 percent iron. Iron recovery
was over 80 percent. Results from the five-
spiral plant led to construction of a larger semi-
commercial plant in 1948. This plant used 12
first-stage spirals, 6 second-stage and 6 third-
stage spirals. Plant capacity was about 16 to 18
tons of feed per hour. This spiral plant was
used to produce several thousand tons of martite
concentrates for sintering tests on this type of
ore. Following successful agglomeration and
blast-furnace tests, the spiral plant was enlarged to include 160 spirals and full commercial
production began in 1952. Pierce [8] reported in
1954 that this plant had a capacity of 2700 tons
of ore per day and produced a concentrate containing 61 to 62 percent iron. A significant part of
Pierce's paper points out, "Whereas the immediate
result of this metallurgical step is important,
the long-range effect is probably more significant.
By economical use of the martite ores, the reserves of the Benson Mines are more than doubled,
and other nearby horizons beckon the men who un-
cover and extract our mineral resources."

Further pioneering in iron ore beneficiation
took place at Benson Mines in 1953 when a second
martite spiral section began operation. The
grinding unit for this section was a 17 foot by
5 foot Aerofall mill. Fleck and Durocher [9] reported on this important development in 1955. The
primary objective in using this new grinding mill
was to reduce the quantity of minus 100-mesh
material in the feed to the spirals. Laboratory
tests had shown conclusively that an Aerofall
ground product gave superior metallurgy as compared

(8) Pierce, J.C.:Stripping is Big Mining Too,
      Compressed Air Magazine, vol 59, June 1954,
      p 161-164.
(9) Fleck, R.G. & R.E. Durocher:A Progress Report
      on the Aerofall Mill, Mining Congress Jnl.,
      vol 41, Dec. 1955, p 52-54.

to a wet rod mill product. Tables II and   III
give a comparison of screen analyses of the products from the two types of mills as well   as
metallurgical results. One feature of the spiral
concentration process at Benson Mines which is
different than other similar operations   is the
presence of considerable quantities of   garnet.
Due to its high specific gravity, the garnet tends
to report in the concentrate. As a consequence,
a third stage of spirals is required for   final
cleaning of the concentrates. Figure 4 is a
flowsheet of the Benson spiral plant. Figure 5
is a photograph of some of the spirals.

     A report by Hubbard [10] in 1953 claimed   that
approximately 4500 spirals were in use   at that
time in all types of plants;of this number, 760
spirals were in use in 10 Lake Superior iron ore
processing plants. These iron ore plants had a
total output of nearly three-quarters of a million
tons of concentrates per year. In Sierra Leone,
Africa 256 molded rubber spirals were processing
a specular hematite ore. Numerous spiral installations have appeared in iron ore plants all over
the world after their high efficiency became
apparent.

The Future for Tables and Spirals

     The future for Humphreys Spiral Concentrators
appears bright in the field of iron ore beneficiation. The same cannot be said for tables unless
improved models appear. Metallurgical results
for processing iron ores on tables and spirals
are not significantly different for most   ores.
It is quite apparent that the spiral has   the
advantage of unclassified feed, no power required,
no moving parts, and less floor space.

     It appears that some progress can be expected
in the direction of less power, more capacity per
unit of floor space and lowered cost of maintain-
ance for future tables. The Bjorksten Research
Laboratories of Madison, Wisconsin fabricated a

(10) Hubbard, J.S., I.B. Humphreys, and W.E.Brown:
     How Humphreys Spiral Concentrator is Used in
     Modern Dressing Practice, Mining World, May,
     1953, (Bulletin 17, Humphreys Invest. Co.)

TABLE II

Comparison of screen analyses--
Rod mill product vs Aerofall product

Mesh	Rod mill product Cum. % Weight	Aerofall product Cum. % Weight
10	0.2	3.7
14	1.0	7.0
20	10.2	22.2
28	22.6	35.9
35	37.2	49.4
48	51.4	62.2
65	63.5	72.0
100	73.5	79.4
150	80.6	85.5
200	85.5	89.4
-200	100.0	100.0

TABLE III

Metallurgical results--Rod Mill vs Aerofall

	Rod Mill Product % Fe	Aerofall Product % Fe
Head	24.40	24.30
Concentrate	60.65	60.60
Tailing	8.80	7.20
Recovery	74.48	79.86
Ratio of Conc.	3.32	3.12

Note: Data from page 54, Mining Congress
Journal, December 1955

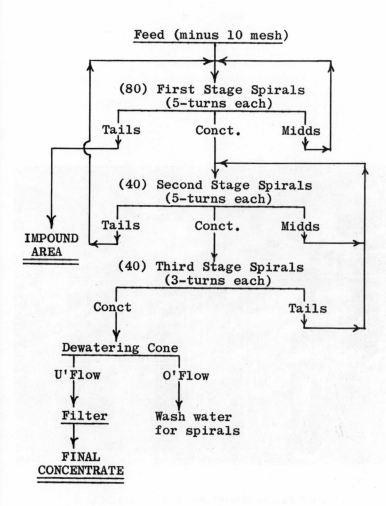

Figure 4. Benson Mines, N.Y. Spiral
Plant Flowsheet

Note: Flowsheet from page 54, Mining
Congress Journal, December 1955

Figure 5.   Benson Mines, N.Y. Spiral Plant
(Photo courtesy Jones & Laughlin
Steel Corp.)

glass fiber reinforced plastic slime deck for a
laboratory-size Wilfley table in 1952. Preliminary testing of this unit gave encouraging results
and indicated that a light-weight plastic deck
could be developed for commercial use. In the
test unit the riffles were cast as an integral
part of the deck. Wear was rapid and indicated
that rubber covering would be desireable.
Hughes [11] reported on the use of aluminum decks
and riffles in a Florida phosphate plant. In the
same plant spirals are operated in parallel with
tables. The operators felt that the tables gave
the sharpest separation on this ore.
    Spirals do have their maintenance problems.
Many iron ores are very abrasive and rapidly wear
deep grooves in the surface of the spirals.
Most spirals in service are made from cast iron.
The Benson Mines plant has installed spirals cast
from a special alloy with good results. Various
types of rubber liners and solid rubber spirals
have been applied to non-ferrous ores with some
success. Lenhart [12] and others [13] described
methods of rubber coating spirals at a Florida
spiral plant which processes large tonnages of
beach sands to recover ilmenite and other minerals.
This Florida plant uses a total of 1100 spirals
to process about 20,000 tons of sand per day.
Various glass and ceramic coatings have also been
applied to spiral surfaces with some success.

(11) Hughes, C.V.O.:Modern Hydraulic Mining in
     Florida With a Survey of Beneficiation
     Practice, Mining Eng. vol 8, Jan. 1956,
     p 31-38.
(12) Lenhart, W.B.:Spiral Concentrators for Grav-
     ity Separation of Minerals, Rock Products,
     vol. 54, Dec. 1951, p 92-95,131.
(13) Anon:Spiral Linings Successful with Abrasive
     Sands at Trail Ridge Plant, Eng. & Mining
     Jnl., vol. 154, Jan. 1953, p 102-104.

ADDITIONAL REFERENCES

Coghill, W.H., G.D. Coe, and H.N. McDonald:Class-
ification and Tabling of Birmingham (Ala.) Red
Iron Ores With Recommendations for Added Recovery, U.S. Bur. Mines Rept. of Inv. 3789, Jan.
1945, 18 pp.

Clemmons, B.H.:The Future of Birmingham Red Iron
Ore, Jefferson County, Ala., Part II - Concentration, U.S. Bur. Mines Rept. of Inv. 4988, July,
1953, p 21-71.

DeVaney, F.D., B.W. Gandrud, and W.H. Coghill:
Gravity Concentration of Alabama Oolitic Iron
Ores, U.S. Bur. Mines Rept. of Inv. 2937, 1929,
7 pp.

DeVaney, F.D.:Differential Grinding as an Aid to
Ore Concentration, Eng. & Mining Jnl., vol 139,
1938, p 43-45.

Coghill, W.H. and P.H. Delano:Differential Grinding of Alabama Iron Ores for Gravity Concentration
U.S. Bur. Mines Rept. of Inv. 3523, 1940, 6 pp.

Singewald, J.T.:Concentration Experiments on the
Siliceous Red Hematites of the Birmingham District, Ala., U.S. Bur. Mines Bulletin 110, 1917,
91 pp.

Coghill, W.H., G.D. Coe, and I.L. Feld:Performance
of Hydraulic Classifier Designed to Incorporate
Four Hitherto Neglected Principles, U.S. Bur.
Mines Rept. of Inv. 3844, 1945, 13 pp.

Gandrud, B.W., A.C. Richardson, and B.S. Followill:
Classification and Tabling of Alabama Red Iron
Ore, U.S. Bur. Mines Rept. of Inv. 3224, 1934,
7 pp.

Coghill, W.H., G.T. Adams, and H.S. Hardman:
Improved Laboratory Concentration Table, U.S.
Bur. Mines Rept. of Inv. 3831, Oct. 1945, 3 pp.

Bradwell, E.S.:Application of Hindered Settling
to Hydraulic Classifiers, Trans. AIME, vol 46,
1913, p 266-276.

Fahrenwald, A.W.:Classifier Efficiency, Trans.
AIME, vol. 87, 1930, p 82.

Bird, B.M. and H.F. Yancey:Hindered-Settling
Classification of Feed to Coal-Washing Tables,
Trans. AIME, vol 88, p 250-271.

DeVaney, F.D. and W.H. Coghill:Concentration of
the Rake Discharge From a Bowl Classifier in a
Washing Plant of the Mesabi Range, U.S. Bur.
Mines Rept. of Inv. 3148, 1932, 7 pp.
Taggart, A.F.:Handbook of Mineral Dressing, John
Wiley & Sons, New York, 1945, Section 11, p 59-90.
Gandrud, B.W.:Concentrating Tables, Coal Prepara-
tion, Chapt. 13, AIME, New York, 1950.
Fahrenwald, A.W. and W.F. Meckel:The Relation of
Table Feed Preparation to Table Efficiency, U.S.
Bur. Mines Rept. of Inv. 2949, July 1929, 15 pp.
Finkey, J.:The Scientific Fundamentals of Gravity
Concentration, English Translation by C.O. And-
erson and M.H. Griffitts, Missouri School of
Mines Bulletin, vol 11, No. 1, Nov. 1927, 295 pp.
Roe, L.A.:Taconite Plants, New Processes Come
First in Iron Ore Plans, Eng. & Mining Jnl., vol.
153, Feb. 1952, p 125-127.
Lee, O.:U. S. Patent 2,514,958, July 11, 1950,
Concentration of Oolitic Iron Ores, (assigned to
the Republic Steel Corp.).
Carpenter, R.D.:Mineral Beneficiation by Gravity
Concentration, A Fundamental Study, Idaho Bur.
Mines & Geology Pamphlet No. 84, April 1949, 16pp.
Kenworthy, H., W.A. Calhoun, and M.M. Fine:Invest-
igation of Concentration Sections at the Central
Mill of the Eagle-Picher Mining & Smelting Co.,
Cardin, Okla., U.S. Bur. Mines Rept. of Inv.
4511, May, 1949, 37 pp.
Odintsov, D.Y.:Lining Slide Surfaces of Coal Bene-
ficiation Equipment With Hard Glass, Ugol, vol.
28, No. 8, 1953, p 44-45;Chem. Abs. vol. 47,
Nov. 10, 1945, p 11694c.
Humphreys, I.B. and J.S Hubbard:Where Spirals
Replaced Tables, Flotation Cells, Eng. & Mining
Jnl., vol. 146, March 1945, p 82-84.
Gleeson, G.W.:Why The Humphreys Spiral Works,
ibid, p 85-86.
Humphreys, I.B.:U.S. Patents 2,431,559 and
2,431,560, Nov. 25, 1947,(assigned to the Hum-
phreys Investment Company).
Thunaes, A. and H.R. Spedden:An Improved Method
of Gravity Concentration in the Fine-Size Range,
Mining Eng. vol. 187, Aug. 1950, p 879-882.
Huttl, J.B.:Modern Device Makes Tin Plant Possible,
Eng. & Mining Jnl. vol. 147, May 1946, p 85-87.

Thompson, J.V. and W.E. Brown:The Humphreys
  Spiral - Some Present and Potential Applications,
  Eng. & Mining Jnl. vol. 151, Aug. 1950, p 87-89.
Detweiler, J.C.:Jacksonville Plant Produces Tit-
  anium from Beach Deposit, Mining Eng. vol. 4,
  June 1952, p 560-562.
Hudspeth, W.R.:Spirals Recover Heavy Mineral By-
  Product - Kings Mountain, N.C., Mining Eng. vol.
  4, Aug. 1952, p 767.
Anon:Florida Sands Boost Supply of Titanium Min-
  eral, Eng. & Mining Jnl. vol 153, May 1952,
  p 82-87.
Otto, H.H., V.H. Wilson, and W.L. Dennen:Prepar-
  ation of Anthracite Silt for Boiler Fuel in a
  Humphreys Spiral Test Plant, Trans. of the Fifth
  Annual Anthracite Conf., Lehigh Univ. May 1947,
  p 270-291.
Anon:Manual of Operating Instructions for the
  Humphreys Spiral Concentrator, Bulletin 10A,
  May 1952, 28 pp. The Humphreys Investment Co.,
  Denver, Colorado.
Hubbard, J.S.:Spiral Concentration, Mining World,
  vol 10, Sept. 1948, p 40-44.
Gillingham, W.P.:Concentrating Minerals in Cast-
  Iron Spirals, Compressed Air Magazine, April
  1949, p 91-93.
Carpenter, J.H. et al:Mining and Concentration of
  Ilmenite and Associated Minerals at Trail Ridge,
  Florida, Mining Eng. vol 5, Aug. 1953, p 789-795.
Roberts, A.E.:How New 3 Million Dollar Highland
  Plant Recovers Titaniferous Minerals, Mining
  World, vol 17, Oct. 1955, p 52-55,72.
Snedden, H.D.:Tuning a Humphreys Spiral Concen-
  trator Plant for Efficient Operation, Paper
  presented at Feb. 1956 annual meeting AIME,
  New York, 4 pp.

Chapter VII

FLOTATION

"The Cleveland - Cliffs Iron
Company and the Ford Motor
Company today announced they
soon will begin mining operations to produce 400,000
tons of concentrates a year
from the Marquette Range at
Humboldt on a property which
has lain dormant to commercial
mining since 1920."--- The
Mining Journal, Marquette,
Michigan, Nov. 21, 1951.

The above announcement marked the beginning of
commercial iron-ore flotation in America. The
Humboldt plant is small as compared to other
iron-ore beneficiation plants used in the Lake
Superior District but has made a definite contribution to the industry. Flotation is the art or
science of separating particles from each other
in a liquid pulp by causing and utilizing prefer-
ential affinity of certain particles for air bubbles. In the case of iron ores, either the iron
minerals or the gangue minerals can be so activated that either will become attached to air bubbles and be removed as a froth product.

The recorded history of the flotation process
begins with the writings of the historian Herod-
otus wherein he mentions the recovery of gold by
use of pitch-covered feathers which were dipped
into gold-bearing muds. The first patent on the
subject was issued to William Haynes in 1860
(British Patent 488). Froth flotation, as we
know it today, matured rapidly during the period
1903 to 1910. Then, after several years of
patent litigation, the flotation process emerged
as the greatest minerals beneficiation advance of
the twentieth century. Practically all the early
successful applications involved flotation of

sulphide ores. The use of soaps for the flotation of non-metallics in 1925 marked the application of the flotation process to ores similar in behavior to iron oxide ores. From 1925 to the present time, the major advances in the art of iron ore flotation have been in the flotation of the gangue minerals from iron oxides. Gaudin [1], in 1932, predicted, "Magnetite and crystalline (specular) hematite may be expected to display fairly high floatability under proper conditions because of their relatively macrocrystalline condition, but hydrated oxides such as limonite may be refractory";this has been true and development of processes for activation and flotation of goethite and hematite has been slow.

In 1931 an attempt was made by the Manganiferous Iron Company at Crosby, Minnesota to float iron oxides on a plant scale. The flotation plant processed five tons of feed per hour and made concentrates containing about 54 percent combined iron and manganese and 13 to 14 percent silica. Recovery was low and the plant was soon shut down. Other attempts to float iron ores were made on a pilot-plant scale but none succeeded in developing a commercially successful operation. As of early 1956 there were only two commercial iron ore flotation plants in America and several small plants in the rest of the world.

Iron ore flotation processes can be classified by the two very inclusive terms, (1) anionic and (2) cationic flotation methods. Either of the methods can be utilized to recover the economic iron minerals in the froth product or in the underflow product.

Anionic Flotation

The three general types of flotation reagents are collectors, frothers, and modifiers. The function of the collector reagent is to promote affinity between mineral particles and air bubbles by formation of a water repellent coating on the

(1) Gaudin, A.M.:Flotation, McGraw-Hill Book Company, New York, 1932, p 375.

surface of the mineral. Flotation reagents which
ionize to yield a negatively charged ion, are
called anionic collectors. Examples of such collectors are fatty acids, resin acids, soaps, and
alkyl sulfates or sulfonates. Table I lists some
of the more common flotation reagents which have
been used in the flotation of iron ores. Approximate prices and the usual consumption in pounds
per ton of feed ore are also given.

The earliest attempts to float iron oxide minerals involved the use of anionic collectors such
as oleic acid or sodium oleate. Such a process
was used at the Cuyuna Range plant which processed
manganiferous iron ore in 1931. The only successful domestic iron ore flotation plants (Marquette
County, Michigan) use an anionic flotation process.
Anionic flotation of iron oxides has been accomplished in both acid and basic circuits. The acid
circuits are, of course, unsuited to ores containing large amounts of calcite or other acid-consum-
ing minerals. Work by the American Cyanamid Company has shown good results using sulfonated tall-
oels or petroleum sulfonates in strongly acid circuits. Many batch and pilot-plant tests on a wide
range of iron oxide ores have demonstrated the
versatility of sulfonated reagents, but no large
scale commercial application has been reported.
The commercial success of strongly acid circuits
in feldspar, garnet, glass sand, and mica flotation plants provides proof that corrosion problems
can be overcome at reasonable cost.

Keck and Jasberg[2] were pioneers in the field
of sulphonate-type flotation reagents. They first
reported tests on a xanthate-soap process being
investigated for processing copper ores. They
used a petroleum sulphonate product which was
supplied by the Sherwood Petroleum Company. The
sulphonate-type reagents were described in detail
by Runke[3] in connection with some U.S. Bureau of

---

(2) Keck, W.E. and P. Jasberg:Mahogany Soap As a
    Flotation Reagent, Eng. & Mining Jnl., vol
    140, June 1939, p 49-51.
(3) Runke, S.M.:Petroleum Sulphonate Flotation of
    Beryl, U.S. Bur. Mines Rept. of Inv. 5067,
    July 1954, p 5.

TABLE I

IRON ORE FLOTATION REAGENTS

Reagent	Function	Price per lb., 1956/cts.	Appr.cons. lbs./ton feed ore
Fatty acids	Collectors	.05-15	.5-5.0
Starch	Slime control	.07-.08	.1-2.0
Amines	Collectors	.29-.45	.1-1.0
Fuel Oil	Coll. frother	.02	.2-4.0
Sulphuric Acid	pH control	.01-.02	.5-4.0
Sulphonates	Collectors	.03-.10	.5-2.0
MIBC	Frother	.16	.01-.1
Xanthates	Collectors(a)	.25	.05-.3
Lime	Activator	.01-.02	1.0-25.0
Talloel	Collector	.02-.04	.5-5.0
Sod. Hydroxide	pH control	.03-.05	.5-3.0

(a)for iron sulphides

Note: Prices from reagent bulletins and The Oil,
        Paint and Drug Reporter.

Mines flotation work. His description of the
chemistry and uses of petroleum sulphonates is
repeated here:
   "Petroleum sulfonates are surface-active
agents obtained as byproducts of petroleum
refining. These were once regarded as
worthless, but in recent years they have
assumed major importance in at least three
fields: As emulsifying agents in cutting
oils, as textile spinning lubricants, and
as sludge-dispersing agents in engine oils.
The name 'petroleum sulphonate' may be
applied to any of the various chemical
compounds containing sulfonic acid or
sulfuric ester radicals that are obtained
by the direct action of a strong sul-
phonating agent on a suitable petroleum
stock. Most petroleum sulphonates are
still being discarded. Those recovered
for use, however, are obtained largely in
the drastic refining of white oils, deodor-
ized kerosenes, or lubricating stock. These
products vary widely in chemical composition
and physical properties, depending upon the
nature of the stock being refined. They
are tan-to-dark-brown viscous liquids and
usually contain a considerable portion of
unsulphonated oil. They may be classified
roughly into two types, those that are
water-soluble (the so-called green acids)
and those that are hydrocarbon-soluble
(the mahogany acids).
   In general, the molecular weight of 400
is considered to be the dividing line
between water-soluble and hydrocarbon-soluble
petroleum sulphonates. Those below 400 are
water-soluble, whereas those above are
hydrocarbon-soluble."
The nature of gangue minerals associated with
iron oxides has an important bearing on amenability to flotation. Gangue minerals which break
down and slime readily often consume large quantities of reagents. Desliming is an extremely
important operation in most iron ore flotation
processes proposed to date. The advent of low-cost
hydrocyclone desliming methods has been an

important cost reduction development. Some of
the gangue minerals which tend to report with the
values when anionic collectors are used include
garnet, hornblende, greenolite, biotite, apatite,
and grunerite.

Most flotation processes using fatty-acid type
anionic collectors are very sensitive to water
quality. Some of the earliest flotation plants
using anionic collectors found that it was
economical to provide water softening facilities
for processing the total flotation plant water
supply. In spite of the fact that this may cost
from 2 to 6 cents per ton of ore processed, reagent savings and better metallurgy will often jus-
tify the installation of a water softening plant.
Hazen[4] showed that use of ion exchange materials
in flotation pulps gave excellent results when
iron oxides were floated with fatty acid collectors. The theory involved is that ion exchange
materials have a stronger absorption coefficient
for calcium than do the gangue minerals (silica
is activated by calcium). Calcium is not only
removed from solution by the ion exchangers, but
is actually stripped from the mineral surfaces.
Sodium and hydrogen cations are absorbed on quartz
or other silicate gangue minerals thus decreasing
their tendency to float. Considerable laboratory
work has been done on use of ion exchange materials in ore pulps. For intimate contact of the
exchanger with ore particles, the exchange material is allowed to circulate freely in the condi-
tioner tank with the pulp; this allows abrasion
to take place and thus complicates the ion exchanger recovery step. The exchange materials are
relatively expensive and must be recovered, regen-
erated, and used over again. The ion exchanger is
usually screened from the pulp between the condi-
tioning and the flotation steps. While the selective adsorption of unwanted ions from flotation
pulps has not been applied on a plant scale, it
seems logical that future developments in the
flotation art will include such techniques.

(4) Hazen, W.C.:Ore Flotation Employing Ion
     Exchange Materials, U.S. Patent 2,557,361,
     June 19, 1951.

The development of anionic flotation processes for manganese ores has resulted in considerable technical information which is of interest to any investigation of the flotation of iron ores. One of the pioneer companies in this field was the Cuban-American Manganese Corporation. Norcross[5] gives an excellent picture of their plant which upgraded large tonnages of 20% manganese ore containing 30% silica to 51% manganese and 8.3 to 11% silica. The reagents used were fatty acid (17-24 lbs.), gas oil (12-16 lbs.), caustic (5-8 lbs.), quebracho (1.5-2.9 lbs.) and lime (7.5-9.6 lbs.) -- all weights in pounds per ton of ore. A more recent U.S. manganese oxide flotation plant which uses fantastic quantities of reagents was described by McCarroll.[6] Here ores averaging 18% manganese are upgraded to over 46% manganese and 10 to 12% silica. Many of the problems of manganese oxide ore flotation are similar to iron oxide ore flotation.

Pryor[7] recently discussed many of the important aspects of floating oxide ores and phenomenon associated with the use of fatty acids. He discusses the solubility characteristics of oleic acid and three common methods of improving results with fatty acids. These are softening the water, use of heat, and repeated recleaning of products. Pryor points out that all these are costly operations and to overcome these conditions he developed a "chemically-modified" oleic acid which even gave good flotation results in ice water. While Pryor worked primarily with fluorspar ores, his observations on fatty acid collector phenomena apply to iron ores as well. The vivid descriptions of frothing problems and froth characteristics are excellent and show keen insight into many problems

(5) Norcross, F.S.,Jr.:Development of the Low-grade Manganese Ores of Cuba, Trans. AIME, vol 153, 1943, p 97-110.

(6) McCarroll, S.J.:Upgrading Manganese Ore, Mining Eng. vol 6, March 1954, p 289-293.

(7) Pryor, E.J.:Some Aspects of the Flotation of Oxidized Minerals, Recent Developments in Mineral Dressing, The Institution of Mining & Metallurgy (London) 1953, p 555-570.

associated with anionic flotation.

Generally speaking, anionic flotation reagents are considerably lower in cost than are cationic reagents. The lure of low-cost reagents has directed much effort toward anionic flotation of gangue minerals from iron ore minerals. In addition, soft water is not required and naturally occurring calcium salts in the ore may even aid in the separation. Anionic flotation of siliceous gangue has been applied experimentally to barite, phosphate, magnesite, manganese, and iron ores. In all cases it was found that selection of suitable depressing agents which would keep the ore mineral in the underflow was difficult. Some of the more promising anionic flotation methods which have been developed for removing siliceous gangue minerals in the froth product are:

(1) Hydrated-lime method. The pH of the pulp is maintained above 11.0 with large additions of hydrated lime in order to depress iron oxides into the underflow product. Desliming of the feed is necessary.

(2) Minerals Separation lime-starch method. The pH of the pulp is maintained above 11.0 with lime and solubilized starch is used to depress the iron minerals. This method was pilot-planted for several years on the Mesabi Range. It differs from (1) in that desliming in unnecessary.

(3) U.S. Bureau of Mines caustic metaphosphate method. The use of metaphosphates and lime permit anionic flotation of silica at high pH with good depression of slime and iron minerals. Pilot-plant tests on calcareous red iron ores of Alabama gave good results.

It seems likely that further advances in the art of anionic flotation of siliceous gangue minerals will continue. As more specific depressing agents for iron oxides are developed, the anionic method will become more attractive. No commercial use has been reported at the present time.

Flotation of Specular Hematite at Humboldt

The first commercial iron ore flotation plant
in America is operated by the Humboldt Mining
Company in Marquette County, Michigan. This
company is a joint venture of the Cleveland-Cliffs
Iron Company and the Ford Motor Company. The
plant started operations in February, 1954 and
processes a low-grade ore which is referred to
as "jasper" in the Michigan Iron districts. The
principal iron mineral is specular hematite and
the ore averages about 34 percent iron. Figure 1
is a flowsheet of the Humboldt flotation plant.

Early plans for beneficiation of Humboldt ore
by flotation were based on use of petroleum sulphonate collectors in an acid circuit. Later, as
pilot plant operations progressed, a shift was
made to soap flotation methods in alkaline pulps.
The sulphonate circuit gave a very "fast" float,
but reagent costs were higher than for the alkaline-
oleic circuit. Laboratory and pilot plant testing
with oleate type collectors indicated that concentrate grades of 57 to 58 percent iron could be
expected in the commercial plant. Fortunately,
this grade was exceeded and plant concentrates
averaged about 62.5 percent iron. Table II lists
typical plant results;

Table II

Humboldt Flotation Plant Data

	%Fe	%SiO2	%Wt
Flot. Conct.	62.39	8.99	44.38
Flot. Tailing	6.84	–	51.10
Slime Tailing	30.43	–	4.52

The pulp density of the flotation feed is about
35% solids and the iron recovery about 89%. The
flotation feed is ground through 48 mesh. Plant
capacity is about 250,000 long tons per year.
Considerable difficulty was experienced at the
Humboldt plant with iron-soaps which blocked pipe
lines, pumps, and launders. Careful blending of
red oil and other oleic acid containing reagents

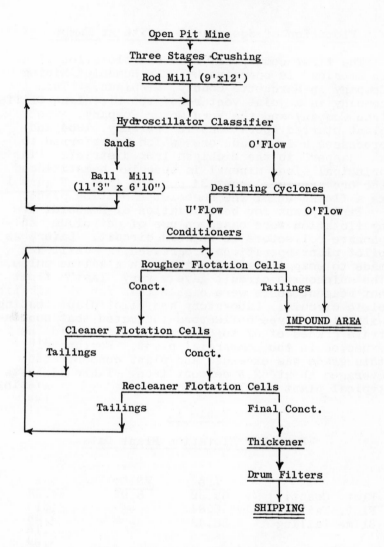

Figure 1. Flowsheet of Humboldt, Michigan
Iron Ore Flotation Plant

solved this difficulty. The Humboldt plant[8] shipped 153,738 tons in 1954 and 173,544 tons in 1955. Figure 2 is a photograph of the flotation section of the Humboldt plant.

A second and larger plant began operations near Republic, Michigan in 1956. This plant uses a very similar flotation flowsheet to beneficiate a specular hematite ore.

Cationic Flotation

Those flotation reagents which ionize to give a positively charged organic ion are called cationic reagents. The most important types of cationic collector reagents in use at present are the fatty amine reagents. The commercial use of cationic collectors to float siliceous gangue minerals dates back to the mid-nineteen thirties when the Valley Forge Cement Company began using dodecyl amine hydrochloride to float mica and talc from argillaceous limestone. The same plant used fatty acid collectors to float calcite. Engelhart gave a description of the Valley Forge flotation plant which is a real contribution to froth flotation history.[9] Earlier laboratory investigations of cationic reagents are described by Dean and Ambrose.[10] A summary of early test results by various U.S. Bureau of Mines investigators relating to the flotation of silica from iron oxides is given in Table III. These encouraging laboratory flotation tests promoted extensive efforts by many to advance cationic flotation of silica from iron ores to commercial status.

Scott and coworkers[11] published results of

(8) Eng. & Mining Jnl. vol 157, April 1956, p 144.
(9) Engelhart, G. K.:Flotation as Applied to Modern Cement Manufacture,Indust. & Eng. Chemistry vol 32, May 1940, p 645-651.
(10) Dean, R.S. and P.M. Ambrose:Development and Use of Certain Flotation Reagents, U.S. Bur. Mines Bulletin 449, 1944, 89 pp.
(11) Scott, D.W.,A.C. Richardson, and N.Arbiter: Amine Flotation of Gangue from Magnetite Concentrates, Trans. AIME vol. 169, 1946, p 466-475.

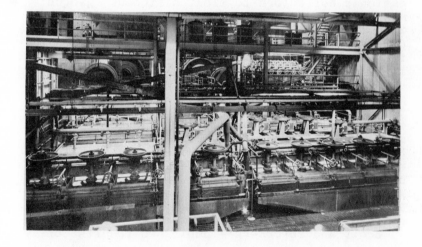

Figure 2.   Photograph of Humboldt, Michigan
            Iron Ore Flotation Plant.
            (Photo courtesy Cleveland-Cliffs
            Iron Co.)

TABLE III[a]

Cationic Flotation of Silica
From Iron Ores -- Laboratory Results

Material	Cationic Collector	%Fe Ore	Concentrates % Fe	%SiO₂	Recov. %
Hematite	DLT 699	17.8	67.4	3.5	92.8
Micaceous Hematite	DP 243	45.2	66.6	4.6	63.1
	(duPont lauryl amine hydrochloride)				
Magnetite	Emulsol	34.8	66.1	6.2	93.3
	660B (quaternary ammonium compound)				

(a) Compiled from U.S. Bureau of Mines Bulletin
    449, 1944 and Report of Investigations 3333,
    1937.

extensive laboratory and pilot plant tests involving amine flotation of siliceous gangue from magnetite concentrates. Lauryl amine hydrochloride was used as the silica collector with the pulp at a pH of 11. Softened water gave best results and total reagent cost was estimated at 8 cents per short ton of feed to flotation. The magnetite concentrates were upgraded from 60.9% Fe and 13.3% SiO_2 to 68.2% Fe and 3.9% SiO_2. DeVaney [12] patented a similar process covering work done independently for Erie Mining Company. Later DeVaney was issued additional patents covering cationic flotation of siliceous gangue minerals from iron ores.[13] Perhaps the earliest patent on the subject was issued to Kirby and Gillson [14] in 1940. No commercial applications for cationic flotation of gangue from iron ores has been reported.

Large tonnages of phosphate ores are upgraded by amine flotation of silica from lower-grade concentrates. The process has been very successful and offers much information to any future large-scale use of the cationic flotation process in iron ore processing.

Future of Iron-Ore Flotation

Any conclusion based on the present status of the art or science of iron ore flotation would concede that for the immediate future commercial installations will be relatively small in size. The economic attractiveness of the magnetic taconites is not conducive to intensive efforts to process the non-magnetic taconites by froth flotation. The science of magnetic roasting is making steady advances toward the goal of a low-cost

(12) DeVaney, F.D.:Beneficiation of Magnetite Concentrates by Flotation, U.S. Patent 2,388,471, Nov. 6, 1945.
(13) DeVaney, F.D.:Froth Flotation of Siliceous Gangue From an Alkaline Magnetic Iron Ore Pulp With an Amine, U.S. Patent 2,450,720, Oct. 5, 1948; Cationic Froth Flotation of Iron Ore, U.S. Patent 2,483,890, Oct.4,1949.
(14) Kirby, J.E. and J.L. Gillson: Flotation Process for Concentrating Oxides of Iron, U.S. Patent 2,217,684, Oct. 15, 1940.

method for production of synthetic magnetic minerals which can be easily recovered by low-cost magnetic processes. This situation discourages efforts in the flotation field.

Continuing research studies by a few laboratories report some progress in the effort to develop new and better reagents for iron ore beneficiation. Cook and Talbot[15] show that certain perfluoro acids and their derivatives are promising candidates for iron ore flotation reagents. One of the most interesting aspects of these new reagents is the possibility of floating iron ores without the usual desliming step. All tests reported were on a laboratory basis only and will require further investigation.

The wide variation in gangue minerals associated with the non-magnetite taconites also mitigates against flotation since some of the iron silicate minerals report in the iron oxide concentrates. Present advantages of roasting and magnetic separation over flotation are higher grade of concentrate, ability to cope with a broad variation in mineral composition and decreased grinding costs.

(15) Cooke, S.R.B. and E.L. Talbot:Fluorochemical Collectors in Flotation, Mining Eng. vol 7, Dec. 1955, p 1149-1152.

ADDITIONAL REFERENCES

Hoover, T.J.:Concentrating Ores by Flotation,
The Mining Magazine, Salisbury House, London,
1916, 320 pp.

Cunningham, J.:Bibliography--Concentrating Ores
by Flotation, Missouri School of Mines Bulletin,
1916, 106 pp.

Rickard, T.A.:The Flotation Process, Mining and
Scientific Press, San Francisco, 1916, 364 pp.

Megraw, H.A.:The Flotation Process, Second Edit.,
McGraw-Hill Book Company, New York, 1918,359 pp.

Taggart, A.F.:A Manual of Flotation Processes,
John Wiley & Sons, Inc., New York, 1921, 181 pp.

Weinig, A.J. and C.B. Carpenter:The Trend of
Flotation, Colorado School of Mines Quarterly,
Fourth Edition, 1937, 189 pp.

Taggart, A.F.:Handbook of Mineral Dressing, John
Wiley & Sons, New York, 1945.

Gaudin, A.M.:Principles of Mineral Dressing,
McGraw-Hill Book Company, New York, 1939.

Michell, F.B.:The Practice of Mineral Dressing,
Electrical Press, Ltd., London, 1950.

Wark, I.W.:Principles of Flotation, Australian
Inst. Mining & Met., Melbourne, 1938.

Petersen, W.:Schwimmaufbereitung, Verlag von
Theodor Steinkopff, Dresden and Leipzig, 1936.

Rabone, P. Flotation Plant Practice, Mining
Publications Ltd., London, 1938.

Coghill, W.H. and J.B. Clemmer:Soap Flotation of
the Nonsulfides, Trans. AIME, vol 112, 1934,
p 449-465.

Adams, A.S., S.M. Kobey, and M.J. Sayers:Flotation
of Hematite, a Laboratory Success, Eng. & Mining
Jnl. vol 132, 1931, p 54-55.

Patek, J.M.:Relative Floatability of Silicate
Minerals, Trans. AIME, vol 112, 1934, p 486-508.

Keck, W.E. and P. Maijala:Iron Concentration Tests
Lick Hard-Water Problem, Eng. & Mining Jnl. vol
145, Jan. 1944, p 79-80.

Clemmer, J.B.:Flotation of Iron Ores, Paper pres-
ented at the Eighth Annual Mining Sumposium,
Center for Continuation Study, Univ. of Minn.,
January, 1947.

Chang, C.S., S.R.B. Cooke, and R.D. Huch:Starches
and Starch Products as Depressants in Amine
Flotation of Iron Ore, Mining Eng., vol 5, Dec.
1953, p 1282-1286.

Counselman, T.B.:Dollars in Current Tailings of
Mesabi Washing Plants, Eng. & Mining Jnl., vol
140, April 1939, p 34-36.

Searles, J.N.:Some Tests With Flotation on Mesabi
Wash-Ore Tailings, Eng. & Mining Jnl., vol 139,
June 1938, p 42-44.

Taggart, A.F. and N. Arbiter:Collector Coatings
in Soap Flotation, Trans. AIME, vol 153, 1943,
p 500-507.

Clemmer, J.B., H.A. Doerner, and F.D. DeVaney:
Experimental Flotation of Washington Magnesite
Ores, Trans. AIME, vol 153, 1943, p 547-556.

Milliken, F.R.:Metallurgy at National Lead Company,
MacIntyre Development, Trans. AIME, vol 183, 1949,
p 101-115.

Pallanch, R.A.:Flotation of Ores an Individual
Problem, Mining & Met., vol 26, March 1945,
p 167-169.

Crago, A.:Three New Steps in Treating Florida
Phosphate Rock, Eng. & Mining Jnl, vol 151,
Nov. 1950, p 78-83.

Ludt, R.W. and C.C.DeWitt:The Flotation of Copper
Silicate from Silica, Mining Eng., vol 1, Feb.
1949, Section 3, p 49-51.

Falconer, S.A.:Pretreatment of Mineral Surfaces
for Froth Flotation, Trans. AIME, vol 184, 1949,
p 247-255.

Cooke, S.R.B. and M. Digre:Studies on the Activation of Quartz with Calcium Ion, Trans. AIME, vol
184, 1949, p 299-305.

Cooke, S.R.B.:The Flotation of Quartz Using Calcium
Ion as Activator, Trans. AIME, vol 184, 1949,
p 306-309.

Gaudin, A.M. and F.W. Bloecher, Jr.:Concerning the
Adsorption of Dodecylamine on Quartz, Mining Eng.
vol 187, April 1950, p 499-505.

Kingman, R.I.:Cyclone Proves Satisfactory for
Thickening, Desliming Flotation Feed, Mining Eng.
vol 187, August, 1950, p 867-870.

Weems, F.T.:Metallurgical Applications of the
Dorr-Clone, Mining Eng., vol 190, August, 1951,
p 681-690.

Keck, W.E., G.C. Eggleston, and W.W. Lowry:A Study
  of the Flotative Properties of Hematite, Bulletin
  of the Michigan College of Mining & Technology,
  July 1937, 24 pp.
Keck, W.E. and P. Jasberg:A Study of the Flotative
  Properties of Magnetite, ibid, 17 pp.
DeVaney, F.D.:Flotation of Lake Superior District
  Iron Ores, Skillings Mining Review, vol 38, Feb.
  11, 1950, p 1,4,6,15.
Iverson, H.G.:Flotation of Gray Iron Ores from
  the Talladega Area, Alabama, U.S. Bur. Mines
  Rept. of Inv. 4570, Dec. 1949, 18 pp.
Zinner, P., and C.L. Holmberg:Investigation of
  the Iron-Bearing Formation of the Western
  Gogebic Range, Iron County, Wisconsin, U.S. Bur.
  Mines Rept. of Inv. 4155, Dec. 1947, 48 pp.
Dahlstrom, D.A.:High-Speed Classification and
  Desliming With the Liquid-Solid Cyclone, Mining
  Eng. vol 190, Feb. 1951, p 153-165.
Gaudin, A.M. and C.S. Chang:Adsorption on Quartz,
  From an Aqueous Solution, of Barium and Laurate
  Ions, Mining Eng. vol 4, Feb. 1952, p 193-201.
Gaudin, A.M., H.R. Spedden, and P.A. Laxen:
  Adsorption of Sodium Ion on Quartz, Mining Eng.
  vol 4, July 1952, p 693-696.
Cooke, S.R.B., N.F. Schulz and E.W. Lindroos:The
  Effect of Certain Starches on Quartz and Hematite
  Suspensions, Mining Eng. vol 4, July 1952,
  p 697-698.
Hertzog, E.S.:A Test to Determine the Lime
  Abstraction of Iron Ores, U.S. Bur. Mines Rept.
  of Inv. 3929, Sept. 1946, 11 pp.
Gaudin, A.M. and D.W. Fuerstenau:Quartz Flotation
  with Cationic Collectors, Mining Eng., Oct. 1955,
  p 958-962.

Chapter VIII

MAGNETIC SEPARATION

                    "First, then, know,
Ceaseless effluvia from the magnet flow;
Effluvia whose superior powers expell
The air that lies between the stone and steel.

A vacuum formed, the steely atoms fly,
In a linked train, and all the void supply:
While the whole ring to which the train is
                              joined
The influence owns and follows close behind."
---Lucretius (c. 96-55 B.C.)

Magnetic separation is a simple, yet effective
method of ore processing. A patent was issued to
William Fullarton in England in 1792 covering the
separation of iron ore by magnetic attraction. The
first United States plant was operated in New York
state in 1853, only four years after the first U.
S. magnetic separator patent was issued to Ransom
Cook (U.S. Patent 6,121 Feb. 20, 1849). This plant
failed but a plant at Benson Mines in up-state New
York produced over a thousand tons of 63 percent
iron concentrates in 1888. The separators used
were the first Ball-Norton dry-belt separators.
These concentrates, shipped to Braddock furnaces
in Pennsylvania, were probably the first magnetic
iron concentrates used in a blast furnace. A new
Benson Mines plant now yields over a million tons
of iron ore concentrates per year. In 1855 a
sponge iron plant in France used electromagnetic
separators [1] . By 1900 several magnetic plants
had been successfully operated and this method of
separation advanced rapidly. The U.S. patent office records show that over 200 patents were issued
on the subject of magnetic separation of ores during the period 1890-1910. A frequent contributor to

_____
(1) Blair, T.S.:The "Direct Process" in Iron Man-
    ufacture, Trans. AIME vol 2, 1874, p 175-199.

this patent group was Thomas A. Edison who patented seventeen different methods and devices for
separating magnetic ores. These were included in
Edison's impressive list of between 50 and 60
patents on ore milling. He also built a large
plant for magnetic concentration of iron ore at
Edison, N.J. which had a designed capacity of 4000
tons per 24 hours. According to F.L. Dyer[2] this
plant contained many radical departures from conventional milling methods. Among these were new
giant crushing rolls, giant cranes (up to 215 foot
span), vertical dryers, air separation methods and
new briquetting techniques. A total of 477 Edison-
type magnetic separators were used according to
Gunther.[3] Unfortunately this large plant was
never operated except in an experimental way.
Factors against its success were a sudden drop in
the iron-ore market due to Mesabi discoveries and
the low ratio of concentration; ore as low as 12
percent iron was processed. The venture cost
Edison and associates over two million dollars
and was the largest single loss sustained by the
great inventor during his career. Edison also
operated a small magnetic plant at Humboldt, Michigan until it was destroyed by fire.

After failure of Edison's New Jersey plant,
interest in large-scale application of magnetic
separation of iron ores dropped in the United
States. However, in Norway and Sweden there was
no slackening of interest since these countries
were dependent on low-grade magnetite ores in
spite of the Mesabi discoveries. The famous
Sydvaranger plant at Kirkenes, Norway started operations in 1910. This plant installed over two
hundred No. 5 Grondal separators to process
1,200,000 tons of ore per year.[4] By 1938 plant
capacity had grown to 1,982,600 metric tons of
crude ore, yielding 880,000 metric tons of high-
grade concentrate. In 1939 Sydvaranger produced

(2) Dyer, F.L. et. al.:Edison--His Life and Inven-
      tions, vol 2, Harper & Bros.,1929, p 473-
      1036.
(3) Gunther, C.G.:Electro-Magnetic Ore Separation,
      Hill Publishing Co., New York, 1909, 193 pp.
(4) Ibid.

1,349,408 metric tons of concentrates.   This
plant was destroyed during World War II but is
now rebuilt and in full operation.   Sydvaranger
can be considered a true ancestor of the modern
taconite plants on the Mesabi Range.

Types of Machines

In his 1921 book, "Magnetic Concentration of
Iron Ore," E. W. Davis[5] classifies magnetic concentrating machines into three types: "(1) those
in which the particles are acted upon more or less
separately by the magnets, the particles being
allowed to fall away, (2) those in which the mass
action predominates and in which the non-magnetic
material is freed by strongly agitating the mass
of particles in the magnetic field, and (3) those
machines in which the polarity of the magnets is
rapidly and continuously reversed." Dean and
Davis in their classic "Magnetic Separation of
Ores"[6] use the following classification:

    Class 1) Separation by attraction of magnetic
             particles to magnet poles
             (a) Separation Using Permanant Magnets
             (b) Separation Using D.C. Electro-
                 magnets
                 I. Separation by attraction of
                    magnetic particles for D.C.
                    electromagnets at drum surface
                II. Belt and disk types
               III. Reciprocating machines
                IV. Drag separators
                 V. Falling-stream separators
                VI. Other separators-including
                    Grondal slime separator, Wheel-
                    Magnets and Frantz isodynamic
                    machine
    Class 2) A.C. separators.

(5) Davis, E.W.:Magnetic Concentration of Iron
    Ore, University of Minnesota Mines Expt.
    Station Bulletin No. 9, 1921, 138 pp.
(6) Dean, R.S. and C.W. Davis: Magnetic Separation
    of Ores, U.S. Bur. Mines Bulletin 425, 1941,
    417 pp.

This Dean-Davis classification of machines is inclusive and accurate, but their statement regarding Class 1 (b) machines --"Separation by attraction of magnetic particles to the poles of a
permanent magnet is of historic interest only, because machines operating on this principle offer
small chance of practical application"-- must be
revised. The rapid development of Alnico and other
newer permanent magnet materials since 1941 has
had great impact upon the field of magnetic separation. These new permanent magnet materials rapidly replaced many electromagnets used for tramp
iron removal, but were more slowly accepted in
ore beneficiation processes. At this writing,
there are a considerable number of large commercial ore-processing machines utilizing permanent
magnets. An early forerunner of present permanent
magnet separators was patented in England in 1792.[7]

Practically all magnetic separation of iron
ores (except for cobbing operations) is now
accomplished by wet separators. These machines
are also used in great numbers in heavy-media
plants to recover magnetic medium. They can be
divided into (1) belt and (2) drum types activated
by permanent magnets or electromagnets. The present
trend is to the drum-type separators due to their
better performance on fine-sized ores. In Sweden,
where much work has been done on magnetic beneficiation, the drum separator has been preferred
for many years. Among the advantages of the drum-
type separator are minimum floor space requirements and flexibility in the flow sheets.

It does not seem at all improbable that
in the future most of the magnetic separators
in magnetite plants and in heavy-media plants
will utilize permanent magnets. These machines
have the advantages of (1) no power required
except to drive drums or belts, (2) greatly
simplified maintenance, (3) high field intensity, and (4) lower cost. In a 1946 paper
on permanent magnets Goss[8] stated, "the progress made in the development of permanent-magnet

(7) Gunther: Op. Cit.
(8) Goss, J.H.:Ductile Permanent Magnets Offer
    New Design Possibilities, Product Engineer,
    Jan. 1946.

alloys during the past decade probably exceeds
the total progress made between the discovery of
natural magnets prior to the Christian Era and
the beginning of the present decade. Fewer than
a dozen alloys that were useful as permanent magnets were on the market a decade ago. More than
20 are available today." Among the newer permanent magnet materials which do not require critical metals (as does Alnico) are Magnadur, a ceramic permanent magnet material and Bismanol, a
bismuth-manganese containing material which was
developed in the Magnetics Division of the Naval
Ordnance Laboratory. Bismanol exhibits a coercive
force of 3000 oersteds, the highest recorded coercive force of any known permanent magnetic material. Because of this high coercive force,
Bismanol exceeds any other permanent magnet (except a platinum-cobalt alloy) in available flux
density in short magnets where length to diameter
ratio is one or less. Since Bismanol magnets are
made by powder metallurgy techniques, complicated
shapes can be processed to close tolerances
without machining. Another new magnetic material
is made from $BaCO_3$ and Fe_2O_3; this material is a
'ferrite.' Alley [9] gave a good technical description of these new materials in the Bell System
Technical Journal: "The term "ferrite" as used
here refers to a class of ferromagnetic oxides
that are structurally the same as magnetite and
as the mineral spinel from which the structure
derives its name. These compounds form extensive
solid solutions of both the substitutional and the
subtractional type. Nickel, zinc and manganese
zinc ferrites are important examples of the substitutional type. In these, the Zn and Ni or
Mn are thought to be solid solution in magnetite
(Fe_3O_4) where they have directly replaced equivalent amounts of iron in the lattice. An example
of the subtractional type of solution is gamma
hematite. Here, oxygen is considered to be in
solution in magnetite, not, however, having replaced iron, but having eliminated it, thus

(9) Alley, R.E., Jr.:A Review of New Magnetic
    Phenomena, The Bell System Tech. Jnl, vol 32,
    Sept. 1953, p 1155-1172.

leaving vacant sites in the lattice. Magnetically ferrites are thought of as consisting of two
interpenetrating lattices of metal ions whose
magnetic moments point in opposite directions.
Since, however, these moments are in general not
equal, the material has a net magnetic moment."
   The forerunner of the modern drum separator
was the Grondal separator patented by Gustaf
Grondal (U.S. Patents 812,170 and 812,172 Feb. 6,
1906). Hundreds of these separators were in use
within 5 years of patent issuance. The Sydvaranger plant in Norway has favored this type separator for many years. Other early installations of
Grondal drum separators were at Benson Mines, N.Y.,
Hanover-Bessemer Iron & Copper Co., Fierro, N.M.,
Bethlehem Steel Co., Lebanon, Pa., and Showa Steel
Works, South Manchuria. At the Lebanon installation the Grondal separator acquired several notable revisions among which was the lowering of the
drum to a submerged position. This overcame the
disadvantage of pulling the magnetic particles
through the air-water interface. Further revisions, including redesign of pulp boxes to confirm
with aerodynamic principles, better washing techniques, and more efficient pulp routing has taken
place in recent years. Thus, beginning in 1906
and continuing through a fifty year period, an
efficient drum-type separator has evolved and is
now seen in most of the magnetic iron ore con-
contration plants of the world. Figure 1 is a
sectional view of a drum-type separator installed
for pilot-plant use. Figure 2 shows a late-model
double-drum high intensity separator. This unit
is popular in taconite plants.

Magnetic Iron Ores

   Iron containing materials of importance to the
iron industry which can be beneficiated by commercial magnetic separation are:

   (1) Magnetite
       (a) low titanium (under 1%
           titanium)
       (b) titaniferous magnetites (over 1%
           titanium)

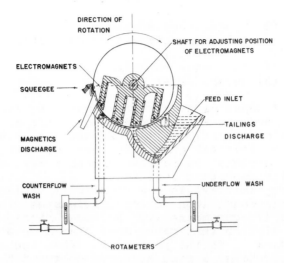

Figure 1. Sectional view of a one-cell Jeffrey-
Steffensen magnetic separator. (From
U.S. Bureau of Mines Report of Investigations No. 4847)

Figure 2. Double-drum magnetic separator.
(Photo courtesy Magnetic Engineering
& Manufacturing Co.)

(2) Products of Roasting
    (a) ferrosoferric oxide (artificial mag-
       netite)
    (b) gamma hematite
(3) Sponge metal

All of these materials are being or have been
processed on a pilot-plant or full commercial
scale of operations. At present the natural magnetites lead all others in tonnage, but within
a few decades the roasted products may occupy an
equally important position.

Singewald [10], in his classic treatise on
titaniferous iron ores, designates the term
"titaniferous magnetite" to cover "those magnetic
ores of iron that carry more than 2 or 3 percent
titanium." In the preface to this publication
J. A. Holmes, a past director of the U.S. Bureau
of Mines, stated, "Iron ores containing over one
percent of titanium are troublesome to smelt in
the blast furnace." This statement is still quoted
by many blast furnace operators today in spite of
the fact that burdens containing considerably
more titanium have been successfully used. There
is some question as to whether blast furnace
operators are prejudiced in favor of non-titaniferous burdens since there has been little sys-
tematic research to support such claims. If small
amounts of titanium are harmful, then operators
will have to learn to live with it as there is
every indication that the titanium content of
furnace burdens will increase as more and more
magnetite ores are beneficiated for furnace use.

Attempts to beneficiate titaniferous magnetite ores by magnetic means date back to the
active 1890-1910 period when many magnetic
plants were planned and built. These efforts are
summarized in Singewald's book, "Moreover, examination of many samples by metallographic methods
has demonstrated that although a large part of the
titanium in these ores is in the form of ilmenite,

(10) Singewald, J.T. Jr.:The Titaniferous Iron
     Ores in the United States - Their Composi-
     tion and Economic Value, U.S. Bur. Mines
     Bulletin 64, 1913, 145 pp.

much of this ilmenite is far more intimately associated with the magnetite than has generally been
supposed. Part of the magnetite and ilmenite occurs in such large and distince aggregates that
their separation by a magnetic concentration after
fine crushing is practicable, but in by far the
larger number of samples examined and in practically all the ore bodies that are known to be large
enough and rich enough in iron to be of much importance, most of the ilmenite occurs as such fine
intergrowths in the mass of the magnetite that a
complete separation of the two minerals by any
process based on difference of physical properties
still seems impractical. Crushing even to 200
mesh would not insure a clean separation of the
two minerals. Consequently the problem of utilizing titaniferous magnetites involves the application of chemical rather than physical methods.
In short, the problem is not one of eliminating
the titanium by milling but of reducing the ores
directly by some smelting process." Some of
Singewald's results obtained by magnetic separation
of domestic titaniferous magnetite ores crushed
to 0.3 mm (48 mesh) and then to 0.15 mm (100 mesh)
are given along with similar data, in Table I.
    The Sorel, Quebec operation of the Quebec Iron
and Titanium Corporation is a good example of
use of a smelting process to beneficiate an
ilmenite ore. In 1955 a total of 311,230 tons of
ore were processed to yield 145,343 tons of titanium dioxide slag and 108,314 tons of iron[11].
The pioneering efforts of the Sorel plant will be
useful in the development of pyro-processing methods for titaniferous magnetite ores.

Magnetic Products of Roasting

    With the magnetic taconite beneficiation pro-
gram now well under way, iron ore producers are
investigating another future ore source which will
involve processing of the enormous quantities of
low-grade non-magnetic iron ores. The leading

(11) Buck, W.K.:Iron Ore In Canada, 1955   (Pre-
        liminary), Department of Mines and Techni-
        cal Surveys, Ottawa, Canada, 9 pp.

TABLE I

Magnetic Separation of Titaniferous Magnetites

Products	% Fe	% TiO$_2$	Recovery of Fe, percent
Lincoln Pond, N.Y.			
Ore	64.66	5.88	
0.3 mm Conct.	66.08	4.82	96.0
0.3 mm Tails	30.59	31.45	
0.15 mm Conct.	66.27	5.12	95.6
Sanford, N.Y.			
Ore	55.07	19.02	
0.3 mm. Conct.	61.23	11.15	78.2
0.3mm Tails	32.99	47.20	
0.15 mm. Conct.	61.23	10.47	75.9
Iron Lake, Minn.			
Ore	53.30	24.30	
0.3 mm. Concts.	54.93	23.15	93.3
0.3 mm. Tails	30.59	40.37	
0.15 mm. Conct.	54.13	23.58	92.0
Iron Mountain, Wyo.			
Ore	54.48	19.47	
0.3 mm Conct.	60.76	12.58	77.7
0.3 mm Tails	32.61	43.47	
0.15 mm Conct.	61.97	10.32	76.0
Iron Mountain, Colo.			
Ore	51.96	14.50	
0.3 mm. Conct.	56.93	13.50	86.0
0.3 mm. Tails	21.42	20.97	
0.15 mm. Conct.	57.77	13.10	80.4
Sands from Lower St. Lawrence River			
Ore	54.8	18.6	
Conct. No. 1	69.6	2.3	---
Conct. No. 2	70.5	1.5	---
Tails	44.0	--	
Natashkwan Sands, Lower St. Lawrence River			
Ore	9.60	2.26	
Conct. No. 1	64.61	2.36	---
Conct. No. 2	68.37	1.61	---
Tails	5.61	2.69	

Note: Data for Natashkwan Sand from Canadian Dept. of Mines Bulletin 617, 1923. All other data from U.S. Bureau of Mines Bulletin 64, 1913.

contenders in the race for processing methods
are froth flotation and magnetic roasting (which
is followed by magnetic separation). In reviewing past history we find that commercial experience has been in favor of roasting processes.
With the exception of small Swedish plants and two
plants in Michigan, there have been no really
large-scale applications of the flotation process
to non-magnetic iron ores. On the other hand there
have been many roasting plants which have processed millions of tons of iron ore. These include
rotary kiln installations in Europe, a large
plant in Manchuria, and several very early pilot
plants which roasted siderite ores prior to magnetic processing. Ingalls[12], in his early book
on the economics and processing of zinc ores, gives
a good review of prior art in the magnetic roasting of various iron minerals to facilitate their
removal from zinc ores. The flowsheet of a plant
at Monteponi, Sardinia is described in detail.
Ferraris magnetic separators were used to remove
magnetic iron oxides produced by roasting a
"hemimorphite-limonite" ore. A rotary kiln type
furnace was used and 2 to 3 percent of coal slack
provided the reducing agent. Six magnetic separators processed about 1000 kg. of calcined ore per
hour. The machines required 100 watts of current
(2 amperes at 50 volts). Ingalls also mentions
the magnetic separation of roasted siderite from
zinc blende at Przibram, Bohemia and in Spain
during the decade 1870 - 1880. At Friedrichssegen,
Germany siderite was roasted in Herreshoff-type
furnaces and processed by Wenstrom magnetic separators to produce zinc concentrates and iron ore
concentrates.
    American attemps in the field of magnetic
separation of roasted iron ores include the Tennessee Coal Iron & Railroad Company plants at
Ensley and Bessemer, Alabama[13], The Goltra Process

(12) Ingalls, W.R.:Production and Properties of
     Zinc, The Eng. & Mining Jnl. Press, 1902,
     328 pp.
(13) Phillips, W.B.:Notes on the Magnetization
     and Concentration of Iron Ore, Trans. AIME
     vol. 25, 1895, p 399 - 423.

plant at Iron Hill near Waukon, Iowa [14] , the
Cooley, Minnesota plant by the University of Minnesota and Butler Brothers[15] , and the Sloss Shef-
field plant in Alabama[16] . One of the early
(1894) pilot plants which roasted Alabama hematite
used a Hoffman magnetic separator operating on 10
to 15 amperes at 110 volts. This machine produced
concentrates analyzing 58.86 percent iron and
11.51 percent silica from roasted ore containing
45 percent iron and 30 percent silica.

The recorded history of magnetic processing of
fine-sized (minus 200 mesh) artificial magnetite
from roasting operations shows that several investigators have recognized that cleaning operations are difficult when such ores are processed[17,18,19,20] . The high coercive force of
artificial magnetite is objectionable even in
roughing and desliming operations. When gangue
and low-grade middlings become entrapped in
tightly-bound magnetic floccules they are very
difficult to reject. The net result is, with presently available magnetic separators, the roasted
ores are usually highly overground before acceptable silica rejection is obtained. Since fine-
grinding is one of the most expensive steps of the

(14) Phillips, W.B.:Concentration by the Goltra
     Process, Iron Age, vol 94, 1914, p 1148-
     1150.
(15) Craig, J.J.:Magnetic Concentration on the
     Mesabi Makes Progress, Eng. & Mining Jnl.,
     vol 139, Jan. 1938, p 48-52.
(16) Rose, E.H.:Beneficiation Methods for South-
     ern Iron Ore, Regional Technical Meetings
     of Amer. Iron & Steel Inst. 1949, p 221-242.
(17) Ibid.
(18) Luyken, W. and H. Kirchberg:Results Obtained
     by Magnetizing Roast of Carbonate Ores,
     Mitteilungen K.W. Institut Eisenforschung,
     vol 22, No. 6, 1940, p 81-92.
(19) Gaudin, A.M.:Principles of Mineral Dressing,
     McGraw-Hill Book Co. New York, 1939, p 456.
(20) Davis, E.W.:Magnetic Roasting of Iron Ore,
     Univ. of Minnesota Mines Experiment Station
     Bulletin 13, May, 1937, 90 pp.

process, it is obvious that some control of the
magnetic properties of artificial magnetite is
desireable. The simplest and oldest method of ov-
ercoming at least part of this difficulty is to
re-oxidize the magnetite to gamma hematite. Chapter IX, which covers pyrometallurgical processing,
gives some details of this process. Little technical information is available regarding the comparison of magnetic properties of gamma hematite
with those of artificial and natural magnetite.
It is possible, by extremely close control of the
reduction and oxidation steps, to produce a magnetic hematite which is less magnetic than artificial magnetite. Furthermore, gamma hematite
often undergoes a loss of magnetic susceptibility
as a function of its age. Controlled ageing may
eventually find use in iron ore beneficiation.

Sponge iron is another important iron-containing
material which is produced by pyrometallurgical
processes and is sometimes beneficiated by magnetic separation. No unusual difficulties are experienced in the magnetic separation of sponge iron
concentrates [21].

Magnetization of Iron Ore Concentrates

While the electrical and electronic industry
has been much concerned with magnetization and
demagnetization of metals for many years, little
attention has been given similar studies of magnetic iron ore concentrates. In spite of the
great volume of magnetic separator patents appearing during the last hundred years, serious studies
of magnetizing and demagnetizing of ores did not
begin until twenty years ago. Wuensch[22] patented
the addition of magnetic solids to oil well drilling fluids; by magnetization of the particles, the
density of the fluid could be controlled. By
mentioning that, "magnetized particles of all
grain sizes settle more rapidly than unmagnetized

(21) Barrett, E.P.:Sponge Iron and Direct Iron
        Processes, U.S. Bur. Mines Bulletin 519,
        1954, 143 pp.
(22) Wuensch, C.E.:Drilling Fluid, U.S. Patent
        2,276,075, March 10, 1942.

or demagnetized materials due to the agglomeration of the grains into flocs", Wuensch encouraged investigation leading to several iron ore process patents which make use of the technique. Braund[23], Vedensky[24], Martin[25], and Roe[26] patented various uses of magnetization in concentrating iron ores. The simplicity of a magnetizing step is sufficient guarantee that further use will be made of this technique in the future.

Mention should also be made that magnetization of iron ore concentrates has been found indispensible in the Nicaro Nickel plant[27,28]. Here artificial magnetite is passed through magnetizing coils to allow use of magnetic flocculation to increase settling rates. Early pilot plant results showed that settling area required varied with the percent of iron in the material as follows:

Fe Content - %	Sq. ft. Thickener Area per ton per day
12 - 15	23
25 - 30	3
30 - 36	2.5
36 - 38	2.0

Magnetizing of magnetite and ferrosilicon pulps is an indispensible step in media recovery circuits of heavy-media plants.

(23) Braund, R.W.:Method of Treating Low Grade Iron Ores, U.S. Patent 2,468,586, April 26, 1949.

(24) Vedensky, D.N. and L.J. Bechaud, Jr:Process for Treating a Magnetic Iron Ore, U.S. Patent 2,558,635, June 26, 1951.

(25) Martin, H.K.:Method and Apparatus for Separating Materials, U.S. Patent 2,560,809, July 17, 1951.

(26) Roe, L.A.:Concentration of Iron Ores, U.S. Patent 2,711,248, June 21, 1955.

(27) Tobleman, H.A. and H.J. Morgan:Review of the Nicaro Nickel Project, Oriente, Cuba, Dept. of Commerce, Washington, Plancor 690, 1948.

(28) Hills, R.C.:Magnetic Separation and Settling for Serpentine Ores, U.S. Patent 2,400,461, May 14, 1946.

Demagnetization of Iron Ore Concentrates

From the earliest production of very fine-sized magnetite concentrates it was probably apparent that passage of the concentrates through a direct current magnetic separator resulted in the formation of enough residual magnetism to cause difficulties in classification and further cleaning of these concentrates. In the course of early experimental work on magnetic iron ores, the Mines Experiment Station of the University of Minnesota designed and built the first demagnetizer for use in ore processing plants[29,30]. Operating on the same principle as the instrument used for demagnetizing watches, the ore demagnetizer consists simply of a conical coil of wire surrounding a pipe. An alternating current is supplied to produce an alternating magnetic field within the pipe which carries the ore. The field strength decreases with the decrease in the number of turns as the pulp moves towards the bottom of the coil. As ore passes through the pipe it loses most of its residual magnetism because of the rapidly reversing magnetic field. Artificial magnetites are more difficult to demagnetize than natural magnetites. This was recognized by Gottschalk and Davis as early as 1933[31].

The difficulty in demagnetizing fine-sized particles of magnetite has been put to constructive use in magnetic taconite plants. Some rejection of middling particles can be accomplished by simple water classification of magnetized pulps. Craig[32] mentions use of this procedure in his description of the first magnetic roasting plant on the Mesabi Range. When pulps were magnetized in this plant it was shown that the larger particles of artificual magnetite acted as collectors

(29) Davis, E.W.:Apparatus for Treatment of Magnetic Ore, U.S. Patent 1,286,247, Dec. 3, 1918.
(30) Davis, E.W.: op cit. reference 20.
(31) Gottschalk, V.H. and C.W. Davis:A Magnetic Material of High Coercive Force, Nature, vol 132, 1933, p 513.
(32) Craig, J.J.:op cit.

for the fine-sized magnetite particles. By processing this pulp in a rake classifier most of the
iron values were recovered in the underflow and
low-grade middlings were discarded in the overflow. Davis utilized a similar procedure in pilot
plant tests on magnetic taconite at the University
of Minneosta. In 1945 he reported[33], "In order to
remove these higher grade middling particles, the
pulp flows from the three-drum Steffensen machine
through a demagnetizing coil into a special FS
classifier. It has been found that if the demagnetizing force is properly adjusted, the fine
particles of magnetite are not demagnetized but
the middling particles are, with the result that
by properly adjusting the uprising water in the
classifier tank, some of these objectionable middling particles will overflow and can be eliminated
from the circuit". It should be noted that the
plant described by Craig processed artificial
magnetite while Davis processed natural magnetite.
The author knows of two instances were artificial
magnetite concentrates were so strongly magnetized
that they caused handling difficulties after com-
pletion of the magnetic separation stage of processing. A sinter plant in Germany experienced
difficulty in processing artificial magnetite
since it formed a tightly packed bed which would
not allow sufficient air passage which is a prime
requisite for good sintering. Davis mentions the
difficulty of demagnetizing artificial magnetite
concentrates from the Butler Brothers roasting
plant at Cooley, Minnesota[34]. He reported, "The
demagnetizing of artificial magnetite was primarily of academic interest until trouble developed
with the concentrate shipped by Butler Brothers
from the magnetic roasting and concentration plant
at Cooley, Minnesota, in 1934. After the first

(33) Davis, E.W.:Beneficiation of Eastern Mesabi
    Magnetic Taconite, Univ. of Minn. Mines
    Experiment Station Information Circular No.
    5, Sept. 1945, p 31-34.
(34) Davis, E.W.:Foreword, Information Circular
    No. 7, "Demagnetization of Magnetite" by
    Hartig, Onstad, and Foot, Univ. of Minnesota
    Mines Experiment Station, May, 1951.

shipment, the report came back that this concentrate was so strongly magnetized that it would not mix readily with other ores and demagnetization would be necessary before the material could be mixed or even properly sampled. A strong, water-cooled demagnetizing coil was made which improved the situation materially, although the trouble never was completely cured".

Hartig, Onstad and Foot[35] published an excellent report on the demagnetization of magnetite. Their work covers both artificial and natural varieties. They found, as Davis had earlier reported, that demagnetization of natural magnetite was not difficult. Accomplishing similar results with artificial magnetite presented many new problems. Careful studies of magnetic ore particles in a magnetic field under a microscope revealed that the behavior of natural magnetite was different than that of artificial magnetite. Natural magnetites usually show a "chaining" effect after the application of an alternating magnetic field. Artificial magnetites (which have a higher coercive force) do not form chains when similar fields are applied. Instead, the particles bound about and follow a rotary path. By increasing the cycles-per-second value from the usual 60 for natural magnetite to a value of 300 to 400 cycles-per-second, good demagnetization of artificial magnetite was obtained. Onstad and Foot[36] patented some features of their findings in 1954.

Two Mesabi Range pilot plants processing magnetic taconite have reported that several small demagnetizers are more effective than one large installation of equal electrical characteristics. This seems reasonable since control of the magnetic effects is better in a small cross-section than in a large area.

(35) Hartig, H.E., N.I. Onstad, and N.J. Foot: Demagnetization of Magnetite, Univ. of Minnesota Mines Experiment Station Inf. Circular No. 7, May, 1951, 22 pp.

(36) Onstad, N.I., and N.J. Foot:Demagnetizing Roasted Iron Ore, U.S. Patent 2,678,130, May 11, 1954.

The use of damped oscillatory discharges to
effect partial demagnetization was observed by
Henry and subsequently studied by Raleigh,
Rutherford, Marconi, and Tschetveikowa[37]. Some
work has been done by the U. S. Bureau of Mines
in subjecting magnetic powders to a magnetic field
generated by damped oscillatory discharge[38] but
no commercial applications are known. Lee[39] in
1931, patented use of an alternating magnetic
field having a frequency between 500 and 50,000
cycles per second as a feature of an ore concentrator.

Typical Plant Flowsheets

Iron ore beneficiation plants using magnetic
separation processes are not usually complicated
in layout or operation. Considerable stress is
placed on efficient materials handling since large
tonnages can be processed in relatively small
plants. The actual magnetic separation step is
one of low cost and high efficiency. Much attention is given the planning of the high-cost crushing and grinding sections in magnetic ore plants.
Whenever possible, magnetic cobbers are used in
the crushing section of the plant to remove pieces
of gangue mineral in as large-sized pieces as
possible. This type of operation is not possible
in the magnetic taconite plants since the iron
ore minerals are intimately associated with the
gangue minerals.

Figures 3, 4, 5, 6, 7, and 8 are flowsheets of
several important magnetic iron ore beneficiation
plants. Figure 3, describes the Sydvaranger,
Norway plant which has been in operation since 1910
with the exception of a period following the World
War II destruction of the plant. This plant is a
pioneer installation which provided information
for today's taconite plants.

(37) Dean, R.S. and C.W. Davis:op cit.
(38) Davis, C.W.:Some Observations on the Move-
        ment and Demagnetization of Ferromagnetic
        Particles in Alternating Magnetic Fields,
        Physics vol. 6, June 1935, p 184-189.
(39) Lee, R.:Ore Concentration, U.S. Patent
        1,829,565, Oct. 27, 1931.

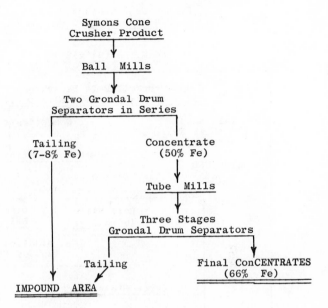

Magnetic Separator Performance

| | Conct. | | Tailings | |
	% Wt.	% Fe.	% Wt.	% Magnetic Fe.
Separator No. 1	71	45	29	1.6
Separator No. 2	66	50	5	2.0
Separator No. 3	52	60	14	1.3
Separator No. 4	45	64	7	2.0
Separator No. 5	44	66	1	2.0

Figure 3.   Flowsheet of Sydvaranger Plant,
           Kirkenes, Norway. (Original plant
           prior to World War II)

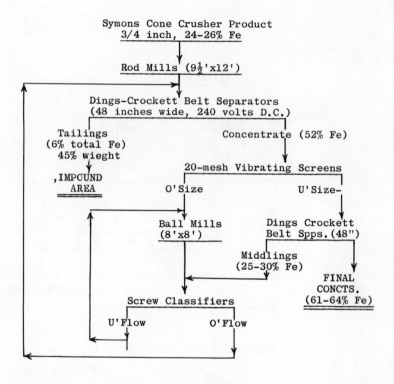

Symons Cone Crusher Product
3/4 inch, 24-26% Fe

Rod Mills (9½'x12')

Dings-Crockett Belt Separators
(48 inches wide, 240 volts D.C.)

Tailings   Concentrate (52% Fe)
(6% total Fe)
45% wieght
                          20-mesh Vibrating Screens
,IMPCUND
AREA   O'Size   U'Size-

              Ball Mills   Dings Crockett
              (8'x8')   Belt Spps.(48")

              Middlings
              (25-30% Fe)
                                  FINAL
                                  CONCTS.
                                  (61-64% Fe)
      Screw Classifiers

  U'Flow   O'Flow

Typical Plant Results

Concentrate			%Sol. Fe	%Mag. Fe	% P	% S	% TiO$_2$	% SiO$_2$
Mesh	Cum. %Wt.							
-20	0.4	Crude	26.75	24.0	.192	.48	.68	40.8
28	4.2	Conct.	63.75	62.5	.024	.21	.77	5.7
35	14.2							
48	26.8		Crude & Conct. each contain 0.25% Mn.					
65	39.8							
100	54.2							
-100	100.0							

Figure 4. Flowsheet of Benson Mines N.Y.
Magnetic Concentration Plant

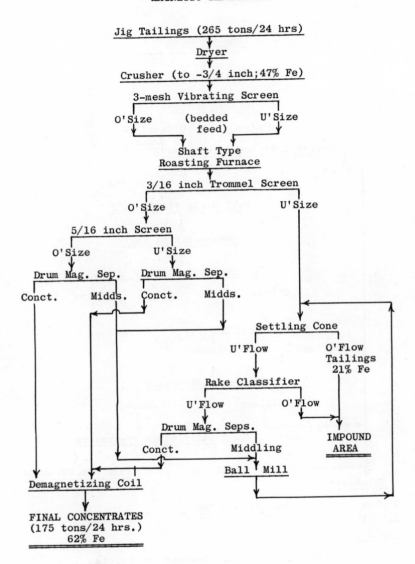

Jig Tailings (265 tons/24 hrs)

Dryer

Crusher (to -3/4 inch;47% Fe)

3-mesh Vibrating Screen

O'Size   (bedded   U'Size
                feed)

Shaft Type
Roasting Furnace

3/16 inch Trommel Screen

O'Size   U'Size

5/16 inch Screen

O'Size   U'Size

Drum Mag. Sep.   Drum Mag. Sep.

Conct.   Midds.   Conct.   Midds.

Settling Cone

U'Flow   O'Flow
                         Tailings
                         21% Fe

Rake Classifier

U'Flow   O'Flow

Drum Mag. Seps.

Conct.   Middling   IMPOUND
                            AREA
                Ball   Mill

Demagnetizing Coil

FINAL CONCENTRATES
(175 tons/24 hrs.)
62% Fe

Figure 5.   Flowsheet of Butler Brothers
            magnetic roasting plant,
            Cooley, Minnesota. (1936)

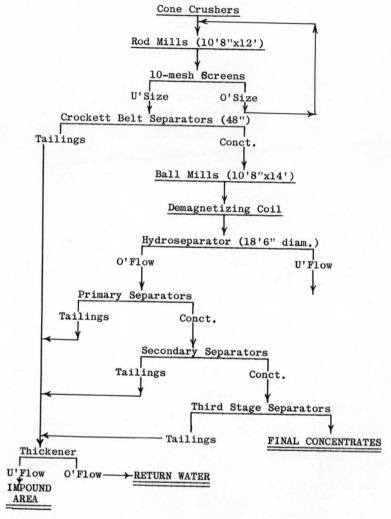

Figure 6.   Typical flowsheet of Pilotac
Magnetic Taconite Pilot Plant
(U.S. Steel Corp.), Minnesota

Note:Concentrator consisted of three identical sections,
except for various comparative test units. Dings
drum separators were compared with 48" Crockett
belt separators in the last three stages of magnetic
separation.

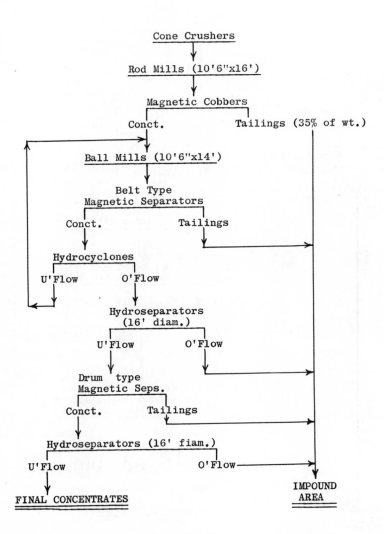

Figure 7. Flowsheet of Silver Bay taconite
plant of Reserve Mining Company,
Minnesota.

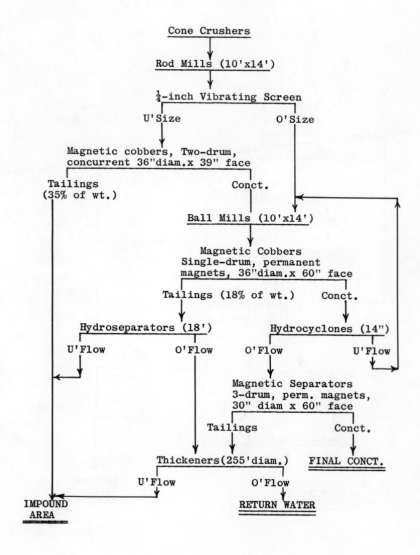

Figure 8. Flowsheet of Erie Mining Company
            magnetic taconite plant, Minnesota

The flowsheet of the Benson Mines plant of Jones & Laughlin Steel Corporation at Star Lake, New York is given in Figure 4. The Benson plant held the distinction of being the largest magnetic ore processing plant in the world for several years before the large taconite plants began operation. Figure 5 describes the operations of the Butler Brothers magnetic roasting plant which contributed much to the technology of magnetic roasting. One of the flowsheets tested in the large Pilotac pilot plant of the U.S. Steel Corporation is given in Figure 6. The flowsheets for the first two large magnetic taconite commercial-scale plants on the Mesabi Range are given in Figures 7 and 8. It is notable that both of these new beneficiation plants use hydrocyclones in the magnetic separation sections.

Due to intensive research programs aimed at more efficient magnetic separation methods, it can be expected that the flowsheets of 1956 may be much improved in another ten years. The static condition of magnetic beneficiation methods has given ground to a new dynamic condition which will give a good account of itself in the years ahead.

Magnetic Superconcentrates

While "superconcentrates" have long been produced in some foreign countries (notably Sweden), it may be only a few years until similar products will be produced domestically. Small quantities of very high-grade magnetite concentrates have been produced at various U.S. plants but never on any large commercial scale. One of the earliest records of superconcentrates dates back to 1891 when Thomas Edison's Humboldt, Michigan plant produced a carload of magnetite concentrates analyzing 71.4 percent iron. This material was produced from a low-grade ore containing about 20 percent iron. No information is available regarding the exact degree of grinding necessary to achieve this excellent concentrate but it was probably coarser than 325 mesh. The author has processed a sample of the same iron formation using a minus 100-mesh grind with the following results:

Product	Wt.%	Fe,%	SiO$_2$,%	Iron Dist.,%
Magnetic				
Conct.	48.7	67.50	5.20	84.3
Tailing	51.3	11.97	61.70	15.7

The crude ore contained 39 percent iron and the results indicate that superconcentrates are possible when the ore is subjected to a fine grinding step.

A 1912 report on briquetting of iron ores [40] gives analyses of magnetite concentrates from two Swedish plants which produced superconcentrates. The concentrates described analyzed 70.1 and 71.0 percent iron with recoveries of 93.5 and 95.5 percent respectively.

Luyken and Kirchberg [41] reported on the manufacture of iron powder from magnetite superconcentrates. They described the re-processing of regular magnetite concentrates containing 67.1 percent iron, 3.14 percent silica and 66.3 percent iron and 3.04 percent silica. The re-processed concentrates contained only 0.34 and 0.23 percent silica respectively. These superconcentrates were reduced with hydrogen in four separate steps in order to observe the progress of reduction. An intermediate purification step removed even more gangue minerals. These were released from magnetite middling particles by differential expansion during roasting. Both ores were of Swedish origin and the final iron powder was of good quality.

Ross [42] described the production of magnetite superconcentrates in Sweden by the re-processing

(40) Hansell, N.V.:The Briquetting of Iron Ores, Trans AIME vol 43, 1912, p 394-411.
(41) Luyken, W. and H. Kirchberg:Manufacture of Iron Powder for Sintered Parts from Pure Concentrates, Arch. Metallkunde, vol 1, 1947, p 335-345.
(42) Ross, H.U.:Iron Ore Concentration in Sweden, Skillings Mining Review, Dec. 10, 1949, p 1,4,13.

of magnetic concentrates on Wilfley tables. An
iron content of 71.8 percent was produced with
little difficulty.

A pilot plant, operated by the U.S. Bureau of
Mines in 1944, produced superconcentrates from
Cranberry, N.C. magnetite ore[43]. The ore contained about 30 percent iron and the concentrate
70.30 percent iron with a magnetic iron recovery
of 93.60 percent. Davis tube tests showed that
a 71.7 percent iron concentrate could be made.

Future Problems

Since the "commercial" liberation size of magnetic iron ores is becoming increasingly finer,
new problems appear in the separatory processes.
Of prime importance is solution of the problem of
rejecting middlings from fine-sized magnetic concentrates. The highest single item of cost (ex-
clusive of agglomeration) in processing low-grade
magnetic iron ore is the grinding operation. With
every ore, there is an optimum grind where locked
mineral grains should be removed from the circuit
and ground separately before returing to the
magnetic separation section. In present practice
this is carried out to some extent by classification steps between magnetic concentration steps.
None of the commercial separators now available
can selectively and quantitatively remove middlings from fine-sized ores.

The magnetic reflux classifier[44] has shown that
careful control of magnetic fields and a carefully
regulated water supply can separate middlings from
magnetite in fine-sized concentrates. The classifier has not as yet been developed in commercial
size units. The largest pilot unit tested was only 4-inches in diameter.

(43) Lamb, F.D. and D.A. Woodard:Pilot-Plant Pro-
     duction of High-Grade Magnetite Concentra-
     tes, Cranberry, N.C., U.S. Bur. Mines Rept.
     of Inv. 3980, Dec. 1946, 7 pp.
(44) Roe, L.A.:Magnetic Reflux Classifier, Mining
     Eng. vol 5, p 312-315, March, 1953.

Eketorp[45,46] proposes improved A.C. separators
to accomplish similar results.

Problems of magnetizing and demagnetizing
operations were described earlier in this chapter.
Fundamental studies by the fast-growing magnetic
powder industry can be expected to provide additional information regarding the magnetic properties of iron oxide powders. Magnetic powders are
now being used in special magnetic inks as well
as on sound-recording tapes and films.

Improved automatic control of magnetic beneficiation plants will be an immediate objective
of the large taconite plants. Laurila[47] has
published information regarding a magnetite and
ilmenite analyzer.

The concentrated effort now being applied to
magnetic beneficiation equipment and methods is
resulting in a slow evolution of new techniques.
With the aid of research in solid-state physics,
electricity and other basic sciences some of the
present mysteries of magnetism will be solved to
the benefit of the iron ore processing industry.

(45) Eketorp, S.:Magnetic Separation of Minerals,
     Canadian Metals vol 13, March 1950, p 6,
     9,46,47.
(46) Eketorp, S.:Three-Phase AC Can Improve Fine-
     Size Magnetic Separation, Eng. & Mining Jnl.
     vol 152, Oct. 1951, p 82-83, 118.
(47) Laurila, E., O. Jantti and R.T. Hukki:Magne-
     tic and Chemical Analyses of Ores and Mill
     Products Containing Magnetite and Ilmenite,
     Mining Eng. vol 190, Sept. 1951, p 797-802.

ADDITIONAL REFERENCES

Fowle, J.C.:Magnetic Concentration at the Michigamme Iron Mine, Lake Superior, Trans. AIME vol 19, 1891, p 62-70.

Cook, R.A.:The Wenstrom Magnetic Separator, Trans. AIME vol 17, 1889, p 599-606.

Crane, W.R.:Investigation of Magnetic Fields, with Reference to Ore-Concentration, Trans. AIME vol 31, 1902, p 405-446.

Birkenbine, J. and Thomas A. Edison:The Concentration of Iron Ore, Trans. AIME vol 16, 1889, p 728-744.

Ball, C.M.:The Ball-Norton Electromagnetic Separator, Trans. AIME vol 19, 1891, p 187-194.

Ball, C.M.:The Magnetic Separation of Iron Ore, Trans. AIME vol 25, 1895, p 533-551.

Norton, S. and S. Lefevre:The Magnetic Concentration of Low Grade Iron Ores, Trans. AIME vol 56, 1917, p 892-916.

Sosman, R.B. and J.C. Hostetter:The Ferrous Iron Content and Magnetic Susceptibility of Some Artificial and Natural Oxides of Iron, Trans. AIME vol 58, 1918, p 409-433.

Sosman, R.B. and J.C. Hostetter:Zonal Growth in Hematite and its Bearing on the Origin of Certain Iron Ores, ibid, p 434-444.

DeVaney, F.D. and W.H. Coghill:Concentration Tests on Tailings from the Washing Plants of the Mesabi Range, Minnesota, U.S. Bur. Mines Rept. of Inv. 3052, Nov. 1930.

Kellogg, L.O.:Iron Concentrator of Unusual Design Eng. & Mining Jnl. vol 96, Aug. 9, 1913, p 243-245.

Peterson, G.W.:Magnetic Separation of Iron Ores, Eng. & Mining Jnl. vol 83, May 11, 1907, p 889-896.

Schilling, E.W. and H. Johnson:Separation of Hematite by Means of Hysteretic Repulsion, AIME Tech. Publication 654, 1936.

Snow, C.:Magnetic Fields of Cylindrical Coils and Annular Coils, U.S. Dept. of Commerce, Natl. Bur. of Standards--Applied Mathematics Series 38, Dec. 30, 1938, 29 pp.

Roche, H.M.:Evaluation of Magnetic Milling at Scrub Oak, Eng. & Mining Jnl. vol 134, 1933, p 241-244.

Stringfellow, G.E.:Edison Pioneered Low-Grade Ore Concentration, Mining Congress Jnl. vol 23, Feb. 1937, p 44-45.

Linney, W.J.:Operations of Chateaugay Division of Republic Steel at Lyon Mountain (N.Y.), Mining & Met. vol 24, Nov. 1943, p 505-508.

Dean, R.S. and C.W. Davis:Magnetic Concentration of Ores, Trans. AIME vol. 112, 1934, p 509-537.

Hagar, I.D.:The MacIntyre Development--New Source of Titanium, Eng. & Mining Jnl. vol 143, Dec. 1942, p 47-49.

Bockman, K.L.:Mining Flourishes in Norway, Eng. & Mining Jnl. vol 141, March 1940, p 41-42.

Manegold, R.L.:Magnetic Separation Comes Into Its Own, Eng. & Mining Jnl. vol 144, Aug. 1943, p 86-88.

Anon:Double Pick-Up Features New Magnetic Separator, Eng. & Mining Jnl. vol 145, July 1944, p 85.

Sosman, R.B. and E. Posnjak:Ferromagnetic Ferric Oxide, Artificial and Natural, Jnl. Washington Academy of Science, vol 15, Aug. 19, 1925, p 329-342.

Hayes, E.T.:Ferromagnetic Properties of Hematite, U.S. Bur. Mines Rept. of Inv. 3570, June 1941.

Armagnac, A.P.:Magic With Magnetism, Popular Science, June 1944, p 130-132,222.

Anon:How Republic Concentrates Adirondack Iron Ores, Eng. & Mining Jnl. vol 146, July 1945, p 90-93.

Davenport, H.:New Magnetic Concentrator Treats Mount Hope Iron Ore, Eng. & Mining Jnl. vol 146, Sept. 1945, p 85-89.

Davis, E.W.:Mesabi Taconite, A Study of Concentrating Characteristics, Univ. of Minn. Mines Expt. Station Inf. Circular No. 4, March 1944.

Members of British Intelligence Objectives Subcommittee:Iron Ore Preparation in Germany, B.I.O.S. Trip No. 1234, Nov. 1945 (London).

Luyken, W.:Lean Ores, German Experience in Their Preparation, Iron & Steel, London, October, 1947, p 471-475.

Anon:Norwegians Conquer Taconite, Mining World vol 9, Oct. 1947, p 22-26.

Hoff, R.C.:Demagnetizing Influences on Permanent
Magnets, Magnetic Age, No.4, 1950, p 7.

Marsh, A.:The Grangesberg Iron Mines, Mine & Quarry Eng. (London) vol 16, August, 1950, p 249-256.

Bruckshaw, J.M. and E.I. Robertson:The Measurement
of Magnetic Properties of Rocks, Jnl. of Scientific Instruments and of Physics in Industry,
vol 25, Dec. 1948, p 444-446.

Fieldner, A.C. and S. Gottley:Annual Report of
Research and Technologic Work on Coal, Fiscal
Year 1950, U.S. Bur. Mines Inf. Circular 7618,
Nov. 1951.

Milliken, F.R.:Metallurgy at National Lead Company, MacIntyre Development, Trans. AIME vol 183
1949, p 101-115.

Scott, D.W., A.C. Richardson, and N. Arbiter:Amine
Flotation of Gangue from Magnetite Concentrates,
Trans. AIME vol 169, 1946, p 466-475.

Derkach, V.G.:Increasing The Efficiency of Electromagnetic Separators, Gornyi Zhur vol 120, No.
2, 1946, p 34-35; Chem. Abs. vol 40, Aug. 10, 1946,
p 4325.

Webb, W.R. and R.G. Fleck:Beneficiation of Adirondack Magnetite, Mining Eng. vol 187, April 1950,
p 444-448.

Vickers, W.A.:Magnetic Iron Sampler, Eng. & Mining Jnl. vol 151, Aug. 1950, p 104.

Hubbell, A.H.:Work on Taconite Now Heads Toward
Commercial Goal, Eng. & Mining Jnl. vol 153,
July, 1952, p 72-75.

Ruppert, J.A.:Manganese Concentrates from Open-
Hearth Slags by Lime-Clinkering (Sylvester) Process, U.S. Bur. Mines Rept. of Inv. 4847, Feb.
1952.

Wiig, R.C.O.:Determination of the Content of a
Mineral in Ores and the Like, U.S. Patent
2,489,066 Nov. 22, 1949.

Ramsey, R.H.:Teamwork on Taconite, Eng. & Mining
Jnl. vol 156, March 1956, p 71-93.

Martin, H.K.:Proposed Flowsheet for Taconite Concentration at Babbitt, Blast Furnace, Coke Oven
& Raw Matls. Committee, AIME, 1948 Proceedings,
vol 7, p 68-72.

Zinner, P., and C.L. Holmberg:Investigation of the
Iron-Bearing Formation of the Western Gogebic
Range, U.S. Bur. Mines Rept. of Inv. 4155, 1947.

Emery, P. and J. Givaudon:Magnetizing Roast Tests on French Iron Ores, Pubs. Inst. Recherches Siderugie (St. Germain-en-Laye) Ser. A. No. 60, 1953, p 5-119.

Williams, M.F. and L.G. Hendrickson:Depolarizing of Magnetite Pulps, Paper given at Annual Meeting of AIME, Feb. 1955, Chicago, Ill., 51 pp.

Anon:Paper Mill Waste Water Clarified 1000 Times Faster, Chemical Processing vol 17, May 1954, p 38.

Anon:Super Purity Equals Super Magnet, Industrial Laboratories, vol 7, Oct. 1956, p 30.

Bozorth, R.M.:The Physics of Magnetic Materials, Electrical Engineering, Feb. 1956, p 134-140

Chapter IX

PYROMETALLURGICAL PROCESSING

"Much less attention has been
paid to the roasting of iron
ores in this country, and notably in the Eastern States,
than the subject demands. --
We note that metallurgists are
beginning to devote more attention to this subject."-----
The Engineering & Mining Jnl.
July 22, 1882 (editorial).

A significant trend in the chemical, ceramic,
power, atomic and metallurgical industries is the
use of higher processing temperatures. For chemical engineers, higher temperatures open the door
to new processes which often result in products
which are impossible to make at what are considered normal operating temperatures. In the field
of metallurgy higher temperatures often result in
faster and more efficient processing of ores.
Metallurgists have known that processing costs
often increase in direct proportion to the operating temperature; thus the tendency has been to
shy away from high temperature beneficiation
methods. Recent jet and rocket developments
demand new and improved materials which will
withstand extreme temperatures over long periods
of time. Also some of the new materials must
exhibit resistance to sudden temperature changes.
Alert ·metallurgists have been quick to adopt new
high-temperature materials to ore processing.
This opens the way to new processes, improvement
of existing processes, and reappraisal of old
processes which may have failed because of high
costs due to short service life of high temperature equipment. Future progress in the field
of iron ore beneficiation will include new and
improved pyrometallurgical processes.

The tie between iron ore beneficiation (in its
strictest sense) and the smelting of iron minerals
is growing tighter. The most important fact encouraging this observation is the rapid increase
in electric furnace steel production in recent
years. From 1949 to 1953 electric furnace steel
production increased 60 percent. Should this
trend continue, it seems probable that steelmaking plants will become more closely integrated
with ore and concentrate producing facilities.
Some discussions of this reevaluation of electric
furnace potential are given by Ramseyer[1],Reinartz[2],
and King[3]. A report on early Swedish electric
furnace practice was given by Stansfield[4] in his
1915 report.

Interest in pyrometallurgical iron-ore beneficiation methods is steadily increasing. Unless
new and drastic changes in present gravity and
flotation processes show up soon or other entirely
new beneficiation methods evolve, it seems reasonably certain that magnetic roasting and other
relatively high-temperature processes will be
used in beneficiating much of the nonmagnetic
iron ore reserves.

Drying of Iron Ores

One of the earliest and simplest iron ore
pyro-processing methods is the drying of ores.
This is sometimes done in order to reduce shipping
costs, but may also be a preliminary step in a

(1) Ramseyer, C.F.:Can the Electric Furnace Com-
    pete With the Open Hearth? Jnl. of Metals,
    vol 5, Dec. 1953, p 1617-1621.
(2) Reinartz, L.F. and H.C. Barnes:Electric Fur-
    nace vs. Open Hearth in Cold Metal Shops,Iron
    & Steel Engineer, vol 31,Jan.1954, p 114-119
(3) Moore, D.D.:Cost Comparisons of the Open Hearth
    and Electric Furnace, Iron & Steel Engineer,
    vol 31, March 1954, p 55-69.
(4) King, C.D.:Steelmaking Processes. Some Future
    Prospects, Jnl. of Metals, vol 6; Trans. AIME
    vol 200, April 1954, p 455-465.
(5) Stansfield, A:Electrothermic Smelting of Iron
    Ores in Sweden, Canada Dept. of Mines Report
    No. 344, 1915, 65 pp.

beneficiation process. Drying is used on hygro-
scopic, soft ores and usually entails a dust loss.
Drying plants have operated in the Lake Superior
region [6] but only on a limited scale.

A large-scale drying plant handling Cuban lateritic ore prepares this ore for a roasting operation in a nickel and cobalt recovery plant. The
ore contains 25 to 30 percent moisture as mined.
A drying operation reduces the moisture to 1 to
3 percent. Details of operation of the drying
plant were given at the February, 1954 meeting of
the AIME[7]. It is necessary to reduce the moisture of this ore prior to grinding and roasting
operations. This ore contains over 50 percent of
minus 325-mesh material as it is mined. Concurrent
fired rotary dryers are fired with Bunker C fuel
oil using 100 percent excess air. The total ore
lost as dust is less than one percent; this is
due to use of efficient electrostatic dust pre-
cipitators. About 1560 Btu are required per pound
of water evaporated and an average of 2.38 pounds
of water are evaporated per hour per cubic foot
of dryer volume.

Recent developments in drying methods include
highly efficient flash dryers and fluidized-bed
type dryers. The latter type is finding use in
drying limestone and coal.

Roasting of Siderite Ores

Another process involving somewhat higher fuel
cost than simple drying of ores but also used to
reduce shipping cost is the roasting of carbonate
ores. Siderite (iron carbonate) looses about 28
percent of its weight when its carbon dioxide is
driven off by roasting. Also the iron content of
the roasted product is considerably higher. For
example, a Canadian siderite ore analyzing 34.7
percent iron can be upgraded to 50.64 percent
iron after undergoing a roasting step to drive

(6) Hansell, N.V.:The Concentration of Iron Ores,
      Trans. AIME vol 44, 1913, p 37-68.
(7) Marquis, B., H.J. Reed and E.R. Sweet:The
      Drying of Lateritic Ores, Feb., 1954 AIME
      annual meeting, New York, N.Y., 8 pp.

off carbon dioxide. Table I lists other significant changes which occur upon roasting this same
ore:

TABLE I

Upgrading Siderite Ore by Roasting

	Crude Ore	Roasted Ore
Iron	34.70%	50.64%
Silica	7.88%	11.74%
Manganese	2.09%	3.08%
Phosphorus	.013%	.014%
Alumina	1.01%	1.60%
Lime	2.70%	3.68%
Magnesia	5.22%	7.30%
Sulphur	2.42%	.051%
Loss on Ignition	27.72%	-----

The removal of sulphur by roasting siderite is
beneficial in two ways. The sulphur provides part
of the fuel for roasting and its removal often results in a final product meeting Bessemer ore
specification. When about 5 percent sulphur (10
percent pyrite, for example) is present in a dry
siderite ore, external fuel is required only to
bring the process to ignition temperature; then
the process is self-fueling. Richter[8] reported
on the economy of roasting spathic (siderite) ores
in 1928. He compared roasting costs and quality
of product when processed in double-conical Siegerland furnaces, the old Donawitz shaft furnaces,
and roasting furnaces used in the San Fernando
and Apold-Fleissner processes. In some early observations on the desulphurization of pyritiferous
iron ores Valentine[9] drew some significant conclusions which modern experience proves valid. He

(8) Richter, L.A.:Economy of Roasting Spathic Ore
        Archiv fur das Eisenhuttenweses, vol 1, June
        1928, p 725-727.
(9) Valentine, S.G.:The Desulphurization of Pyrit-
        iferous Iron Ores, Trans. AIME, vol 18, 1890,
        p 78-87.

He concluded, "Fusion, or sintering of ore is likely to prevent any further desulphurization", and, "an efficient roaster must allow easy control of heat, abundant access of air to the hot ore, and rapid removal of the products of combustion."

Some siderite ores contain arsenic as well as sulphur. Removal of arsenic is somewhat more difficult than sulphur displacement, but can be effectively removed by close control of roasting. A detailed report on removal of arsenic by roasting was published by Luyken and Heller[10] in 1938. Their report and unpublished data on a Canadian siderite ore indicate that roasting in rotary kilns will provide efficient removal of arsenic from iron ores. Conventional sintering machines are usually very efficient in sulphur removal operations but fail to obtain good removal of arsenic. The rotary kiln provides a more prolonged period of heating, good mixing action, and better atmosphere control. All of these conditions are essential to efficient arsenic removal.

W. Luyken[11] described European siderite roasting practice as of 1947 in a British journal. He described the early Siegerland shaft furnaces which were relatively low in height and had various designs including conical, double conical, and cylindro-conical. In these kilns interspersed coke was burned in the natural kiln draft; fuel consumption amounted to 5 percent of the weight of ore, capacity was low, and only minor amounts of fines could be tolerated. Later developments included forced draft and mechanical discharge devices. This greatly increased capacity and coke consumption dropped to one or two percent. The latest kiln Dr. Luyken described was a cylindrical kiln 36-feet high and 12-feet 6-inches in diameter with a 3 1/4-inch layer of insulation between the refractory lining and the steel shell to reduce radiation losses. Daily capacity of

(10) Luyken, W. and L. Heller:Arsenic in Iron Ores and Its Elimination Before Smelting, Archiv fur das Eisenhuttenwesen, vol 11, 1938, p 475-481.

(11) Luyken, W.:Lean Ores, German Experience in Their Preparation, Iron & Steel, (London) October, 1947, p 471-475.

this kiln was 100 tons if the proportion of fines
was about 9 percent. When fines content increased
to 26 percent, kiln capacity dropped to 65 tons
per 24-hour day. The 100 ton figure corresponds
to about 0.76 tons per cubic yard of kiln volume
every 24 hours. Dr. Luyken also reported, "As the
decomposition of the spar in air sets free 322
Btu per pound of iron, it is possible to roast
the previously enriched spar without the use of
fuel. Two factors are essential for success;
first the iron and copper sulphides in the ore
must allow evolution of heat, and secondly, care
must be taken by accurate temperature control to
maintain the heating zone at about half the height
of the kiln." A similar utilization of exothermic
reactions is exemplified by the Battelle roasting
process for low-grade taconite ores.

The two largest North American siderite roasting operations are the plants of Algoma Ore Properties Limited in Ontario, Canada and the Lone
Star Steel Company in northeast Texas. The Canadian plant utilizes Dwight-Lloyd sinter machines
to roast and sinter siderite ore. As of 1955,
five sinter machines were producing about 120,000
tons of sinter per month. The roasting operation
upgraded Algoma ore from 35 percent iron to over
51 percent iron. The Texas plant uses rotary
kilns to calcine ore at 1700 to 1900 degrees F.
Both goethite and siderite are upgraded by roasting operations. Bond[12] reported that when goethite ores are roasted in the kilns some beneficiation other than dehydration takes place. About 6
to 7 percent of the silica is eliminated as dust
from the kiln operation. Alternating goethite
and siderite ores in the rotary kilns was helpful
in removing "rings" from the kilns. Longenecker[13]
also reported on the Lone Star plant. The two
kilns used were 278 and 300-feet in length; diameters were 11-feet, 6-inches and 9-feet, 6-
inches respectively.

(12) Bond, W.R.:Beneficiation of East Texas Iron
     Ores, Blast Fur.,Coke Oven & Raw Matls. Com-
     mittee, AIME, Proc. vol 12, 1953 p 6-17.
(13) Longenecker,C.:Lone Star Rapidly Increasing
     Service in the Southwest, Blast Furn & Steel
     Plant, vol 38, Sept. 1950, p 1042-1049.

Roasting of Iron Ores to Magnetic Oxides

No one really knows when man first discovered that non-magnetic iron ores could be converted to magnetic oxides by heat. It seems reasonable that the phenomenon occurred many times at many places when prehistoric men built their camp fires near iron-bearing rocks or minerals and later discovered synthetic lodestones in the ashes. Metallurgical literature indicates that siderite roasting has been commercially practiced for about 100 years.

Reduction of Iron Carbonates

The roasting of siderite as a beneficiation method in itself has been discussed earlier in this chapter. Now we will discuss roasting to produce magnetic oxides which can be subsequently beneficiated by magnetic separation. Siderite is converted to a magnetic form by heating in a slightly oxidizing atmosphere at 700 to 800 degrees Centigrade. Carbon dioxide begins to evolve at 300 degrees. Differential thermal analysis studies of siderite[14, 15, 16, 17, 18] show that the endothermic decomposition reaction of siderite extends from approximately 400 to 670 degrees. As Rowland and Jonas[17] point out, "The effect of

(14) Kerr, P.F. and S.L. Kulp:Differential Thermal
     Analysis of Siderite, Amer. Mineralogist,
     vol 32, 1947, p 678-680.
(15) Speil, S.:Applications of Thermal Analysis
     to Clays and Aluminous Materials, U.S. Bur.
     Mines Rept. of Inv. 3764, July 1944, 36 pp.
(16) Bowen, C.H.:Data for Interpretation of Diff-
     erential Thermal Curves, Ohio State Univ.
     Eng. Exp. Sta. Circ. 56, Sept. 1954, 17 pp.
(17) Rowland, R.A. and E.C. Jonas:Variations in
     Differential Thermal Analysis Curves of Sid-
     erite, Amer. Mineralogist vol 34, July-Aug.
     1949, p 550-558.
(18) Rowland, R.A., and D.R. Lewis:Furnace Atmos-
     phere Control in Differential Thermal
     Analysis, Amer. Mineralogist vol 36, Jan.
     1951, p 80-91.

heating on siderite involves conditions not generally encountered in the thermal analysis of most minerals. When decomposition takes place and carbon dioxide is liberated from the $FeCO_3$, the remaining FeO is very susceptible to oxidation. Whether the oxidation occurs simultaneously with, immediately after, or somewhat later than the loss of carbon dioxide may be dependent on the rate at which the carbon dioxide can escape and allow air to enter." Subsequent studies by Rowland and others showed that special atmosphere control in thermal analysis furnaces enabled definite control of the endothermic reaction caused by carbon-dioxide evolution.

If siderite is roasted in an inert atmosphere, some FeO (which is nonmagnetic) will result. With free access to air, the nonmagnetic Fe_2O_3 is formed. According to 1909 practice[19], "Siderite is usually mixed with from 3 to 5 percent of fine coal or coke before calcination to aid in its decomposition and to insure a reducing or neutral atmosphere in the furnace; if coal is used it must be of a noncoking variety." Also, "calcined siderite, which is always very strongly magnetic, is usually roasted at 850 degrees Centigrade, at which temperature only 15 minutes is required for the production of magnetic oxide."

In an early ore dressing volume by Ingalls[20], the following is found, "Iron sulphide, carbonate and sesquioxide may under certain conditions be converted into the magnetic oxide, Fe_3O_4, in which form it is easily attracted by the magnet and thereby may be separated from compounds of zinc, all of which are nonmagnetic, or at least only feebly magnetic. Processes depending upon that principle were first applied many years ago, perhaps as early as 1855." Specific examples of early roasting plants were given. These included the Lill plant at Przibram, Bohemia, a Spanish plant,

(19) Gunther, C.G.:Electro-Magnetic Ore Separation
       Hill Publishing Co. New York, 1909.
(20) Ingalls, W.R.:Production and Properties of
       Zinc, The Eng. & Mining Jnl. Press, 1902,
       328 pp.

and a plant at Friedrichssegen, Germany.   These
plants removed siderite from zinc minerals by
roasting and magnetic separation during the 1870-
1880 decade.

T. Twynam in 1907 disclosed in his British
patent number 1615 the calcination of siderite
ores in a closed kiln, furnace, or oven (in the
absence of free oxygen) with subsequent magnetic
separation of the magnetic oxide formed.

Work on a siderite roasting process was carried
out at the Kaiser-Wilhelm Institute[21] just prior
to World War II. This process (Austrian patent
154,368, April 15, 1938) used two rotary kilns,
one for roasting and one for the cooling step.
The siderite was decomposed in an atmosphere containing very little uncombined oxygen. The waste
gases, which were rich in carbon dioxide, were
used to cool the roasted material. The process
was designed to produce a final product having
"uniform magnetic properties."

Gunther[22] refers to an Allevard, France plant
which calcined siderite at the unnecessarily high
temperature of 1000 degrees Centigrade. The plant
had a capacity of 210 to 220 metric tons in 10
hours and produced a final product, after magnetic
separation, containing 50 percent iron and manganese. The weight loss, due to expelled carbon
dioxide, was 28 percent.

Reduction of Iron Oxides

The reduction of iron oxides is a subject of
extreme importance to the minerals engineer.
Several volumes could easily be compiled on the subject from the literature. Those phases most interesting to minerals studies are found in widely scattered sources. Ralston's, "Iron Oxide Reduction Equilibria:A Critique from the Standpoint
of the Phase Rule and Thermodynamics," was published by the U.S. Bureau of Mines in 1929 and
sold for sixty cents. This was a 326-page bargain

(21) Luyken, W. and H. Kirchberg:Results Obtained
         by Magnetizing Roasting of Carbonate Ores
         Mitteilungen, K.W. Institut Eisenforschung,
         vol 22, No. 6, 1940, p 81-92.
(22) Gunther, C.G. op cit.

of information which included a critical discussion of existing data and presented new data   col-
lected by the Bureau of Mines. From the introduction of this volume[23] we quote, "This paper, better
than any other means, will indicate the surprising
lack in our knowledge concerning the properties of
one of the most important metal-oxide systems
known to man." It is with a similar thought in
mind that these observations are presented.

Interest in reducibility of iron ores, concentrates and agglomerates has been rapidly in
creasing as furnace operators look more closely
at their burdens. Reducibility is the relative
rate of deoxidation of a material and can be measured or determined by various methods. A common
method is to plot the loss in weight which occurs
when heated samples are exposed to a reducing gas.
An easily reduced ore will lose weight (oxygen)
rapidly while an ore which is difficult to reduce
will lose weight slowly. When several ares are
being compared, a comparison of the weight losses
over a given period of time, with identical temperature and atmosphere conditions, will indicate
relative reducibility. Foreign blast furnace operators, especially Swedish, have often emphasized
the importance of good reducibility of ores and
concentrates. It is a well established fact that
hematite is much more easily reduced than magnetite.
This is primarily due to its more porous structure.
Yet as late as 1950 a survey of the U.S. iron-ore
sinter plants showed than an average of three-
fourths of the iron contained in U.S. sinter was
present as magnetite. The present trend to utilization of reducibility tests for control of sinter plants is encouraging. European practice
strives for maximum hematite content in agglomerated iron-bearing materials. One point in favor
of U.S. physically-strong "magnetite sinter" is
that big U.S. furnaces require an ore with greater
physical strength. The smaller European furnaces
can use burdens with less physical strength.

---

(23) Ralston, O.C.:Iron Oxide Reduction Equilibria:
      A Critique from the Standpoint of the Phase
      Rule and Thermodynamics, U.S. Bur. Mines
      Bulletin 296, 1929, 326 pp.

The greater ease of reducibility of some pelletized concentrates may become an important factor
influencing their future popularity. Agglomeration of tailor-made iron concentrates allows considerable control over some of the most important
variables involved in reducibility. These are
porosity, particle size, and use of additives.
Barrett and Wood[24] showed that as little as one-
half of one percent (by weight) addition of sodium
carbonate or sodium aluminate greatly accelerated
the deoxidation of magnetite by hydrogen at 600
degrees Centigrade.

The relative ease of reducibility is approximately proportional to the porosity of the ore. In
most cases reducibility if inversely proportional
to the ferrous iron content of the ore. Most of
the published results on the order of reducibility
of iron ores compare favorably with the following:

Order of Decreasing Ease of Reducibility for Common Ores & Concentrates

By author	Barrett & Wood[24]
(1)goethite(Mich)	(1)limonite ore
(2)hematite(Minn.)	(2)hematite ores
(3)martite(N.Y.)	(3)glomerules(low ferrous)
(4)magnetite(N.Y.)	(4)sinters(high ferrous)
	(5)nodule
	(6)magnetite ore

The effect of "contaminating" and "trace elements" on the reduction of iron oxide materials
has been given little attention and study. Among
the common elements often present either in the
space lattice or very intimately associated with
the iron oxide structure are titanium, chromium,
nickel, cobalt, aluminum and magnesium. Of these
elements titanium shows the greatest variation in
content and is present in quantities ranging from
a trace to over 15 percent. The rapid develop-

(24) Barrett, E.P. and C.E. Wood:Relative Reduci-
          bility of Some Iron Oxide Materials, U.S.
          Bur. Mines Rept. of Inv. 4569, Oct. 1949,
          17 pp.

ment of the titanium metal industry has resulted
in development of much new information regarding
the iron-titanium association in several minerals.
Singewald[25] points out that in general the
titaniferous magnetite ores exhibit a ratio of
titanium to iron of 0.1323 to 0.1747. In discussing Udy and Lorig's paper[26] on reduction of magnetite, Payne points out that when titanium is present the reduction temperatures must be higher
than when pure magnetites are reduced.

Table II lists a comparison of apparatus and
conditions used by various investigators to determine reducibility of iron ores. These data
show that the methods used are still in a state
of flux. There seems to be no universal agreement
as to the best method, but the direct weighing of
sample weight loss seems to be gaining preference
over older absorption methods. It seems probable
that when the volume of reducibility determinations becomes great enough to interest some laboratory equipment manufacturer, we can expect a
standard apparatus and method to appear. Figures
1 and 2 are schematic drawings of equipment used
for reducibility determination.

Hydrogen finds favor over carbon monoxide or
hydrocarbon reducing gases since the latter require
a carbon correction in final calculations. The
carbon may be present in the reduced material as
surface deposits or in combination with the iron.
Klemantaski[27] reported on the action of inhibitors
such as cyanogen, ammonia and hydrogen sulphide
which prevented carbon deposition when magnetite
was reduced at 450 degrees Centigrade with pure
carbon monoxide.

(25) Singewald, J.T.Jr.:The Titaniferous Iron
          Ores in the United States-Their Composition
          and Economic Value, U.S. Bur. Mines Bulle-
          tin 64, 1913, 141 pp.
(26) Udy, M.C. and C.H. Lorig:The Low-Temperature
          Gaseous Reduction of a Magnetite, Trans.
          AIME vol 154, 1943, p 162-181.
(27) Klemantaski, S.:Action of Inhibitors of Car-
          bon Deposition in Iron Ore Reduction, Jnl.
          of the Iron & Steel Inst. (London) vol 171,
          Part 2, June 1952, p 176-182.

TABLE II

Comparison of Various Reducibility
Apparatus and Methods

	A	B	C	D	E
Reducing agent	H_2	H_2	CO	H_2	H_2, CO, water gas, bosh gas.
Gas flow	2G/hr	600cc/ min.	725 to 2750cc/ min.	28.3cc/ min./gm ore	.12 - .70 cu.ft./ min.
Sample particle size	$-\frac{1}{4}$" to plus 1/8"	9/16" cubes	10 to 30 mesh, 2 cm. lumps	minus .525" plus .263"	minus .742" plus .371"
Reduction temp. °C.	750	800	600- 900	800	600-900

Notes: Reducing gases are purified by passage through
platinized asbestos, magnesium perchlorate, KOH,
H_2SO_4, $CaCl_2$ or P_2O_5. The water produced by
combination of hydrogen with oxygen from the ore
is absorbed and weighed. "E" measures loss of
oxygen from the sample by direct, continuous
weighing of the hot sample.

References
(A) Joseph, T.L.:Porosity, Reducibility and Size Preparation
of Ores, Trans. AIME vol 120, 1936, p 72-98.
(B) Gillings, D.W., et al:The Sintering of Northamptonshire
Iron Ore, A Production-Plant Study of Factors Affect-
ing Sinter Quality, Jnl. of the Iron & Steel Inst.
(London) April 1954, p 433-435.
(C) Kamura,Het al:Reduction of Iron Ores by Carbon Monoxide,
Trans. AIME vol 71, 1925, p 549-567.
(D) Firth, C.V.:Agglomeration of Fine Iron Ore, Blast Fur-
nace and Raw Materials Conference, AIME, Proceedings
vol 4, 1944, p 62-64.
(E) Barrett, E.P. and C.E.Wood:Relative Reducibility of
Some Iron Oxide Materials, U.S. Bur. Mines Rept. of
Inv. 4569, Oct. 1949, 17 pp.

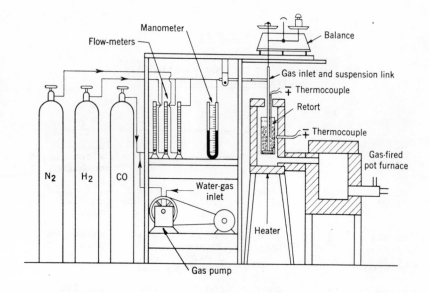

Figure 1. - Schematic drawing of apparatus for studying the deoxidation of iron oxides by various gas mixtures.

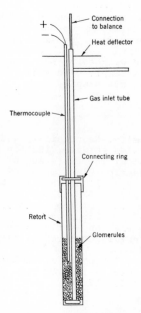

Figure 2. - Schematic sketch of retort for loss-in-weight apparatus. (From U.S. Bureau of Mines Rept. of Inv. 4569)

In spite of publicity given high top-pressure blast furnaces and the beneficial effect on the reduction rate of iron oxides in blast furnaces and the beneficial effect on the reduction rate of iron oxides in blast furnaces, there is little information concerning the effect of pressure on magnetic roasting of iron ores.

Tenenbaum and Joseph[28,29] reported some significant findings on the effect of pressure on reduction of iron ores in 1940. Using 9/16-inch ore cubes they noted that the rate of reduction of solid iron oxides with hydrogen increased about 40 percent by doubling the pressure. When carbon monoxide was used, doubling the pressure increased the rate of reduction about 23 percent. The basic patent on the so-called high top-pressure blast furnace was issued to Julien Avery[30], a chemical engineer, in 1938. According to figures reported in 1953, more than 20 high top-pressure blast furnaces were in use throughout the world[31]. Operation at pressures of less than 5 psi (gauge), which is only 2 to 3 pounds higher than normal top pressure, shows little beneficial effects. Limitations of physical equipment has held most pressurized furnaces to only 12 psi (gauge). The main advantages of pressurized furnaces are that iron production can be increased 10 percent or more with no increase in coke rate, finer-sized raw materials can be used and dust losses are reduced. The information gained by pressurization of blast furnaces may be useful in future magnetic roasting plants. With the possible exception of recent work on fluidized bed roasting of iron ores, most

(28) Tenenbaum, M. and T.L. Joseph:Reduction of Iron Ores Under Pressure by Hydrogen Trans. AIME vol 135, 1939, p 59-72.

(29) Tenenbaum, M. and T.L. Joseph:Reduction of Iron Ores Under Pressure by Carbon Monoxide, Trans. AIME vol 140, 1940, p 106-125.

(30) Avery, J.M.:Method of Operating Blast Furnaces, U.S. Patent 2,131,031, Sept. 27, 1938.

(31) Pepper, E.L.:The High Top-Pressure Blast Furnace, Metal Progress, vol 63, Feb. 1953, p 71-73.

magnetic roasting operations have been carried out
at atmospheric pressure. The excellent results
now being obtained by chemical beneficiation methods which utilize high-pressure leaching methods
may encourage the development of high-pressure
roasting operations in the future.

Blair[32] gives an interesting account of the
pioneering efforts in the reduction roasting of
iron ore by Adrian Chenot of France. Chenot's
plant was located at Clichy-la-Garenne, near Paris
and utilized magnetic roasting followed by magnetic
separation. This beneficiated product was then
reduced to sponge metal. Chenot died an accident-
al death when his plant was still in an experimental stage, in 1855. This date, 1855, is the earliest date known to the author for a magnetic
roasting-magnetic separation process for low-grade
iron ores.

The earliest reference on the subject of magnetic roasting of iron ore in America is that of
Clemens Jones[33] in an AIME publication in 1891.
He briefly describes magnetic roasting of goethite
and hematite followed by magnetic separation.
Quoting from his paper, "The only statement now
possible is, that the hydrated oxides of iron
become magnetized at a red heat in contact with
carbon or carbon monoxide." Jones was issued U.
S. Patent 480,405 covering his process on August
9, 1892. This patent is believed to be the first
U.S. patent on the reduction roasting of iron
oxide ores.

In 1895, W.B. Phillips[34] reported the observations of George B. McCormack (Tennessee Coal, Iron
and Railway Company) that a piece of soft, red,
fossiliferous ore turned black when subjected to
the heat and reducing gases in a coke oven flue.
Since the black ore resembled magnetite, McCormack

(32) Blair, T.S.:The "Direct Process" in Iron
     Manufacture, Trans AIME, vol 2, 1874, p
     175-199.
(33) Jones, C.:The Magnetization of Iron Ore,
     Trans AIME, vol 19, 1891, p 289-296.
(34) Phillips, W.B.:Notes on the Magnetization
     and Concentration of Iron Ore, Trans. AIME
     vol 25, 1895, p 399-423.

tested the ore with a hand magnet and found that it was magnetic. Further tests showed that ore which contained 46 percent iron could be up-graded to over 60 percent iron by roasting and magnetic separation. McCormack and A. E. Barton secured U.S. Patent 519,902, May 15, 1894, on the process of magnetizing hematite ores and concentrating them magnetically.

Phillips continued this early work and reported operations of an experimental plant at Ensley, Alabama which would process 3000 pounds of ore at a time. Then, at Bessemer, Alabama, for several weeks, he operated a Davis-Colby gas-fired kiln which processed 110 tons per 24 hours. The reducing gas was supplied by a Wellman producer. Kiln temperature was 900 to 1350 degrees Fahrenheit, with an average of 1100 degrees. The reduced ore was fed to a Hoffman belt-type magnetic separator at the rate of 700 pounds per hour with the following results:

	Fe, %	SiO_2, %
Feed	45.0	30.0
Concentrate	58.86	11.51
Middlings	51.12	21.00

Tailings analyses were not given. The phosphorus content of 0.3 percent was not reduced by magnetic separation but could be reduced to 0.008 percent by a sulphuric acid leach. The estimated cost for the operation of a plant treating 100 tons, per day was $1.15 per ton of concentrates. These results are significant in the early history of magnetic roasting and also represent the beginning of the beneficiation of iron ores from the Birmingham area.

The next significant American attempt to utilize a magnetic roasting process was a 450-ton pilot-plant built in 1913 to utilize the Goltra process[35,36]. The plant was located at Iron Hill

(35) Spilsbury, E.G.:Goltra Process for Concentrating Iron Ore, Eng. & Mining Jnl. vol 95, 1913, p 475-476.
(36) Phillips, W.B.:Concentration by the Goltra Process, Iron Age, vol 94, 1914, p 1148-1150.

near Waukon, Iowa. The process included preliminary roasting to dry the ore and screening to
separate the coarse from the minus ½-inch material.
The fines, while hot, were sprayed with crude
petroleum in a sealed rotary kiln to produce magnetic iron oxide. The roasted ore was subjected
to magnetic separation in Ball-Norton separators.
In trial runs on a Texas brown ore analyzing 32.74
percent iron, a magnetic concentrate containing
63.33 percent iron and a tailing product containing 34.05 percent iron was obtained.

In 1925 a rotary kiln was used in a roasting
plant at Gijon, Spain by the Sociedad Industrial
Asturiana[37]. Low-grade hematite ore was converted
to artificial magnetite in a 100-foot long by 5-
foot diameter kiln. The furnace capacity was only
two tons of ore per hour and only 80 percent of
the iron in the ore was converted to a magnetic
state. Fuel consumption was about 600 pounds of
coke breeze per ton of roasted product. The oolitic type ore, which contained 43 percent iron, was
crushed to minus 3/8-inch before feeding to the
kiln. The roasted product was crushed to minus
150 mesh, concentrated magnetically, and briquetted. The final product contained 61 percent iron.
Good control of furnace temperatures was never
attained and the plant was shut down after intermittent operation during the summer of 1925.

Dr. Davis[38] included in a report on magnetic
roasting of iron ore a letter from Dr. Umene,
Director of Showa Steel Works, which described
the "largest magnetic roasting plant in the world."
This title may still apply since large-scale operations are scarce. The plant described by Umene
was the Anzan, Manchuria plant which used shaft-
type furnaces for reduction of hematite. A more
recent reference to this plant is found in an
issue of the U.S. Bureau of Mines Mineral Trade

(37) Davis, E.W.:Magnetic Roasting of Iron Ore,
        Univ. of Minnesota Mines Experiment Sta-
        tion Bulletin No. 13, May, 1937, 90 pp.
  (38) Davis:op cit.

Notes[39]. The furnaces are about 10 meters high
and use powdered coal for preheating the ore to
650 degrees Centigrade. Then coke oven gas is
used in the reducing zone and the reduced ore is
quenched in water. This plant began operations
in 1926 and expansions of facilities occurred in
1935, 1937 and 1939.

The U.S. Bureau of Mines[40], in connection with
beneficiation studies on Southern Iron ores,
published a report on extensive laboratory and
pilot-plant work involving magnetic roasting of
Alabama ores in 1927. Pilot-plant roasting was
done in a multiple hearth-type furnace using minus
1/4-inch ore containing from 32.6 to 36.3 percent
iron. The reduction time was 15 to 30 minutes at
550 degrees Centigrade. The magnetic product was
ground to minus 200 mesh and separated by magnetic
log washers operated in series. Table III sum-
marizes laboratory magnetic roasting tests with
Alabama ores. It should be noted that the magnetic roasting process showed high lime rejection.
This is undesirable in processing these ores and
Lee[41] reported on a flotation process which could
recover limestone from the magnetic separator tailings. This flotation concentrate could be combined
with the magnetic concentrate as needed to provide
a self-fluxing final product. The Bureau's process
was never applied on a commercial scale, presumab-
ly because of the high roasting cost.

Activity in the magnetic roasting field was not
lacking in England, France and Germany during the
period the U. S. Bureau of Mines was studying
applicability of the process to Alabama ores.
Several British Patents were issued on the subject

(39) Harrington, J.F. and B.M. Page: Sources of
       Iron Ore in Asia, Economic and Scientific
       Section, Natural Resources Div. Rept. No.
       154, March 1952, Reprinted by U.S. Bur.
       Mines as Mineral Trade Notes Special Supple-
       ment No. 38 to vol 34, No. 5, May 1952.
(40) Lee, O., B.W. Gandrud and F.D. DeVaney: Mag-
       netic Concentration of Iron Ores of
       Alabama, U.S. Bur. Mines Bulletin 278,
       1927, 75 pp.
(41) Lee: op cit.

TABLE III

Summary of Laboratory Magnetic-Roasting
Tests with Alabama Ores (a)

Ore Seam	Feed %			Concentrate %			Tailing %	
	Fe	Insol.	CaO	Fe	Insol.	CaO	Fe	CaO
Irondale	40.3	23.1	7.6	53.5	14.8	1.9	5.2	22.8
Big Seam	37.2	28.3	7.3	53.7	13.8	3.5	4.8	14.6
" "	33.0	22.0	13.3	53.4	10.6	4.7	6.1	24.7
" "	38.0	14.7	14.5	54.0	10.5	3.0	3.9	39.1
" "	32.9	13.9	16.0	51.6	10.2	4.4	7.5	31.1

Leached, high-silica ores

Ore Seam	Feed %			Concentrate %			Tailing %	
Ida	40.9	39.4	Tr.	61.5	11.3	-	3.6	-
Upper Big	37.2	38.1	2.4	57.1	13.2	0.7	4.7	5.2

Ferruginous sandstones

Ore Seam	Feed %			Concentrate %			Tailing %	
Upper	18.2	69.7	Tr.	57.3	15.0	-	3.3	-
Middle	31.9	34.7	8.1	51.1	20.1	2.5	4.3	16.1

Notes:
   (a) Adapted from U.S. Bureau of Mines Report of
   Investigations 4988, July 1953, p 31.
   Minus ¼-inch ore was roasted at 550 degrees C.
   for 30 minutes. Magnetic separation in Davis
   tube at minus 100 mesh.
   Recovery of iron ranged from 86.4 to 97.0 %.
   Lime rejection into tailings ranged from 68.3
   to 86.2 %.

in 1936. Luyken and Kraeber[42] described magnetic
roasting tests on brown hematite ores of Lower
Silesia in 1936. A concentrate containing 50 percent iron with a total recovery of 88.7 percent
was obtained. In France, at about the same time,
the St. Jacques Turbulent Furnace[43] was receiving
much publicity. This apparatus consisted of a
vertical cylinder-type furnace which processed
ore fines fed as a "dust suspension". The intimate ore-flame contact allowed reduction to take
place in as little as four seconds time. A heat
exchanger utilized extracted heat from the reduced
ore to preheat combustion air. Tests with a 42
percent iron ore resulted in magnetic concentrates
containing 53 and 50 percent iron with recoveries
of 92 and 98.5 percent respectively.

In the United States a magnetic roasting pilot
plant was built by Butler Brothers at Cooley,
Minnesota under a cooperative agreement with the
University of Minnesota in 1934. The plant processed 29,074 tons of jig plant tailings and
recovered 15,870 tons of merchantable concentrates
during the 1934-1935 period of operation. The
plant was operated over a period of four years.
The last two years (1936-1937) were considered
semi-commercial operations. As a result of several years of laboratory testing, the plant utilized
a shaft-type reduction furnace. The plant had a
capacity of 265 tons per hour and consisted of
three sections. The first was a preparation plant
where minus 1-1/4 inch jig tailings containing 42
to 50 percent iron were dried in a vertical shaft-
type dryer to reduce moisture from an initial 8 to
10 percent to approximately 3 percent. The dried
ore was then crushed to minus 3/4-inch and screened at 3 mesh. The over- and undersize ore was fed
separately to the kiln to control dust losses, to
decrease power cost of fan operation and to pre-

(42) Luyken, W. and L. Kraeber:Magnetic Dressing
       of Brown Hematite Ores of Lower Silesia,
       Eisenforschung, Mitt. Kaiser Wilhelm Inst.,
       Dusseldorf, vol 18, 1936, p 35-41.
(43) Dean, R.S. and C.W. Davis:Magnetic Separation
       of Ores, U.S. Bur. Mines Bulletin 525, 1941
       p 262-263.

vent channeling of reduction gases. The second
section contained the roasting furnace through
which ore traveled continuously by gravity. Ore
was heated in the upper part by hot gases derived
by combustion of fuel oil and then reduced to magnetic state in the lower part by an oil vapor reducing agent. Water quenching of the roasted product took place at the bottom of the furnace. The
third section consisted of a concentration plant
where the artificial magnetite was concentrated
by wet magnetic separators. The plant superint-
endent of this operation made the following statement regarding the possibility of a skin roast,
"At an earlier date, it had been felt that a thin
film of magnetite on the outside of a piece of ore
was all that was necessary to cause its retention
in a magnetic field. In the experimental work
conducted at the Mines Experiment Station previous
to the erection of the plant, it was found that
this was not true, but that the force of attraction, for a given field strength, depended on the
ratio of the weight of magnetic iron in the piece
to the total weight of the piece. This is an all-
important factor, affecting not only the concentration of the roasted ore, but also the actual
roasting of the ore, as it is obvious that, for
best results, the furnace operating conditions,
particularly the maximum size of ore particle and
the time for reduction must be such as to accomplish reduction of the entire piece and not just a
"skin" roast. Examination has shown, however,
that a number of the coarser pieces of concentrate
may contain a small core or center of red hematite;
these pieces appear to be high-grade concentrate,
which means that the ratio of the weight of magnetic iron to the total weight of the piece is suff-
iciently high for the piece of concentrate to be
recovered by the magnetic drum."[44]
      The final conclusion reached at the Cooley
plant was that, "roasting costs are still much

(44) Craig, J.J.:Magnetic Concentration on the
      Mesabi Makes Progress, Eng. & Mining Jnl.,
      vol 139, Jan. 1938, p 48-51.

too high for this process to be used generally"[45].
When operations were discontinued at the Cooley
plant, Davis and his colleagues continued their
pioneering work with low-grade iron ores on a
laboratory and pilot-plant scale at the University
of Minnesota. The Minnesota Mines Experiment
Station Report of March, 1944 is typical of the
steady flow of technical information issuing from
this laboratory[46]. This report describes roasting
tests on many Mesabi Range samples including ore
from rock dumps, outcrops, pit walls and drill
cores. The report concludes, "indications are
that after magnetic roasting there is little difference in concentrating characteristics between
oxidized taconite and magnetic taconite." Later
this is somewhat modified by, "The indications are
that after magnetic roasting of oxidized taconite
that is low in carbonate and silicate iron, the
tailings that can be rejected are lower in iron
than the tailings that can be rejected from natural magnetite." More recent work has verified this
conclusion. This, along with the fact that many
of the non-magnetic taconites contain a higher
percentage of iron than the magnetic types, has
been an important factor spurring the development
of processes for beneficiation of non-magnetic
taconites.

Roasting tests on Alabama ores were also renew-
ed in the late nineteen thirties. According to
Clemmons[47], the Sloss-Sheffield Steel and Iron
Company undertook laboratory and pilot-plant
roasting of high-silica ore in Alabama around the
year 1938. The results of the work was not published but Clemmons reported that a 24-ton per
day pilot plant was constructed. Several differ-

(45) Davis, E.W.:First Magnetic Roasting Plant in
      Lake Superior Region, Trans. AIME, vol 134,
      1939, p 389-408.
(46) Davis, E.W.:Mesabi Taconite, A Study of Con-
      centrating Characteristics, Univ. of Minn.
      Expt. Sta. Inf. Circ. No.4, Mar. 1944, 19 pp.
(47) Clemmons, B.H.:The Future of Birmingham Red
      Iron Ore, Jefferson County, Alabama, Part II
      Concentration, U.S. Bur. Mines Rept. of Inv.
      4988, July 1953, p 32.

ent ores were roasted in a 4- by 30-foot rotary
kiln. The reduced product was ground and concentrated in a Crockett-type magnetic separator.
One development resulting from these studies was
U.S. Patent 2,240,718, May 6, 1941 to Schiffman,
Lawson and Blakemore. This unusual patent covers
a procedure for simultaneously roasting and grinding ore in a ball mill at 1200 degrees Fahrenheit.
The current rapid development of new high-temperature metals and ceramics may encourage reconsider-
eration of this process.

During the years 1943-1947 Sloss-Sheffield
installed and operated a 200-ton per day plant
using a rotary kiln with natural gas as the fuel
and finely divided high volatile coal, mixed with
the charge, as the reducing agent[48,49]. Minus
1/4-inch ore was fed to the kiln and the reduced
ore was ground through 65 mesh in a ball mill
operated in closed circuit with a spiral-type
classifier. The classifier overflow as passed
through magnetic separators to produce concentrates containing 50 to 56 percent iron. Recovery
was usually over 85 percent.

Several years before the Sloss-Sheffield pilot
plant began operations, a large-scale commercial
iron ore roasting plant was in operation at the
Herman Goering Works (now Reichswerke A.G.) at
Watenstedt, Germany. The Lurgi process was used
and the plant was designed for 6000 tons of ore
per day. Since little published information has
appeared regarding this plant, some observations
of a British Intelligence Objectives Subcommittee
team are noted here[50]. "In this process, developed by the Lurgi Gesellschaft, crushed ore is
passed through a rotary kiln in which it is subjected to a magnetic roasting operation by the
action of heat and blast furnace gas. Part of the
gas enters the kiln at the exit end, thereby

(48) Clemmons:op cit
(49) Rose, E.H.:Beneficiation Methods for Southern
     Iron Ore, Regional Technical Meetings of
     Amer. Iron & Steel Inst. 1949, p 221-242.
(50) Iron Ore Preparation in Germany, British
     Intelligence Objectives Sub-Committee (BIOS)
     Trip No. 1234, November, 1945.

cooling and to some degree reducing the ore in the
lower one-third of the kiln. Additional gas and
excess air are introduced in the upper sections
of the kiln to generate the necessary heat. The
ore charge to the Lurgi kiln is normally below one
inch, but it is reputed to be capable of dealing
with ore up to four inches. At the time of the
visit some of the ore remaining in the feed chutes
was over three inches. The kiln is 165-feet long
by 11-feet, 6-inches in diameter and is inclined
at four degrees. Operation is at the rate of 35
to 40 tons charged per hour per kiln and the
consumption of blast furnace gas is 420,000 cubic
feet per hour. There are eight such kilns at
Watenstedt. The kiln is of uniform external
diameter and is lined with firebrick except for a
short unlined section at the discharge end; the
ore charge is turned over by means of lifters fitted to the kiln wall. These lifters are simply
curved corrugated plates projecting about 9 inches
from the wall. Gas and air are introduced to the
kiln at intervals along its length and gas alone
is introduced at the discharge end. There are 12
burners along the kiln, arranged in a two-start
spiral. Each burner pipe projects approximately
to the center of the kiln. An inspection glass
is incorporated in the outer end of the burner
pipe. Normally it is not necessary to use all
the burners simultaneously.
     The gas for reduction is introduced into the
kiln through the centre of the discharge end and
amounts to approximately 280,000 cubic feet per
hour. Burner gas delivered through the burners
along the length of the kiln amounts to approximately 140,000 cubic feet per hour. Gas is
delivered at a pressure of 10 inches, water gauge.
Air used totals approximately 360,000 cubic feet
per hour. A water pipe projects through the
reduction gas tube to be used only if the discharge temperature exceeds 80 degrees Centigrade.
This was reported to be quite frequently the case.
The use of water reduces the efficiency of the
process, as it diminishes the partial pressure
of carbon monoxide in the kiln, but the overall
efficiency of the process benefits by improved
magnetic separation. Exhaust gases pass through

cyclones and a precipitator. The carbon dioxide content is about 18 percent with less than one percent carbon monoxide. The kiln revolves once in $1\frac{1}{2}$ - 3 minutes; this variable speed is used as the main control of the process. Power consumption of the kiln was said to be 35 kwh. Thermocouples are fitted at ten points in the kiln and are connected to recorders by slip rings on the kiln. Dust production is excessive, due to high exit gas velocities and appears to have been quite a serious problem. It was considered that this could be reduced by redesigning the kiln at this point. The very fine dust was sold to the colour industry. Elaborate equipment has been installed to reintroduce the dust to the kiln at a point beyond that of maximum gas velocity. This is done through a central pipe which extends into the kiln 30 feet from the charging end. The dust is carried in by a stream of air. Temperature of the exit gases averages 250 degrees Centigrade. The highest temperature attained in the kiln for efficient operation is about 750 degrees. Early operation was at 850 degrees Centigrade, but it became evident that better results were obtained at 750 degrees. The opinion has been expressed that at the higher temperature a thin slag film may form on the surface of the oolites which will of course reduce the efficiency of the magnetic separation.

After leaving the kiln, the product has to pass through the magnetic separating plant. Magnetic separation is very inefficient unless the material is finely crushed. The roasted ore, therefore, is crushed to -1/8 inch, every effort being made to reduce the particle size to -1/16 inch. This is done in two stages through two-roll crushers with plain rolls and after screening the material then goes to the separating plant. The total power consumption for mechanism and magnetic separation amount to 17 kwh per ton of concentrate. For the eight Lurgi kilns there are 24 magnetic separators. Using D.C.at 120 volts, the primary separators each take 10 to 11 amps and the secondary separators 7 to 9 amps. The separators are installed in tandem, the primary drums running at 120 r.p.m. and the secondaries at 60 to 90 r.p.m.

It was stated that semi-A.C. had been tried for material of 1/8 - 1/16 inch size without any significant change in efficiency. For the finer material such as cyclone dust semi-A.C. was said to give much better results than D.C. and two separators had been installed for this.

Dust is a problem; the whole of the plant has to be fully enclosed and dust extraction apparatus fitted and at the end of it all the material has to be sintered. In this connection the operators say it is impossible to sinter successfully more than 25 or 30 percent of Lurgi concentrates.

A typical analysis of the ore at the various stages of the operation is as follows:

	Raw Ore	Roasted Ore	Magnetic Conct.
Fe	27.00	31.25	40.0%
SiO_2	28.00	30.1	23.56%
Al_2O_3	10.6	-	9.21%
CaO	5.72	5.6	4.4%
MgO	1.81	-	2.3%
Mn	0.20	0.19	0.18%
P	0.42	0.34	0.47%
L.O.I.	13.25	-	-
Moisture	7.9	0.16	0.05%
Fe/SiO_2	0.96	1.04	1.70

The yield data of the Lurgi process are given as follows:

	Raw Ore = 100 tons		Mag. Conct. = 57.4 tons		Non-mag & dust = 34.7	
	%	Tons	%	Tons	%	Tons
Fe	27.0	27.0	40.0	23.0	11.5	4.0
SiO2	28.0	28.0	23.6	13.5	41.8	14.5
Al_2O_3	10.8	10.6	9.2	5.3	15.3	5.3
CaO	5.7	5.7	4.4	2.5	9.2	3.2
MgO	1.8	1.8	2.3	1.3	1.4	0.5
Mn_3O_4	0.3	0.3	0.25	0.15	0.4	0.15
P_2O_5	1.0	1.0	1.15	0.65	1.0	1.35

Operation is reported as not too easy. Close temperature control is necessary for efficient working and crushing before separation is also critical.

One point in favor of the Lurgi process is that kiln linings have a long life because of the comparatively low temperatures employed. The lifters previously referred to are made of a special nickel chromium steel and have a life much shorter than that of the refractory.

A point which impressed the team was that the capital cost of the plant must have been very high in relation to the tonnage handled."

Another report in the British literature[51] gives considerable details regarding German magnetic roasting practice. In this report Dr. Luyken points out the adviseability of producing gamma hematite, the brown strongly magnetic ferric oxide. He states, "The oxide has the cubic space lattice of magnetite and is of equal magnetizability. Its production is conditional on the temperature of oxidation not being higher than about 550 degrees Centigrade; it is hardly necessary to add that if the temperature is not exceeded no excess of oxygen or air during cooling can be harmful because the oxidation stops at gamma hematite."

Dr. Luyken also describes a large experimental magnetic roasting plant at Landsberg, Upper Schleswig which operated in 1942 and 1943. A rotary kiln 65-feet long with a capacity of 26 cubic yards was used in conjunction with a cooling kiln 39-feet long. A gas seal was used on the discharge end of the kiln and producer gas was used as fuel. Operating temperatures in the kiln were 620 to 850 degrees Centigrade. A summary of results on four ores was given:

	Ore % Fe	Yield Wt.%	Mag. Conct. %Fe	Rec. of Fe, %
Iron Sandstone	16.1	--	49.4	76.5
Salzgitter ore	25.0	59.5	40.1	82.8
Thuringian brown ore	25.2	49.8	47.7	94.0
Krompach waste slimes (iron carbonate)	27.1	51.2	50.7	95.8

(51) Luyken, W.:Lean Ores, German Experience in
      Their Preparation, Iron & Steel (London)
      Oct. 1947, p 471-475.

Some suggestions for improving the Lurgi kiln were given by Wahlbrecker[52]. He suggests a lower roasting temperature (500-550 degrees C) than was used at the Watenstedt plant. In addition, spiral blades are proposed for equalizing load distribution and to improve gas generation.

Another example of a very large magnetic roasting plant is the Nicaro nickel plant in Cuba. Strangely enough, the artificial magnetite produced in this plant is literally thrown away, since only nickel and cobalt are recovered. The magnetite contains too much chromium and nickel to be valuable as an iron ore. The operations of this plant are briefly described in the chapter on hydrometallurgy and by-products.

Intensive research during the 1940-1955 period has resulted in the development of three significant roasting processes which are contenders in the race for a more efficient magnetic roasting process. The three processes are:

    (1) The fluidized bed process
    (2) The Battelle reduction-oxidation process
    (3) The DeVaney process

None of these processes use rotary kilns for the roasting operation and none have been proven by commercial operation on iron ore. The Battelle and DeVaney processes use shaft-type furnaces; the fluidized bed process is carried out in a vertical furnace generally referred to as a "reactor". The "fluidized-bed reactor" is a modification of equipment developed by the Standard Oil Development Company for fluid catalytic cracking of hydrocarbons. The Dorr Company is licensed under Standard's patents to use the fluidizing technique in non-petroleum, non-catalytic processes. Table IV compares the three magnetic roasting processes. A study of these processes reveals certain advantages for each. If it is possible to combine the best features of the three processes, then a magnetic roasting process of high efficiency can be applied to the beneficiation of nonmagnetic taconites.

The end product of all magnetic roasting opera-

---

(52) Wahlbrecker, W.:Problems of Magnetizing Roasting of Iron Ores in a Rotary Furnace, Z. Erz. v. Metall. vol 5, Feb. 1952, p 54-61.

TABLE IV

Comparison of Fluidized Bed, DeVaney
and Battelle Roasting Processes

	Fluidized Bed	DeVaney	Battelle
Preferred feed size	8-10 mesh	10 mesh to 2-inch	10 mesh to 1-inch
Feed limitations	prefers fine sizes	prefers max. of 20%-10mesh	prefers max. of 20% -10mesh
Reducing gas composition	producer gas	5-6% CO, 15% CO_2, bal. N_2	hydrogen or producer gas
Reduction temp.	est. 400-800 deg.C.	816-871 deg. C.	399-449 degrees C.
Recovery Fe in plus 60% Fe conct.	over 90	Over 90	over 90
Btu req. per long ton feed	600,000	312,952	heat required only to start operation
Fuel cost per ton feed (oil @ 10cts/gallon)	$0.50	$0.25	--
Pilot plant feed rate- lbs/hour	200	2240	600
Furnace capacity, long tons feed/ sq.ft. shaft area/ 24 hours	4.4	5-6	5-6
Remarks:	Good process for finer ore fractions	Process easy to operate	Feed must contain min. of 20% of the Fe in form of Fe_2O_3

tions must have one qualification above all others-
it must be susceptible to recovery by commercial
magnetic separators. This means that the product
must be artificial magnetite or gamma hematite.
Gamma hematite has the same chemical composition
as alpha hematite (Fe_2O_3) but has a cubic crystalline structure as compared to a rhombohedral
structure for alpha hematite. Gamma hematite is
strongly magnetic and easily beneficiated by wet
magnetic methods whereas alpha hematite is commercially processed only by gravity and froth
flotation methods. Artificial magnetite has the
same chemical composition as natural magnetite
(Fe_3O_4), crystallizes in the same crystalline
system (cubic), and is strongly magnetic. Most
magnetic-roasting processes have been aimed at
production of artificial magnetite, but recently
much attention has been given the formation of
gamma hematite as an end product. This involves
the added stop of controlled oxidation of the artificial magnetite to gamma hematite. Artificial
magnetite is an intermediate product when any
roasting process is used to produce gamma hematite. The oxidation reaction is exothermic and
provides additional heat units to the process.

Little information is available regarding the
magnetic properties of these two artificial magnetic iron minerals. The reader is referred to
Chapter III for a review of some pertinent work
on the subject.

Metallization of Iron Ores

It is probable that no method of iron ore beneficiation has received more attention and effort
than the so-called "direct iron and sponge iron"
processes. In some cases the starting raw material
is low-grade iron ore; in others the feed is iron
ore concentrates which have been beneficiated to
various degrees. For the purposes of this chapter
no fine line of distinction will be drawn between
processes which may be classed as "ore beneficiation processes" and those which should possibly
be classified as "smelting operations". In many
direct iron processes both are involved.

An early classic on direct iron was presented

by Thomas S. Blair[53] at a New York AIME meeting
in 1874. He observed that "The whole literature
of the art, so far as it relates to the direct
process, is, up to this time, but a history of
failure. It is safe to say that more money, time,
and talent have been fruitlessly spent in the
pursuit of this object than in all the other unsuccessful efforts in the whole line of iron metallurgy. A distinguished authority in patent law
has remarked that the invention records of the
United States and of foreign countries are filled
with the waifs and abandoned relics of these
abortive struggles." Blair mentions Chenot in
France, Renton in America and Gurlt in Germany
as examples of early inventors of direct iron
processes. Since Blair's review there have been
dozens of similar processes developed, but only
three have had real commercial development. These
are the Wiberg, the Hoganas, and the Krupp-Renn
processes. The Wiberg and Hoganas processes are
purely smelting operations while the Krupp-Renn
method includes ore dressing operations.

According to Barrett[54] the Hoganas process has
been used in Sweden for about 40 years to make
some 10,000 tons of premium-grade sponge iron per
year. The process involves firing of ceramic sag-
gers which contain magnetite superconcentrate (70
to 71% iron) surrounded by a mixture of limestone
and coke breeze. The fuel requirements are about
1,000 kg of coal per metric ton of sponge iron.
Most of the final product is consumed by Swedish
steel companies making high-quality special steels.
A similar process was developed by the Ontario Research Foundation in Canada. Cavanagh[55,56] reported on the method in 1951 and was issued a
patent in 1954.

(53) Blair, T.S.:The "Direct Process" in Iron Manufacture, Trans. AIME vol 2, 1874, p 175-199.
(54) Barrett, E.P.:Sponge Iron and Direct-Iron
Processes, U.S.B.M. Bull. 519, 1954, 143 pp.
(55) Cavanagh, P.E.:Sponge Iron a Remedy for Scrap
Shortage? Steel, June 11, 1951, p 92-101.
(56) Cavanagh, P.E.:Method of Making Metal Products Direct From Ores, U.S. Patent 2,686,
118 Aug. 10, 1954.

The Wiberg-Soderfors process claims very low consumption of reducing agent per ton of iron produced. Kalling and Stalhed[57] published details regarding the chemistry of the process, construction of plant, operational results, and suitability of different ores. In this process high-grade iron ore or concentrate is reduced in a shaft furnace with close control of temperature and gas composition. Wiberg made his first experiments at Woxna, Sweden in 1920. The plant at Soderfors, Sweden was first started in 1932 and has been expanded several times. A furnace of 10,000 metric tons capacity per year was in operation by 1941. The shaft and carburetor are lined with high-quality firebrick and surrounded by a gas-proof welded steel cover. The space between the cover and brickwork is filled with Sil-O-Cel powder. From November 10, 1941 until February 28, 1945 the plant operated continuously to prove the reliability of the process. The average analysis of the sponge iron produced is 64.9% metallic-iron, 76.6% total iron, 0.60% carbon, 0.005% sulphur and 0.015% phosphorus. An overall reduction of 84.2% is obtained; this can be increased to 95% with suitable ores and at lower production rates. Normally, sintered ores are preferred as feed materials. Among the advantages claimed for the method are: (1) a wide variety of sintered or pelletized ores can be used, (2) sulphur is effectively removed, (3) sponge obtained is suitable for melting in electric furnaces, (4) fuel consumption is low, (5) a wide variety of fuels can be used, (6) low labor requirements and (7) low-cost plant.

A very favorable feature which will probably continue to interest steel producers in sponge iron methods is the low residual alloy content of steels produced from sponge iron. It is a well known fact that the nickel, copper and tin content of commercial scrap iron is steadily increasing. These are the "positive contaminants" which are recycled in steel-making processes. Nickel, for example cannot be removed by either oxidation or

(57) Kalling, B. and J. Stalhed: Wiberg-Soderfors Method For the Manufacture of Sponge Iron, Steel, Sept. 19, 1949, p 72-75, 102-106.

reduction steps. The current quest for extreme purity iron and steel will encourage further development of sponge iron methods.

The J.T. Jones Step Process

One of the early metallizing processes for low-grade iron ores was the J.T. Jones Step Process. Jones operated a large pilot plant from 1908 to 1912 in northern Michigan. A study of the limited references[58,59,60,61,62] indicates that Jones' work was the real foundation for the well known Krupp-Renn process which did not appear until 1930 in Germany. One report on the Jones process appeared in a 1912 publication of the Michigan Geological Survey[62]. Albert E. White, author of this report, was an instructor in Chemical Engineering at the University of Michigan. White describes the process as follows, "The experiment in brief is to take low grade iron ore and by bringing it into contact with the volatile matters of coal or wood and likewise the fixed carbon which is found in the coal or wood it is expected that the oxygen will be driven out of the iron without in any way fluxing or melting the iron or gangue found in the ore--and then by a process of magnetic concentration the iron will be freed from its gangue and there will be obtained as a result

(58) Anon:The Jones Process for Metallizing Ore, Iron Age, vol 88, Dec. 14, 1911 p 1305.
(59) Anon:The New Step Process Furnace at Iron Mountain, Michigan for Smelting Iron Ores, Iron Trade Review, vol 43, Nov. 5, 1908, p 771-772.
(60) Anon:Making Steel Direct From Ores, Iron Trade Review, vol 68, May 19, 1921, p 1375-1376.
(61) U.S. Patents 880,799 March 3, 1908; 890,234 June 9, 1908: 891,704 and 891,705 June 23, 1908:899,405 Sept. 22, 1908: 930,764 Aug. 10, 1909: 981,280 Jan. 10, 1911: 1,174,729 March 7, 1916.
(62) White, A.E.:The J.T. Jones Step Process for the Metallization of Low Grade Iron Ores, Publication 8, Geol. Series 6, Mineral Resources of Michigan, 1912, p 245-256.

a product by all means fit for blast furnace use
and possibly of such a high grade as to be acceptable for open hearth use."

In his pilot plant experiments Jones used a
rotary kiln 120-feet long and 8-feet in diameter.
Feed ore was crushed to 1/8- to 1-inch size and
maximum reduction temperature was about 940 degrees Centigrade.

The Krupp-Renn Process

The Krupp-Renn process of iron ore beneficiation was invented by Dr. Friedrich Johannsen of
the German Krupp Company during the early nineteen thirties. The initial pilot plant was put
in operation at Borbeck, Germany in 1934. In this
process a mixture of low-grade iron ore and coke
is processed in a rotary kiln at high temperature.
The iron in the ore is reduced by solid carbon
and the metallic particles fuse together to form
small pellets known as "luppen". The metal never
becomes completely molten and is recovered in
solid form. As discharged from the kiln, the
metallic iron is dispersed as rounded granules in
a pasty, glassy slag. The iron pellets are prevented from re-oxidizing by this slag coating.
The process cannot be applied to high-grade ores
unless slag making material is added.

Some of the disadvantages of the process are:
  (a) Most of the sulphur in the burden and
      the fuel goes into the metal
  (b) High temperature and erosive action of
      the slag cause high kiln lining costs
  (c) Dust production is high - 10% of the
      charge at times.

Some advantages of the Krupp-Renn process are:
  (a) It can be used regardless of the form in
      which iron occurs in the ore
  (b) The kiln can be heated with cheapest
      available fuel
  (c) Fine-grinding of ores and agglomeration
      of final beneficiated product are dis-
      pensed with
  (d) Iron content of the final product is
      higher than that obtained by any other
      known beneficiation method.

A critical review of the Krupp-Renn process was
published in 1951 by Henry, Ramseyer and Miller[63].
Their paper covers processing of Czech and French
ores in a large Krupp-Renn plant at the Kraluv
Dvur plant of Czech United Steels Company not far
from Prague. The kiln used was 197-feet long with
an external diameter of 11-feet 10-inches. When
operating on low-grade Czech ores a CaO/SiO_2
ratio of approximately 0.09 was maintained. Ores
containing 26 to 30 percent iron were beneficiated
to 92 to 93 percent iron. A major part of kiln
relining operations (which were quite frequent)
consisted of replacing all brick in the lower 50
to 65 feet of the kiln plus local patching farther
up the kiln. Ring formation is critical in the
Krupp-Renn process and apparently the ideal gangue would be a relatively refractory material with
a short fusion range which melts only after the
iron in it has been nearly completely reduced. In
comparing Czech practice with others, the authors
state, "From what is known of Krupp-Renn operations in Germany and Japan, it can be assumed that
the Kraluv Dvur plant runs far better than the
others, and is in fact the only Krupp-Renn operation on which any opinion as to the value of the
process and its field of usefulness can safely be
based."

Kraluv Dvur engineers recommend increasing both
the length and diameter of the kiln to increase
capacity without additional labor cost. Also they
claim that their present 75 percent available
operating time can be increased.

Difficulties with the Krupp-Renn process in
Manchuria and Japan have been summarized[64] as follows:

"High fuel requirements necessary to heat
the mass of low-grade material.
Difficulties in exact temperature control to
obtain just the right fluidity without stick-
ing.
Furnace product required an extra operation

(63) Henry, P.E., C.F. Ramseyer and J.R. Miller:
Krupp-Renn Tests on French Minette Ore,
Iron & Steel Engineer, Feb. 1951, p 66-78.
(64) Harrington, J.F. and B.M. Page: op cit.

in crushing and separating iron pellets from
the slag.
Serious mechanical difficulties in operation
and maintaining refractories in the kiln.
In brief, the process was a failure and continued
operation could be justified only by the extra-
ordinary demand for iron without regard to cost."

Recent metallizing tests by the Krupp-Renn
process were reported by Astier[65]. Three hundred
tons of Lorraine, France iron ore was processed
in a 60-meter long rotary kiln. Boddeker[66] reported in 1954 on commercial scale tests of the
Sturzelberger process for production of iron from
low-grade ore in a rotary kiln. The ore processed
contained 30 percent iron and 1.85 percent manganese. The slag produced contained 6.70 percent
FeO and 3.85 percent MnO as compared to only 2.03
percent manganese in the final metal product. He
concluded that the process advantages were largely offset by the high cost and complexity of the
installation and by the iron and manganese loss
in the slag.
A tremendous amount of work has been done towards the development of a rotary kiln process
for metallizing of low-grade iron ore. The
physics and chemistry of the process are now
quite well defined and understood. It is primarily lack of suitable equipment which has prevented
commercial success of this process. The rapid development of better refractories, insulation and
heat resistant metals will greatly aid future developments in metallizing processes.

Fuels for Pyrometallurgical Processes

In addition to the "Iron age" and "age of metals" the history of man also includes what Leslie
White of the University of Michigan calls the

(65) Astier, J.:Direct Reduction Tests in the
      Kraluv-Dvur Rotary Kiln, Publ. Inst.
      Recherches, Siderurgie (St. Germain-en-Laye)
      Ser. A, No. 53, 1953, p 1-43.
(66) Boddeker, W.:The Metallurgy of Iron Ore in
      The Rotary Furnace, Metallurgie u.
      Giessereitech, vol 4, 1954, p 148-157.

"Fuel Revolution". It was the fuel revolution
that really brought metals into their own. Man
has utilized wood, coal, oil, gas and now atomic
energy as heat sources. All of these except the
latter have been used as fuels for iron ore beneficiation processes. Coal has been the most
popular of all fuels used to date. As the scale
of operations of iron ore processing grows the
coals of lignite rank will become increasingly
important. In the U.S.A. we use the term "lignite"
to define coal of low rank similar to the well
known Braunkohle of Germany. The ASTM classification establishes 8,300 Btu per pound on the
moist mineral-matter-free basis as the upper limit
for lignite and brown coal. The U.S. Bureau of
Mines has long been prominent in the study and
development of lignite utilization methods. A
comprehensive report by the Bureau[67] in 1954
gives an excellent story of the present day status of the lignite industry. The report gives
the cost of lignite at the minesite as slightly
over 2 dollars per ton or about 15 cents per
million Btu . Annual production in the North
Central States has reached over 3 million tons.
In present industrial practice lignite is burned
with its as-mined moisture content, averaging 36
percent water by weight as mined. The report
also recognizes the fuel potential on the iron
ranges and gives the present delivered cost of
fuels now used on the Minnesota Ranges as about
32 cents per million Btu . Railroad transportation cost to the Ranges for delivering lignite is
about $3.50 per ton so that the delivered cost of
lignite would be about 2.75 times the minesite
cost of $2.00 per ton. "The main opportunities
for substantial reduction in transportation costs
for fuel or power appear to lie in new developments in pipeline transportation of fuel or in
long-distance transmission of power generated at
the minesite. Both of these methods show promise
where demand is large enough, although neither

---

(67) U.S. Bureau of Mines Staff:Technology of
     Lignitic Coals, Parts 1 and 2., U.S. Bur.
     Mines Inf. Circular Nos. 7691, 7692, July
     1954, 142 and 119 pp respectively.

pipeline transportation of solid fuels   nor power
transmission at voltages up to 500,000   volts,
which promise the greatest economy for long dis-
tances, have been commercially developed as yet."
    Peat is a fuel of even lower quality than lig-
nite. It is the product of slow decay of vegeta-
ble matter under water and usually dark brown in
color. Peat varies in   appearance   from a loose
friable earthy product to a hard tough   mass approaching coal. As it occurs in a bog,   peat
may contain as much as 92 percent water. When
air dried, the moisture content may drop to 25
or 30 percent. The obvious fact is that   peat is
a low-quality fuel. Yet its occurrence in close
proximity to the   Minnesota iron ranges   forces
continued efforts towards its utilization.
    The Office   of the   Commissioner of   the Iron
Range Resources and Rehabilitation   published   a
progress report[68] on a "Peat for Heat"   study in
1949. Continued interest   by iron ore producers
indicates eventual use of peat on the iron ranges.
Peat may find use in sponge iron or magnetic roasting processes either   as a source of   roasting gas
or as a solid reductant. Also   peat   may be used
in large   generating   stations   for production of
cheap electric power. Minnesota's seven million
acres of peat land represents approximately fifty
percent of the peat in the United States.
    The rapid depletion of   fuel   supplies in all
parts of the world has focused attention on fuel
economy in all pyrometallurgical operations. A
British authority,   Sir Ernest Smith, states in
the forward of a   book dedicated   to   all those
interested in the conservation of fuel, that not
more than 15 or 20 percent of the energy   of
British coal supplies is   usefully employed[69].
Thus an improvement of only 5 percent would mean
a saving in coal mined of between 50 and 75   mil-

(68) Plummer, C.E.:Report of Progress in Peat De-
      velopment, Office of the Commissioner of
      the Iron Range Resources & Rehabilitation,
      St. Paul   Minnesota, 1949, 142 pp.
(69) Critchley, G.N.:Waste-Heat Recovery from
      Industrial Furnaces, A Symposium, Chapman
      & Hall Ltd., London, 1948, 383 pp.

lion tons a year. It is probably safe to use a
similar efficiency figure in the U.S.A. where
coal production for 1955 was estimated at 465
million tons. As the iron ore beneficiation engineer increases his use of various pyrometallurgical processes he will be increasingly concerned
with efficient use of fuels.

Water-gas plants may become important auxiliary
operations to iron ore magnetic roasting plants.
Water gas is made by passing steam through a bed
of white-hot coke contained in a generator which
is often automatically operated. The gas produced
consists mainly of hydrogen and carbon monoxide
and has a calorific value of 290 to 300 Btu
per cubic foot. The importance of waste heat
recovery in a water gas plant is apparent when it
is noted that less than 50 percent of the heat of
the burned coke remains in the fuel bed during the
blow period with the remainder leaving the generator in the blow gases. The principal method of
heat recovery is by means of a waste-heat boiler.
In British practice it is usual to equip with
waste-heat boilers only those water-gas plants
having a capacity of one million or more cubic
feet of gas per day.

Producer gas is also finding considerable favor
as a reducing agent in some pilot-plant magnetic
roasting operations. The reactions involved in
forming producer gas are essentially the same as
those which take place in a water-gas plant.
However, in producer gas there is contained all
the nitrogen entering with the air for combustion.
This gives a gas which is low in combustible
constituents and its heat value per unit volume
is low. Hermansen[70] gives a detailed discussion
of technical considerations involved in the making of producer gas. He points out that a few
percent of carbon dioxide in the finished gas is
of little importance if the distance between the
producer and the burning of the gas is short.
If the developed gas is cooled before use then a
low carbon dioxide content becomes more desireable.

(70) Hermansen, A.:Industrial Furnace Technique,
     Ernest Benn Ltd. London 1929, 293 pp.

A comparison of the composition of some common
reducing gases is given below:

	CO	H_2	CH_4	CO_2	N_2	C_2H_6	Approx. Btu/cu.ft.
Producer gas	22	10	2.6	5.7	59.7	-	130
Water gas	43	52.2	-	3.5	1.3	-	290
Coal gas*	9	47.1	34.	1.1	2.3	-	575
Natural gas	-	-	84.	-	4.	12	1000

*6.5% C_2H_4

Explosion Hazards of Fine Metal Powders

Since modern iron ore beneficiation processes
involve finer and finer-sized particles it is
important to mention some of the hazards involved
in working with fine-sized fuels, ores, and metals.
It is unnecessary to discuss the well known fire
and explosion hazards of fine coal dust. However,
the fire hazard of such minerals as pyrite is much
less known. Bowes[71] claims that freshly pulverized pyrite presents a greater fire hazard than
does coal. The absence of moisture reduces the
danger. It is recommended that the amount stored
be kept small or that inert gas (such as CO_2) be
introduced into the storage hoppers. Cooling by
ventilation is dangerous since the increased air
flow may promote ignition.

The U.S. Bureau of Mines, in 1943, reported
on the inflammability and explosibility of 53
metal powders[72]. The powders tested included 14
different metals and 2 alloys. The test equipment
and procedure are described and relative inflammability and explosibility ratings were determined.
Reduced iron and carbonyl iron showed high inflammability and low ignition temperatures (315
and 320 degrees C. respectively).

A detailed study of the spontaneous combustion

(71) Bowes, P.C.:Spontaneous Heating and Ignition
      in Iron Pyrites, Ind. Chemist, vol 30,
      1954, p 12-14.
(72) Hartmann, I., John Nagy and H.R. Brown:
      Inflammability and Explosibility of Metal
      Powders, U.S. Bureau of Mines Rept. of Inv.
      3722, Oct. 1943, 39 pp.

of metal powders was reported by Kopelman and Compton[73]. They call attention to the interesting fact that even the hydrides of metals are less pyrophoric than their parent metals at the same particle size. In comparing the very pyrophoric zirconium powder with iron powder they mention that for the same degree of pyrophoricity iron must be about one hundredth the size of the zirconium powder. Particle sizes of the order of 0.01 to 0.03 microns will make iron, nickel or copper pyrophoric. Also low reduction temperatures favor pyrophoricity. A technique called, "doping" which has been known for over a century, has been applied to the preparation of ultrafine (0.03 micron) iron powder suitable for permanent magnets. The doping process consists of adding impurities which prevent sintering of iron particles during processing of the powder. Another reference to pyrophoric iron powder by Stewart[74] describes the influence of additives in the production of high coercivity ultra-fine iron powder. Hayward[75] mentions difficulties caused by pyrophoric action of fine reduced iron ore particles in various iron ore reduction processes.

The high sensitivity to electrostatic spark discharges of some metal powders is mentioned by Hart and Tomlinson[76]. They state that, "under certain conditions the human body may build up and discharge electrostatic spark energies as great as 0.001 joule. This is of the order of that energy required to ignite dust clouds of zirconium

(73) Kopelman, B., and V.B. Compton:Spontaneous Combustion of Metal Powders, Metal Progress vol 63, Feb. 1953, p 77-79.
(74) Stewart, E.W., G.P. Conrad II, and J.F. Libsch:Influence of Additives in the Production of High-Coercivity Ultra-Fine Iron Powder, Jnl. of Metals vol 7, Jan. 1955, p 152-157.
(75) Hayward, C.R.:Hydrogen as a Reducing Agent, Eng. & Mining Jnl. vol 153, Jan. 1952, p 85-87.
(76) Hart, D. and W.R. Tomlinson,Jr.:Use of Finely Divided Metals in Explosives, Metal Progress, vol 59, 1951, p 788-792.

and some types of magnesium powder."

Lihl[77], in a detailed study of pyrophoric iron oxide produced by thermal decomposition of ferrous formate or ferrous oxalate, reports formation of a carbon-containing oxide whose iron content corresponds to the formula FeO. This oxide was designated gamma FeO and was pyrophoric when exposed to air after its formation. It burned to Fe_2O_3, but its spinel structure remained well preserved. Depending upon the reduction temperature, the residual oxide may possess the structure of alpha or gamma FeO. Under some conditions, the two oxides can also exist simultaneously. Lihl also concludes that low reduction temperatures favor pyrophoricity.

(77) Lihl, F.:Concerning a Pyrophoric Iron Oxide, Monatshefte Fur Chemie vol 81, 1950, No. 5 p 632-846.

ADDITIONAL REFERENCES

Anon:The Push to Hotter, Temperatures, Fortune, vol. 49, Jan. 1954, p 114-119, 124-129.

Joseph, T.L.:The Iron Blast Furnace, U.S. Bur. Mines Inf. Circular 6779, May 1934, 29 pp.

Kinzie, R.A.:Fuel Economy in the Lepol Kilns, Mining Eng. vol 187, Feb. 1950, p 289-291.

Howard, J.J.:A New Approach to Taconite Utilization, Mining Eng. vol 187, May 1950, p 560-563.

Lesher, C.E.:Low-Temperature Coke as a Reactive Carbon, Mining Eng. vol 187, July 1950, p 805-810.

Wuerker, R.G.:Beneficiation of Taconites by Pyrometallurgy, Mining Eng. vol 190, Jan. 1951, p 25-26.

Lesher, C.E.:Development of the Disco Process of Low Temperature Carbonization, Mining Eng. vol 4, March 1952, p 287-299.

Gibbs, R.:Estimating Best Output and Fuel Rates of Dry Feed Lime Kilns, Chem. & Met. Eng. vol 53, April 1946, p 99-101.

Gibbs, R.:Estimating Best Output and Fuel Rates of Wet-Feed Lime Kilns, Chem. & Met. Eng. vol 53, May, 1946, p 139-141.

Brower, T.E. and B.M. Larsen:A Survey of the Sulphur Problem Through the Various Operations in the Steel Plant, Jnl. of Metals vol 3, Dec. 1951, p 1163-1171.

Nordberg, B.:America's Largest Dry Process Cement Kiln, Rock Products vol 55, Aug. 1952, p 132-138, 211-216.

Pearson, B.M.:Ring Formation in Cement Kilns, Rock Products vol 55, Aug. 1952, p 158-159.

Warner, I.:Elements of Efficiency in Lime Calcination, Rock Products vol 55, Jan. 1952, p 137-139, 195-197.

Nordberg, B.:Penn-Dixie's 500-Foot Rotary Kiln, Rock Products vol 55, Jan. 1952, p 140-147.

Anon:Britain's Newest Cement Plant, Rock Products vol 55, Feb. 1952, p 110-112.

Weisz, W.H.:Kiln Performance Charted from Studies of Gas Analysis, Rock Products vol 55, March 1952, p 88-91, 113.

Luethge, J.A.:How to Scale Up a Rotary Kiln, Chem.
Eng. vol 58, Dec. 1951, p 151-153.
Phillipp, L.S.:An Electrically-Fired Kiln, Rock
Products vol 52, March 1939, p 84-85.
Atherton, C.R.:Rotary Lime Kiln Capacity-A Recon-
ciliation of Points of View, Rock Products vol
52, June 1949, p 126, 135.
Barkell, Y:Utilization of Low Temperature Kiln
Gases, Rock Products vol 52, Aug. 1949, p 158.
Koyanagi, K.:Simultaneous Manufacture of Cement
and Cast Iron, Rock Products vol 52, May 1949,
p 60-62.
Koyanagi, K. and T. Sudoh:Constitution of Cement
Clinker Obtained By Basset Process, Rock Prod-
ucts vol 53, Feb. 1950, p 129-132.
Josephson, G.W., F. Sillers, and D.G. Runner:Iron
Blast-Furnace Slag Production, Processing, Prop-
erties and Uses, U.S. Bur. Mines Bulletin 479,1949.
Kalbach, J.C.:Fluidization in Chemical Reactions,
Chem. Eng. vol 54, Jan. 1947, p 105-108.
Kalbach, J.C.:Handling Solids-Gas Reactions by
Fluidization, Chem. Eng. vol 54, Feb. 1947, p
136-138.
Linden, H.R. and D.F. Othmer:Combustion Calcula-
tions for Hydrocarbon Fuels, Chem. Eng. vol 54,
April 1947, p 115-119; May 1947, p 148-153.
Otto, F.C.:Estimating Mineral Wool Insulation,
Chem. Eng. vol 54, July 1947, p 102-106.
Kite, R.P. and E.J. Roberts:Fluidization in Non-
Catalytic Operations, Chem. Eng. vol 54, Dec.
1947, p 112-115.
Gibbs, R.:Computing Combustion Volumes for Burn-
ing Fuel Oil, Chem. Eng. vol 56, Jan. 1949, p
112-114.
Schwab, G.M. and J. Philinis:Reactions of Iron
Pyrite:Its Thermal Decomposition by Hydrogen and
Air Oxidation, Jnl. Amer. Chem. Soc. vol 69,
Nov. 1947, p 2588-2596.
Leva, M., et al:Fluid Flow Through Packed and
Fluidized Systems, U.S. Bur. Mines Bulletin 504,
1951, 149 pp.
Counselman, T.B.:Fluo Solids For Roasting, Eng. &
Mining Jnl. vol 151, March 1950, p 84-85.
White, F.S. and E.L. Kinsella:Solids Fluidization
Applied to Lime Burning, Mining Eng. vol 4, Sept.
1952, p 903-906.

Gulbransen, E.A.and R. Ruka:Kinetics and Mechanism of Solid Phase Reactions in Oxide Films on
Pure Iron, Ind. & Eng. Chem. vol 43, March 1951,
p 697-703.

Humphrey, G.L., E.G. King and K.K. Kelley: Some
Thermodynamic Values for Ferrous Oxide, U.S. Bur.
Mines Rept. of Inv. 4870, June 1952.

Bitsianes, G. and T.L. Joseph:The Wustite Phase
in Partially Reduced Hematite, Trans, AIME vol
200, 1954, Jnl. of Metals, Feb. 1954, p 150-153.

Bitsianes, G. and T.L. Joseph:Solid Phase Identification in Partially Reduced Iron Ore, Trans.
AIME vol 197, 1953; Jnl. of Metals Dec. 1953,
p 1641-1647.

Hottel, H.C. and I. Mc. C. Stewart:Space Requirement for the Combustion of Pulverized Coal, Ind.
& Eng. Chem. vol 32, May 1940, p 719-730.

Gibaldo, F.:Calcining With Indirect-fired Rotary
Kilns, Rock Products vol 52, Sept. 1949, p 63-64.

Gibbs, R.:Thermodynamics of Lime Manufacture Part
I, Rock Products vol 53, Feb. 1950, p 118-121,
143:Part II June 1950, p 122-124;Part III Oct.
1950, p 110-112;Part IV, vol 54, Feb. p 108-111,
128.

Emery, P. and J. Givaudon:Magnetizing Roast Tests
on French Iron Ores, Pubs. Inst. Recherches Siderugie (St. Germain-en-Laye) Ser. A. No. 60,
1953, p 5-119.

Othmer, D.F.:Fluidization, Reinhold Publishing
Corp. New York, 1956, 231 pp.

Zinner, P. and C.L. Holmberg:Investigation of
Iron-Bearing Formation of the Western Gogebic
Range, Iron County, Wisconsin, U.S. Bur. Mines
Rept. of Inv. 4155, Dec. 1947, 48 pp.

Counselman, T.B.:How Fluidization Can Serve the
Mineral Industries, Eng. & Mining Jnl. vol 156,
March 1955, p 70-75, 96.

Stephens, F.M.:The Fluidized-Bed Sulfate Roasting
of Nonferrous Metals, Chem. Eng. Progress, vol
49, Sept. 1953 p 455-458.

Matheson, Lewis, Morse et al:Symposium on Dynamics
of Fluid-Solid Systems, Ind. and Eng. Chem. vol
41, June 1949, p 1099-1249.

Anon:Fluidization Nomenclature Proposed, Chem. &
Eng. News, vol 27, March 7, 1949, p 686, 726.

Anderson, T.T. and R. Bolduc:FluoSolids Roasting of Zinc Concentrates for Contact Acid, Chem. Eng. Progress vol 49, Oct. 1953, p 527-532.
Priestley, R.J.:FluoSolids Conversion of Iron Ore to Magnetites, Paper given at AIME meeting, New York, Feb. 1954.
Minet, R.G., H.B. Smith and C.A. Trilling:Economics of Coal Carbonization by the Low-Temperature Process, Chem. Eng. Progress vol 50, July 1954, p 342-347.
Minet, R.G.:Continuous Fluidized Carbonization of Bituminous Coal, Paper presented before American Coke & Coal Chemicals Inst. Rye, N.Y. May, 1955.
Scharf, H.B. and E.C. Dominguez:The FluoSolids Reactor Installation at Sparrows Point, Mining Eng. vol 8, May 1956, p 517-523.
Stephens, F.M., B. Langston and A.C. Richardson: The Reduction-Oxidation Process for the Treatment of Taconites, AIME Blast Furnace, Coke Oven & Raw Materials Committee Proceedings 1953, p 53-81;also abstract published in Journal of Metals, June 1953, p 780-785.
DeVaney, F.D.:Magnetic Roasting of Lean Iron Ores Mining Eng. vol 4, Dec. 1952, p 1219-1223.
Heath, T.D.:Process of Reducing Ferric Oxide to Ferrosoferric oxide, U.S. Patent 2,477,454, July 26, 1949.
Stephens, F.M.:Treatment of Iron Ore, U.S. Patent 2,693,409, Nov. 2, 1954.
Tiddy, W. and F.D. Cooper:Two-Stage Conversion of Iron Oxide into Iron, U.S. Patent 2,545,932, March 20, 1951.
Person, R.A. and W. Mitchell:Effect of Heat Treatment and Magnetic Conversion on the Grindability of Nonmagnetic Taconites, Paper presented at AIME meeting New York, Feb. 1956.
Blue, R.W. and H.H.Claasen:Preparation of Wustite, Jnl. Amer. Chem. Society vol 71, Nov. 1949,p 3839.
Wells, R.G.:Microscopic Identification of Wustite (FeO) in the Presence of Other Oxides of Iron, Paper presented at the 123 Meeting of Amer. Chem. Society, Los Angeles, March 1953.
Paul, R.A.:Magnetic Roasting of Iron Ores, French Patent 982,574, June 12, 1951.
Urquhart, N.J.:Reduction of Iron Oxides, U.S. Patent 2,690,390, Sept. 28, 1954.

Cavanagh, P.E.:Metal Products Directly from Ores, U.S. Patent 2,686,118, Aug. 10, 1954.

Castelliz, L. et al:The Decomposition of Ferrous Oxide, Monatsh, vol 85, 1954, p 487-490;Chem. Abstracts vol 48, Nov. 25, 1954 p 13512c

Khundkar, M.H.:Thermal Decomposition of Iron Pyrites, Jnl. Indian Chem. Society, vol 24, 1947, p 407-408.

Trivedi, H.:Reduction of Iron Ore, Science & Culture, vol 17, 1952, p 423-424.

Scharschu, C.A.:Hydrogen Reduction of Iron Ore, Jnl. of Metals vol 4, 1952, p 250-251.

Walbrecker, W.:Problems of Magnetic Iron Ore Roasting in a Rotary-Tube Furnace, Z. Ergbergbau u. Mettallhutten vol 5, 1952, p 54-61;Chem. Abs. May 25, 1952, p 4445.

Safiullin, N.S.:Production of Magnetic Oxide by Reduction of Ferric Oxide, Khim. Prom., 1954, p 174-177;Chem. Abs. vol 49, Jan. 10, 1955, p 128.

Williams, G.C. and R.A. Ragatz:Low Temperature Reduction of Magnetite Ore-Effect of Catalytic Compounds, Chem. & Met. Eng. vol 28, Jan. 1936, p 130-133.

Dobovisek, B.:Control of Reduction of Iron Ores With Solid Carbon by Applying the D.T.A., Rudar-sko-Met. Zbornik, 1955, p 229-238.;Chem. Abs. June 10, 1956, p 7693.

Hawk, C.O. et al:Conversion of Methane to Carbon Monoxide and Hydrogen, Ind. & Eng. Chemistry, vol 24, Jan. 1932, p 23-27.

Gauger, A.W. et al:Development of Dakota Lignite, Ind. & Eng. Chemistry, vol 24, Jan. 1932, p 36-40.

Anon:U.S. Iron Powder Makers Contest Swedish Domination, Steel vol 130, June 2, 1952, p 74.

Kalling, B. and F. Johannsen:Reduction of Iron Ore Without Melting in a Rotary Furnace, Jnl. of the Iron & Steel Inst. (London) vol 177 Part 1, p 76-85.

Johannsen, F.:Process of Directly Producing Wrought Iron, U.S. Patent 1,964,917, July 3, 1934.

Johannsen, F.:Process of Producing Wrought Iron, U.S. Patent 2,047,562, July 14, 1936.

Howard, J.J. and H.A. Heiligman:Treating Oxide Ores, U.S. Patent 2,450,343, Sept. 28, 1948.

Scortecci, A. and M. Scortecci:A New Process for Direct Reduction of Iron Pyrites, Metal Progress vol 60, Oct. 1951, p 72-75.

Hemminger, C.E.:Process for a Two-Stage Gaseous Reduction of Iron Ore, U.S. Patent 2,481,217, Sept. 6, 1949.

Edstrom, J.O.:Reduction Experiments on Steep Rock Ore, Jernkontorets Ann. vol 140, 1936, p 130-136.

Takahashi, Y. and G. Monma:Erosion of Lining for the Rotary Kiln in the Krupp-Renn Process, Bull. Research Inst. Mineral Dressing Met. Tohuku Univ. vol 8, 59-65, 1952;Chem. Abs. vol 49, 1955, p7210.

Kalling, M.S.:Method of Reducing Ores Without Melting U.S. Patent 2,593,398.

Kalling, B.M.S. et al:Desulfurization of Metals, Swedish Patent 135,751, May 20, 1952.

Kalling, B. et al:Desulphurization of Pig Iron with Pulverized Lime, Trans. AIME vol 191, 1951 p 732-738.

Brown, W.E.:An Experiment in Making Sponge Iron, Eng. & Mining Jnl. vol 145, Nov. 1944, p 83-86.

Specht, O.G. and C.A. Zapffe:The Low-Temperature Gaseous Reduction of Magnetite to Sponge Iron, Trans. AIME vol 167, 1946, p 237-280.

Marek, L.F., A. Bogrow, and G.W. King:Experimental Laboratory Study on Effect of Pressure on Carbon Deposition and Rate of Reduction of Iron Oxides in the Blast-Furnace Process, Trans. AIME vol 172, 1947, p 46-70.

Buehl, R.C., E.P. Shoub and J.P. Riott:Production of Low-sulphur Sponge Iron, Trans. AIME vol 172, 1947, p 76-89.

Morris, J.P.:Determination of Metallic Iron and Oxygen in Sponge Iron, U.S. Bur. Mines Rept. of Inv. 3824, Sept. 1945, 31 pp.

Johnston, T.L.:Sponge Iron in Japan, U.S. Bur. Mines Inf. Circular 7440, March, 1948, 12 pp.

Gottschalk, V.H.:Making Iron Powder in the Tunnel Kiln, U.S. Bur. Mines Inf. Circular 7473, Aug. 1948, 16 pp.

Dean, R.S, S.R.B. Cooke et al:Studies in Direct Production of Iron & Steel from Ore, U.S. Bur. Mines Rept. of Inv. 3229, 1934, 65 pp.

Barrett, E.P.:Some Important Factors in Sponge Iron Production, U.S. Bur. Mines Rept. of Inv. 2955, Aug. 1929, 4 pp.

Ross, D.W.:Production of Sponge Iron in a Shale-
Brick Plant, U.S. Bur. Mines Rept. of Inv. 3822,
Sept. 1945, 27 pp.

Smith, K.M. and S.E. Burton:Manufacture of Sponge
Iron in Periodic Brick Kilns, U.S. Bur. Mines
Rept. of Inv. 3841, Dec. 1945, 38 pp.

Brown, W.E.:Sponge-Iron Experiments at Longview
Texas, U.S. Bur. Mines Rept. of Inv. 3925, Aug.
1946, 58 pp.

Torgeson, D.R. et al:Pilot-Plant Investigations--
Production of Sponge Iron with Producer Gas, U.S.
Bur. Mines Rept. of Inv. 3994, Dec. 1946, 42 pp.

O'Dea, R.J.:Small-Scale Tests of Selective Reduction of Iron in Titaniferous Iron Ores, U.S. Bur.
Mines Rept. of Inv. 3886, June, 1946, 19 pp.

Johnson, T.L. and W.M. Mahan:Laramie Sponge-Iron
Pilot Plant, U.S. Bur. Mines Rept. of Inv. 4376,
Sept., 1948, 44 pp.

Freeman, H.:Direct Iron in Canada, The Canadian
Mining Jnl. vol 49, Aug. 1956, p 566-569.

VanDeusen, E.L.:Bypassing the Blast Furnace,
Fortune, vol 54, Oct. 1956, p 164-167, 174,176.

Chapter X

HYDROMETALLURGY AND BY-PRODUCTS

> "Solidified juices are either
> prepared from waters in which
> nature or art has infused them,
> or they are produced from the
> liquid juices themselves, or
> from stony minerals."---De Re
> Metallica, 1556.

Hydrometallurgy of iron ores involves treatment by "wet" processes such as leaching followed by other accessory operations. The subject of hydrometallurgy of iron ores is destined for much attention in the future. The importance of lateritic ores alone justifies inclusion of a survey of this topic. Nickel and cobalt are already being recovered in large quantities from laterites and chromium recovery may soon be successful. When satisfactory removal of these three elements is accomplished a new source of iron ore will be available. In Cuba and the Phillipines there are very large reserves of lateritic iron ore. Past efforts have resulted in only minor usage of these ores. The Japanese used some Phillipine ore for their World War II efforts and the M.A. Hanna Company is at present using a pyrometallurgical method to beneficiate Oregon laterite ore on a relatively small scale. Neither of these pyrometallurgical attempts can, at present, be considered satisfactory processes for large scale utilization of lateritic iron ore.

The application of hydrometallurgical beneficiation processes to iron ores has included various leaching processes for reduction of the sulphur and phosphorus content of the ores. The production of by-products from iron ores is closely related to application of hydrometallurgical methods. Most of the "chemical" beneficiation methods now under consideration are high-cost processes and must pay their way by production of

high-value products. Among the by-products which
have been recovered from iron ores are nickel,
cobalt, copper, vanadium, cement, feldspar, apatite, ilmenite, crushed stone, gravel, sand, and
sulphur. By-products from future iron ore plants
may include chromium, selenium, arsenic, alumina,
manganese, sillimanite, mica and monazite.

Hydrometallurgical processing has been advanced
considerably by the intensive efforts applied
to beneficiation of uranium ores in recent years.
The "chemical" behavior of uranium minerals is
quite different than that of the iron ore minerals.
However, the chemical response of gangue minerals
associated with uranium minerals is similar to
the behavior of gangue minerals associated with
iron ores. Therefore, information developed by
the uranium beneficiation industry is of interest
to the iron ore industry. The chemistry of many
uranium processing methods has been considered
classified defense information until as recently
as 1955.   Many of the fundamentals involved in
these processes are over fifty years old. One
outstanding development greatly encouraged by the
rapid growth of the uranium industry is the use
of ion exchange resins to abstract values from
solutions. As hydrometallurgical methods gain
further acceptance in iron ore beneficiation
plants it seems likely that ion exchange resins
will find use in the recovery of valuable by-
products from plant liquors.

Removal of Phosphorus from Iron Ores

Phosphorus is an objectionable element when
present in iron ores. Graham [1] offers sage advice
regarding phosphorus in iron ores in his report
on behavorism of elements in iron and steel making. He says, "Phosphorus is completely captured
physically and chemically by the iron which is
undergoing reduction in the blast furnace. The
suppliers of raw materials, geologists, mining
engineers and minerals beneficiation engineers
will do well to remember that every ounce of

(1) Graham, H.W.:Behaviorism of Elements in Iron
    and Steelmaking, Metal Progress, vol 61,
    Jan. 1952, p 87-96.

phosphorus in the burden will appear in the iron produced. To this statement the steel maker and his metallurgist will further attest that phosphorus, though a weak element, is temperamental and annoying and generally contributes to increased costs, to difficulties of control and frequently to poor quality."

Some iron ores contain enough phosphorus(often easily recovered by froth flotaion) to make its separation profitable for use in fertilizer manufacture. Several Russian iron ore plants recover apatite by flotation. Other plants have been operated in Sweden for many years. Gunther [2] reported in 1909 on a Swedish magnetite operation at Svarto which processed an ore containing 3 percent phosphorus. The magnetic separator tailings carried 13.7 percent phosphorus. This tailing was further processed by jigging and fine grinding to produce an apatite concentrate. The concentrate was treated chemically for removal of remaining magnetite, calcined with soda ash and sold as fertilizer containing 30 percent phosphoric acid in soluble form. A recent report by Hedvall [3] describes developments regarding apatite concentrates from Grangesburg ores.

Most iron ores contain phosphorus so intimately associated with the iron minerals that usual gravity and flotation methods of beneficiation do not apply. Then the most feasible method often involves leaching of the ores or concentrates. Apatite(calcium phosphate) is the most common phosphorus containing mineral in iron ores, but occurrences of monazite(a radioactive phosphate mineral) are also known. As early as 1895, W.B. Phillips [4] mentions leaching of phosphorus from iron ores. It seems quite probable that much work

(2)Gunther, C.G.:Electro-Magnetic Ore Separation, Hill Publishing Co. New York, 1909.
(3)Hedvall, J.A. et al:New Uses for Swedish Minerals Other Than Ores--On Transforming Flotation Apatite to Phosphate Fertilizer, Trans. of Chalmers Univ. of Technology, Gothenburg, Sweden Nr. 100, 1950, 22 pp.
(4)Phillips, W.B.:Notes on the Magnetization and Concentration of Iron Ore, Trans. AIME vol 25, 1895, p 399-423.

has been done on the removal of phosphorus from
iron ore by chemical beneficiation methods but
few data have been published. The U.S. Bureau of
Mines reported in some detail on leaching of phosphorus from Alabama ironoores in 1935 and also
studied the reduction of phosphorus content   in
Missouri iron ore [5,6] . In the Alabama work a
series of chemically pure phosphates of calcium,
aluminum, manganese, ferrous iron and ferric iron
were digested by various solutions. All these
synthetic phosphates dissolved very easily. Dist-
illed water dissolved appreciable amounts of all
of the phosphates and yet would not dissolve any
one completely. When sampes of natural phosphate
minerals were digested, they were found much more
difficult to dissolve. The minerals tested included Florida phosphate rock, apatite, dufrenite,
triplite, wavellite and vivianite. With the exception of the last two minerals, acids were
found to be the best solvents. Wavellite and
vivianite could be dissolved with N/2 sodium
hydroxide solutions. Most of the phosphorus in
the Alabama red ores was present as calcium phosphate mixed with small quantities of ferrous,
ferric and aluminum phosphates.
    Mortsell [7] reported on Swedish attempts to re-
move phosphorus with acid solutions. A method for
de-phosphorization of iron ores which has gained
increasing favor in Sweden is acid soaking. With
batch tests on one-ton charges, phosphorus contents
of 0.003 percent were easily attained. Similar
leaching procedures are used in the United States
for the production of high purity glass sands.

(5) Hertzog, E.S.:A Study of the Occurrence and
     Amenability to Leaching of the Phosphorus
     Compounds in Some Red Iron Ores of Alabama,
     U.S. Bur. Mines Rept. of Inv. 3294, Dec.
     1935, 9 pp.
(6) Kenworthy, H.:Reduction of Phosphorus Content
     in Iron Ore and Concentrates from Iron Mount-
     ain Missouri, U.S. Bur. Mines Rept. of Inv.
     4199, Feb. 1948, 20 pp.
(7) Mortsell, S.:Rationalizing Endeavours with
     Swedish Iron Ore Concentration, Jernkontorets
     Annaler, vol 146, No. 9, 1946, p 55.

Iron oxide coatings are leached from the surfaces of silica sand grains by use of acid and steam in wooden leaching towers. The method is reported to be very low in cost.

Results of detailed work on leaching of phosphorus from Scappoose, Oregon iron ore have been published [8] . The investigators concluded that considerable phosphorus may be removed from Scappoose ore by roasting at 800 to 900 degrees Centigrade for 2 hours in the presence of 7 to 10 percent soda ash followed by leaching in hot water. No commercial application has been reported.

The first phosphate plant in South Africa [9] began operations in 1955. The plant processed a magnetite-apatite ore which contains up to 30 percent magnetite. The magnetite concentrate, which is stockpiled for future use, contains 55% Fe, 1-2% P_2O_5, and 2-4% TiO_2 . The crude ore contains only 7 to 10 percent apatite and final apatite concentrates contain about 33% P_2O_5 . Future developments in upgrading the magnetite concentrates will probably involve hydrometallurgical processing.

Production of Extremely High-Grade Iron Concentrates

Utilization of chemical beneficiation methods such as acid leaching has been used on a limited scale to produce extremely high-grade iron concentrates. The method is limited to those materials which contain gangue minerals which are easily dissolved in common acids. Since quartz and other silicates are almost always present in iron ore concentrates, it becomes evident that reagents selective towards these minerals are also desireable. This leads to the caustic-solution method for selectively leaching silicates from ores. A brief patent history of caustic-leaching beneficiation methods includes the following United States

(8) Walsted, J.P.:Metallurgical Tests on Scappoose Oregon Iron Ore, U.S. Bur. Mines Rept. of Inv. 5079, Oct. 1954, 46 pp.

(9) Holz, P.:South Africa's First Phosphate Plant, Rock Products, vol 58, Dec. 1955, p 84-88,154.

patents:

46,619 March 7, 1865-- Improved Process for Desulphurizing and Disintegrating Ores, J.C. Ayer.

52,132 Jan. 23, 1866-- Improved Method of Disintegrating and Desulphurizing Gold, Silver, and Copper Ores, Brower and Campbell.

229,586 July 6, 1880-- Extracting Precious Metals from Ores, T.C. Clark.

236,424 Jan. 11, 1881-- Process of Treating Ore, H.W. Faucett.

487,579 Dec. 6, 1892-- Process of Treating Gold and Silver Ores, G.W. McKee.

664,488 Dec. 25, 1900-- Bath for Rendering Ore Friable, K. Miller.

739,116 Sept. 15, 1903-- Process of Disintegrating Ores, C.T. Snedekor.

862,676 Aug. 6, 1907-- Extraction of Potassium Compounds from Feldspar, A.J. Swayze.

956,381 April 26, 1910-- Process of Treating Ores, A.A. Lockwood and M.R.A. Samuel.

1,237,765 Aug. 21, 1917-- Method of Treating Iron Ore, F.A. Eustis.

1,305,969 June 3, 1919-- Process of Extracting Metals from Silicates, L.L. Jackson.

1,323,124 Nov. 25, 1919-- Method of Recovering Gold, R. Thayer.

1,575,852 March 9, 1926-- Beneficiation of Ores, C.P. McCormack.

1,828,756 Oct. 27, 1931-- Process for the Refining of Chromium Ores, P. Weise and F. Specht.

1,832,069 Nov. 17, 1931-- Method of Roasting Ores, E.J. Wechter.

2,038,399 April 21, 1936-- Process for Treating Siliceous Materials, G.C. Westby.

2,191,819 Feb. 27, 1940-- Treatment of Manganese Ore, T.B. Albin.

2,353,613 July 11, 1944-- Process for Beneficiation of Iron Ores and Recovery of By-Product Values, D. Gardner.

The U.S. Bureau of Mines has undertaken considerable work involving the caustic leaching of silica from manganes ores. The technical aspects

of the work are very similar to caustic leaching
processes which have been attempted with iron
ores. Lundquist [10], in reporting on some of
this work, states that the opaline varieties of
silica respond more readily to caustic leaching
than do the crystalline varieties. This is in
agreement with work done by the author on leaching chert from low-grade Michigan and Wisconsin
iron ores [11] . Heat treatment of iron ores and
concentrates prior to caustic leaching results in
increased silica extraction in some cases. In
carrying out leaching operations with caustic
solutions at elevated temperatures and pressures,
a word of caution is repeated from a U.S. Bureau
of Mines release [12] : "Many industrial processes
require the heating or boiling of caustic soda
(sodium hydroxide) solutions. All too frequently
the vessels involved develop cracks in highly
stressed parts, such as rivet heads, riveted seams,
welds, and pipe connections. These cracks are for
the most part intercrystalline and are identical
to those produced in the seams of steam boilers."
The results of a large number of laboratory tests
were given in the form of a graph showing temperature plotted against caustic concentration. All
the cracking of vessels occurred in a well-defined
zone, roughly above 180 degrees Fahrenheit and
between 15 and 40 percent sodium hydroxide. Avoid-
ance of the severe-cracking zone outlined by this
study should reduce the probability of such cracking in similar operations. The Bureau further
warns that long periods of operation outside the
critical zone may also result in vessel failure.
One caustic soda producer warns [13], "Steel

(10) Lundquist, R.V.:Upgrading Domestic Manganese
        Ores By Leaching With Caustic Soda, Mining
        Eng. vol 5, April 1953, p 413-417.
(11) Roe, L.A.:Discussion of Lundquist Paper,
        Trans. AIME vol 196, 1953, p 1122.
(12) U.S. Bur. Mines Inf. Circular 7618, Nov. 1951;
        Berk, A.A. and W.F. Waldeck:Caustic Danger
        Zone, Chemical Eng. vol 57, June 1950, p 235,
        236, 238.
(13) Caustic Soda Technical Data Book by Wyandotte
        Chemicals Corp., 1952, 56 pp.

particularly if unrelieved stresses are present,
is subject to caustic embrittlement above 200
degrees Fahrenheit. For service above this temperature, a protective lining is recommended."
   The chemical refining of low-grade tungsten
ores by the Salt Lake Tungsten Company [14] is an
example of a modern plant utilizing a high-
pressure chemical leaching method to up-grade ores.
Sodium carbonate solutions are used, but sodium
hydroxide is formed in the closed pressure vessels.
Processing techniques developed in this and similar plants will be valuable in the study of
future hydrometallurgical processes for production
of high-purity iron concentrates. A new process
for production of zirconia [15] uses an acid leach
procedure to remove calcium and magnesium silicates from a synthetic zirconia.
   Many different "acid solution" processes have
been proposed for recovery of iron compounds or
metallic iron from low-grade iron ores. One of
the more recent domestic developments in this field
proceeded as far as a pilot-scale plant. The
process used in this plant was invented by C. V.
Firth of the University of Minnesota [16]. This
method of acid solution recovered metallic iron
powder from a Minnesota carbonate slate ore containing about 26 percent iron. Sulphuric acid was
used to dissolve iron and the ferrous sulphate
produced was calcined to iron oxide. The iron
oxide was then reduced to metallic iron. Figure
1 lists processing steps for the Firth Process.
A pilot plant, which was built near Aurora, Minnesota,was operated for a few months and then dis-
mantled. The high cost of the process defeated
commercial application at that time.

(14) Burwell, B.:Chemical Refining of Tungsten,
     AIME paper given at Salt Lake City, Utah,
     October, 1955.
(15) Anon:Kiln Reactor Key to New Zirconia Pro-
     cess, Chemical Eng. vol 61, Nov. 1954,
     p 124-126.
(16) Firth, C.V.:Method of Producing Iron Oxide
     for Production of Powdered Iron, U.S.
     Patent 2,413,492 December 31, 1946.

PREPARATION OF CRUDE CARBONATE SLATE
    a) Crushing
    b) Grinding
    c) Dewatering

PRODUCTION OF COPPERAS CRYSTALS
    a) Digestion of the carbonate slate
       with dilute sulphuric acid
    b) Evaporation of filtrate
    c) Crystallization of ferrous sulphate
    d) Filtration

DEHYDRATION OF FERROUS SULPHATE

PRODUCTION OF PURE IRON OXIDE
    a) Selective calcination
    b) Solution and extraction of impurities
    c) Filtration of the iron oxide

AGGLOMERATION OF THE IRON OXIDE
IN PREPARATION FOR REDUCTION

METALLIZATION OF THE IRON
    a) Reduction of the iron oxide
    b) Cooling of the pure iron

GRINDING OF THE METAL PELLETS

Figure 1.   Steps Used in Production
             of Powdered Iron by Acid
             Solution of Low-Grade Ore *

As given in U.S. Patent 2,413,492

By-Products from Iron Ores

As iron ore beneficiation metnods become more complex, greater opportunities are presented for recovery of by-products from iron ores. Long-range planning will insure future recovery of products not now recoverable at a profit. In an excellent paper before the 1955 annual AIME meeting, Nelson Severinghaus discussed production problems of the stone industry and needed research of that industry 17 . In mentioning stock-piling of products which at the time of storage are classed as "waste", he stated, "An important thing to remember here is that any excess products should be placed where they may be readily recovered and will not be contaminated with foreign matter. The handling, storage and possible recovery of momentarily unmarketable products presents one more important problem in the stone industry." This statement comes from an executive in an industry which must drill, blast, excavate, crush, size, store, reclaim and load rock for an average sale price of less than $1.25 per short ton. Every individual charged with the responsibility of storing tailings from an iron ore plant will do well to give serious thought to possible future reclamation of middlings and selected portions of tailings.

The first step in the production of by-products from iron ores is a complete, thorough analysis of the ore involved. These should be made either on drill core composites which represent the total known ore body or, in case a beneficiation plant is already in operation, on yearly composites of pertinent plant products. Both elemental and mineralogical analyses are necessary. Analyses for elemental composition may include spectrographic analyses, various "wet" chemical analyses, differential thermal analysis and perhaps even new methods such as "activation analysis". The latter is a method for determining the constituents of a sample by utilizing certain nuclear properties

(17) Severinghaus, N.:Production Problems of the Stone Industry and Needed Research, Paper, AIME annual meeting, Chicago, 1955.

of the isotopes of the elements in the sample.
Nuclear particles are used to produce radioactive isotopes by activation of nuclei of the sample
elements. These radioactive isotopes can be de-
tected and measured by their nuclear radiations.
Thus with an exact knowledge of nuclear characteristics, a determination of the amount of element
present can be made. Analysis by radioactivation
was first suggested by Hevesy and Levi in 1936.
In 1952 the Oak Ridge National Laboratory made
available to the public andactivation analysis
service 18,19 . An excellent comparison of activation analysis with other methods was given by
Meinke 20 in 1955.

There is an important point in terminology to
be considered when any discussion is made of the
unused portions of iron ores or blast furnace
products. This is the frequent reference to
"waste" products. Waste is generally defined as
a product thrown away as worthless after being
used or spent. The sulphite paper industry has
learned a hard lesson regarding the term "waste"
and is now attempting to re-educate the public
into using a less harsh word. For many years the
paper companies referred to their used process
liquor as "waste sulphite liquor" . This liquor
was often dumped into any convenient stream. As
anti-pollution laws became more numerous and
strict and as sportsmen's groups began to apply
pressure to prevent stream pollution by this
"waste" , the paper industry realized that its
choice of words had been unwise. Today, the same
industry refers to its used process liquor as
"spent sulphite liquor". This is a less harsh
terminology and much more acceptable to the public.
Fortunately these same spent liquors are proving
to be the source of valuable by-products. Included
in these are vanillin, yeast, flotation reagents,
coal and iron ore briquetting agents, emulsifying

(18) Anon:Isotopics, vol 2, No. 2, 1954, p 4.
(19) Murphy, W.J.:Analytical Chemistry, vol 24,
       1952, p 1235.
(20) Meinke, W.W.:Trace-Element Sensitivity:Com-
       parison of Activation Analysis with Other
       Methods, Science, vol 121, Feb. 11, 1955,
       p 177-184.

agents, soil stabilizers and soaps. Thus these
liquors are loosing their classification as   a
"waste" product.

Fortunately, in the ore processing industry,
we have referred to our presently worthless mineral by-products as tailings. This term is relatively innocuous but care should be exercised
that it does not become synonymous with waste.

Philip [21] in a 1913 discussion of refuse and
by-products in England stated, "Blast furnace
slag has got the name of "smelter's refuse", and
these slag mounds are simply some of the rubbish
heaps of our modern industrial civilisation. The
name "refuse" is, however, not quite so accurate
a description of slag nowadays, for various ways
have been devised whereby some, at least, of this
waste product is turned to useful account." Early
recognition of the value of this relatively unused
blast furnace by-product by American furnace operators has resulted in a steadily increasing list
of uses for blast furnace slag. The U.S. Bureau
of Mines in cooperation with the National Slag
Association published a book [22] on iron blast-
furnace slag in 1949. This book describes what
can be accomplished in developing markets for a
by-product which could easily have been considered
as waste. The value of this book as a reference
is enhanced by its extensive bibliography of 554
references. It is significant that an output of
24,926,033 short tons of iron blast-furnace slag
valued at $29,480,858 was achieved in 1950 [23].
In processing this quantity of slag, 296,603 short
tons of iron were recovered.

Vanadium from Iron Ores

Vanadium is present in many iron ores.   It may

(21) Philip, J.C.:Achievements of Chemical Science,
     Macmillan & Co. Ltd. London, 1913, 217 pp.
(22) Josephson, G.W., F. Sillers, Jr. and D.G.
     Runner:Iron Blast-Furnace Slag Production,
     Processing, Properties and Uses, U.S. Bur.
     Mines Bulletin 479, 1949, 304 pp.
(23) U.S. Bur. Mines Mineral Market Report MMS
     No. 1968, May 17, 1951.

range from 0.007 percent in Mesabi hematite to
0.40 percent in Tahawus, N.Y. magnetite. The
titaniferous magnetites often carry from 0.10 to
0.60% V_2O_5 ;the Bushveld ores of South Africa contain up to 1.5% V_2O_5 [24]. Kemp, in his treatise
on titaniferous iron ores of the Adirondacks [25],
stated, "One of the most characteristic features
of titaniferous ores is the presence of vanadic
oxide in small amounts, and one can only regret
that it has not oftener been determined. Being
one of the rarer elements, it has seldom been
sought for, and yet enough determinations have
been made to make it characteristic of this type
of ore body. The amount is usually less than half
of one percent, or about 5 to 10 pounds of vanadic
acid to the ton. Vanadium, it is interesting to
remark, was first discovered in pig iron made
from the titaniferous ores of Taberg, Sweden.
When Walz's analyses (1876--vanadium found present
in over twenty iron ores) were reported some attempts were made to recover the vanadium from the
Church mine (N.J.) ore on a commercial scale but
they did not prove successful. At Iglamala,
Sweden, where the ores are similar to those at
Taberg, 0.40 percent V_2O_5 has been determined."

During World War II serious consideration was
given the recovery of vanadium from oolitic iron
ores in southern Germany. With an expansion in
ore mining, a production of 15,000 tons of vanadium per year was envisioned. In fact, considerable production was obtained from some German ores
during the war. Fischer [26] reported on a process
which operated on Thomas converter slag containing one percent vanadium. The slag was treated
by a "sodadizing roast", leached with water, and
the vanadium oxide precipitated by an acid treatment. It is said that Germany produced $6\frac{1}{2}$ million
pounds of vanadium per year by using this process.

(24) Minerals Yearbook, 1945, p 659.
(25) Kemp, J.F.:The Titaniferous Iron Ores of the
      Adirondacks, U.S. Geol. Survey 19th annual
      Report, Part III Economic Geology, 1897-98
      Govt. Printing Office, 1899, p 383-422.
(26) Fischer, R.P.:German Iron Ores Yield Vana-
      dium, Trans. AIME vol 172, 1947, p 71-75.

Cole and Breitenstein [27] described laboratory and pilot plant processing of titaniferous magnetite from New York for recovery of vanadium and chromium. The ore, containing 0.40 percent vanadium, was ground through 200 mesh. After addition of 3 to 5% NaCl and 6 to 10% Na_2CO_3, the ore was roasted at 910 to 930 degrees Centigrade. Seventy five to 90% of the vanadium and 50% of the chromium was changed to water soluble compounds by this process. An acid method for recovering vanadium from chromate liquors was outlined by Perrin and others of the Diamond Alkali Company [28].

Luyken and Kirchberg [29] reported that the maximum amount of vanadium in German iron ores is 0.13 percent. In concentrating titanium bearing magnetites they reported that the vanadium remains with the iron and most of the titanium goes to waste.

An announcement of a new plant for recovery of vanadium from iron ores appeared in the Engineering and Mining Journal in April, 1955 [30]. The new plant was to be Finland's first plant for the extraction of vanadium and was to be built by the Otanmaki Corporation at the site of its mine in northern Finland. The news item further states, "Vanadium will be extracted from magnetite concentrates through a process developed by Matti Merenmies, company metallurgist, and Professor Kauko Jarvinen, mining engineer and technical consultant to the Otanmaki Corporation. The new process differs from earlier methods for extracting vanadium principally in that it is carried out

(27) Cole, S.S. and J.S. Breitenstein:Recovery of Vanadium from Titaniferous Magnetite, Trans. AIME vol 191, 1951, p 1133-1137.
(28) Perrin, T.S., J.N. Jenkins and R.G. Banner: Vanadium Recovery from Chromate Liquors, Industrial & Eng. Chemistry vol 44, Feb., 1952, p 401-404.
(29) Luyken, W. and H. Kirchberg:Vanadium in Iron Ores and Its Behaviour in Ore Preparation, Mitt. Kaiser Wilhelm Inst. Eisenforsch., Dusseldorf, vol 27, 1944, p 29-42.
(30) Anon:Engineering & Mining Jnl. news item, vol 156, April 1955, p 178.

at an earlier stage, before the iron ore is sent
to the smelter. After preliminary drying, the
magnetite concentrate is further treated in a
magnetic separator, raising the concentration to
about 69% iron and 0.6% vanadium. Ore will then
be sent to the new extraction plant, where it will
be milled further and where sodium sulphate will
be added. The next step in the process is pelletization and roasting of the ore to form soluble
sodium vanadate, which can be leached out with
water. The pellets can then be sent to the iron
ore smelter while the sodium vanadate solution is
processed further. Addition of concentrated sulphuric acid to the sodium vanadate solution results in the precipitation of vanadium pentoxide,
which is filtered and smelted. The resulting
commercial product will contain about 90% vanadium
pentoxide. The plant will produce 500 metric tons
of vanadium pentoxide and 70,000 metric tons of
iron ore pellets per year."

One factor which may cause some decline in
efforts being directed toward recovery of vanadium
from iron ores is the production of large quantities of by-product vanadium from uranium ores.
Large tonnages of vanadium are now being obtained
in the processing of sandstone type uranium ore
of the Colorado Plateau region. Vivian [31] described operations of the U.S. Vanadium Company near
Rifle, Colorado which used a sodium chloride roast
followed by a water leach to recover sodium meta-
vanadate. Many modifications and variations of
this process have been covered in numerous studies sponsored by the Atomic Energy Commission in
recent years. Work by the U.S. Bureau of Mines
on the extraction of vanadium from shale was reported by King and Wilson [32]. The investigation
was summarized as follows: "An acid bake of

(31) Vivian, C.H.:Vanadium--A Metal Named for a
     Goddess, Compressed Air Magazine, October
     1945, p 260-264.
(32) King, W.H. and S.R. Wilson:Diamond Drill and
     Auger Sampling of Vanadiferous Shale, Mercur
     Dome Mine, Tooele County, Utah, U.S. Bur.
     Mines Rept. of Inv. 4572, Nov. 1949, p 8.

pre-roasted ore followed by water leach gave the
optimum extraction of the vanadium. An extraction
of 85 percent was obtained, but the acid consumption was high. Caustic leaching of pre-roasted
ore gave a 68 percent extraction and the conventional salt-pyrite roast gave only 23 and 48 percent extractions."

In February, 1944 the Office of Metals Reserve
terminated a purchasing program, "as the result
of the accumulation of large inventories of vanadium in ores and in vanadium products." As long
as large tonnages of uranium-vanadium ores are
being processed, there will exist the possibility
of a decrease in vanadium prices. This situation
is not encouraging to present high-cost methods
for recovering vanadium from iron ores.

Chromium from Iron Ores

Chromium, like vanadium, is almost invariably
present in titaniferous iron ores. The quantity
may range from a trace to nearly 2 percent chromium. Very large tonnages of chromium are contained in the lateritic iron ore deposits.   The
percentage of chromium in lateritic ores may range
from 0.50 to over 4 percent(see Table III, Chapter III).

When commercial processes are developed for
recovery of chromium from iron ores, enormous
tonnages of chromium will be made available. In
view of the tremendous potential for supplies of
chromium, nickel, cobalt and iron offered by the
lateritic iron ore deposits, we can expect an
early solution to this difficult metallurgical
problem. In testifying at hearings before a
Senate Committee in 1953, Mr. O.C. Ralston [33]
made the statement, "If we were to work the Cuban
laterites for those five metals(Fe,Ni,Co,Cr,Ni) or

(33) Special Subcommittee on Minerals, Materials
and Fuels Economics of the Committee on
Interior and Insular Affairs, U.S. Senate:
Stockpile and Accessibility of Strategic
and Critical Materials to the U.S. in Time
of War, Part I, U.S. Dept. of Interior, Bur.
of Mines, 1953, p 339-340.

four metals and alumina as a by-product, not
counting in the alumina, the gross value per ton
of Cuban laterite was said to about 24 and a
fraction dollars. Most of that is the value   of
the nickel, cobalt and chromium. If we can
dissect that ore and pull it to pieces and finally
ship off iron ore, without these alloying elements,
to be smelted in the United States, we have at our
own back door everything needed for self sufficiency in practically everything except possibly
chromium. Up to date there have been no processes for doing that."
The U.S. Bureau of Mines has done and is continuing to do much research on methods of upgrading domestic chromite ores. These studies [34-41]
provide a useful backlog of information for use
in development of methods for recovery of chromium from iron ores.

(34) Doerner, H.A.:Chemistry of the Anhydrous
     Chlorides of Chromium, U.S. Bur. Mines Tech.
     Paper 577, 1937, 51 pp.
(35) Maier, C.G.:Sponge Chromium, U.S. Bur. Mines
     Bulletin 436, 1942, 109 pp.
(36) Boericke, F.S. and W.M. Bangert:Equilibrium
     in the Reduction of Ferrous Chromite by
     Hydrogen and Energy Requirements in the
     Selective Reduction of Iron in Chromite, U.
     S. Bur. Mines Rept. of Inv. 3813, June 1945.
(37) Boericke, F.S. and W.M. Bangert:Effect of
     Variables in Chemical Beneficiation of Chro-
     mite Ores, U.S.B.M. Rept. of Inv. 3817, 1945.
(38) Lloyd, R.R. et al:Beneficiation of Montana
     Chromite Concentrates by Roasting and Lea-
     cning, U.S.B.M. Rept. of Inv. 3834, Feb 1946.
(39) Boericke, F.S.:Selective Reduction of Iron
     in Chromite by Metnane, U.S.B.M. Rept. of
     Inv. 3847, Feb., 1946.
(40) Batty, J.V.:Beneficiation of Chromite Ores
     from western United States, U.S.B.M. Rept.
     of Inv. 4079, June 1947.
(41) Kelley, K.K.:Contributions to tne Data on
     Theoretical Metallurgy, Part X. High Temp-
     erature Heat-Content, Heat-Capacity, and
     Entropy Data for Inorganic Compounds, U.S.B.
     M. Bulletin 476, 1949 and Bulletin 477, 1950.

One popular method of removing chromium from
iron ores is based on an oxidative roast followed
by a water leach to remove soluble chromates. An
excellent report on methods for producing chromate
salts from domestic chromite ores was published
by the State College of Washington in 1939 (42).
The work covered in this report went into considerable detail. A summary of German practice was
given along with a penetrating analysis of weak
areas in hydrometallurgical processing of ores
for recovery of chromium.

A detailed report on bichromate manufacture in
three plants of I.G. Farbenindustrie was published by the Office of Technical Services [43] after
World War II. The report covers the commercial
production of sodium bichromate and potassium bichromate giving many technical details and costs.
In addition, attention is called to the ever-
present hazard of chrome poisoning in these plants.

Cobalt from Iron Ores

The first and oldest example of a domestic iron
ore beneficiation plant which recovers cobalt is
the Lebanon, Pennsylvania plant of the Bethlehem
Steel Company. This plant processes an iron ore
containing about 43 percent iron, 0.40 percent
copper as chalcopyrite, and 1.86 percent sulphur.
The iron concentrate (magnetite) contains 60 percent iron, o.24 percent copper and 0.90 percent
sulphur [44]. The iron concentrates are sintered
to produce a low-sulphur product. The ore contains a little less than one pound of cobalt per

(42) Doerner, H.A. and others:A Study of Methods
     for Producing Chromate Salts from Domestic
     Ores, State College of Washington-Mining
     Expt. Sta. Bulletin V, Sept. 1939, 28 pp.
(43) McBerty, F.H. and B.H. Wilcoxon:Bichromates
     Manufacture, FIAT Final Report 796, Office
     of Technical Services, Dept. of Commerce,
     Washington, D.C.
(44) Yaklish, J.P.:The Iron Ore Deposit of Corn-
     wall, Pennsylvania, Explosives Engineer,
     vol 16, Nov. 1938, p 327-333.

ton. A pyrite concentrate of the following analysis is obtained by froth flotation[45] :

	Percent
Sulphur	48.9
Iron	41.2
Cobalt	1.42
Copper	0.31
Insol.	4.5

The pyrite concentrates are sent to the Sparrows Point plant near Baltimore, Maryland. Here a sulphate roast is used to solubilize the cobalt for subsequent recovery. Other products of the operation are sulphuric acid and iron ore sinter. Beall [46] described operations of the plant in 1950. The 1950 production of cobalt was 793,813 pounds or about one-tenth of the total United States consumption at that time [47].

A report in the Minerals Yearbook for 1945 mentions that the Urals branch of the Academy of Sciences (U.S.S.R.) has carried out successful experiments for obtaining cobalt and nickel from the Elizavetinski iron ore mine.

A study of mineralogical and geographical reports on trace elements in iron minerals leads the author to conclude that every mining operation now throwing pyrite into a tailing product should collect a representative sample of this pyrite and have a complete elemental analysis made of this material. Cobalt is often found in pyrite. A Norwegian reference [48] reported that X-ray spectrographic analyses of 19 samples of pyrite from Norwegian nickel ores gave 0.47 to 1.25 percent cobalt, with very little or no copper or nickel.

(45) Scharf, H.B. and E.C. Dominguez:The Fluo-Solids Reactor Installation at Sparrows Point, Mining Eng. vol 8, May 1956, p 517-523.

(46) Beall, J.V.:Cobalt, Mining Eng. vol 190, Jan. 1951, p 17-24.

(47) O'Connor, J.A.:Chemical Eng. vol 58, Sept. 1951, p 114.

(48) Bjorlykke, H.:The Cobalt Content of Pyrite from Norwegian Nickel Ores, Norsk. Geol. Tids. vol 25, 1945, p 11-15.

Pyrite from a contact zinc deposit contained 0.70
percent cobalt;pyrite from a granitic pegmatite
contained 0.33 percent cobalt. Two pyrite samples
from young hydrothermal dikes and two samples
from shales contained less than 0.05 percent
cobalt. The conclusion was drawn that high cobalt
content in pyrite seems to be characteristic of
pyrite formed at high temperatures.

Sulphur has long been recovered from pyrites
and several plants produce a high-grade iron sinter in the same operation. The sulphur is
usually recovered as sulphuric acid, but at least
one Canadian plant recovers elemental sulphur
from pyrite. The steadily increasing demand for
sulphuric acid by hydrometallurgical operations
has encouraged installation of several new acid
plants which use pyrite as the starting material.
A bibliography published by the U.S. Geological
Survey [49] indicates that pyrite deposits are
available in many areas of the United States.

Cobalt is recovered along with nickel at the
Nicaro Nickel plant in Cuba. Identification of
the nickel or the cobalt minerals is very difficult in all the lateritic iron ores. In some
laterites it appears that there is some correlation between manganese and cobalt contents.
Nakabe [50] reports that problems encountered in
removing cobalt from cupriferous pyrite are similar to those encountered in the removal of
nickel and cobalt from laterites.

Nickel from Iron Ores

Nickel is currently being recovered by various
methods from both oxide and sulphide-type iron
ores. The most extensive operation is that of
the Nicaro Nickel Company in Cuba. Other plants

(49) Espenshade, G.H. and C.H. Broedel:Annotated
        Bibliography and Index Map of Sulphur and
        Pyrites Deposits in the United States and
        Alaska, U.S. Geol. Survey Circular 157,
        1952, 48 pp.
(50) Nakabe, S.:Metallurgy of Cobalt Production
        from Cupriferous Pyrite, AIME Jnl. of Metals
        June 1951, p 445-451.

are at Riddle, Oregon and at Copper Cliff, Ontario
Canada. There may be some objection to classification of these materials as "iron" ores. However, iron oxide pellets are recovered from the
Canadian plant, ferronickel from the Oregon operation, and it appears to be only a matter of time
before iron is recovered from the Cuban ore.
Analyses of some better known iron-nickel ores
are given below:

	Analysis - Percent				
	Fe	Ni	Co	Cr	SiO2
Nicaro, Cuba	50.0	1.25	0.06	1.50	6.00
Riddle, Oregon	14.4	1.50	0.004	0.66	45.9
Tocantins, Brazil	12.1	4.4	0.03	1.1	45.6
Cle Elum, Washington	49.9	0.92	0.11	1.7	8.4
Manicani Island, Philippines	48.4	1.06	--	2.99	1.86

The Nicaro operation is based on the recovery
of nickel and cobalt from a large deposit of
laterite in eastern Cuba. This plant was built
during World War II to alleviate a shortage of
nickel in the United States. An official record
of the operation is contained in a report distributed by the U.S. Department of Commerce [51] .
Several accounts of plant operations have appeared in the technical press and many of these references are given at the end of this chapter.
The Nicaro process is based on U.S. Patent
1,487,145 issued to M.H. Caron on March 18, 1924.
Credit for commercial application of the method
is given to Freeport Sulphur Company. This

(51) Tobelman, H.A. and H.J. Morgan:A Review of
     the Nicaro Nickel Project, Oriente Cuba,
     Plancor 690, Jan. 15, 1948, Office of the
     Publication Board, Dept. of Commerce, Wash-
     ington, D.C.

company pilot planted the Nicaro Process and operated the initial commercial plant. The present Nicaro plant appears to be a successful operation and is an example of hydrometallurgical processing on a large scale. Initial operation of this plant began in 1943. Production reached 32 million pounds of oxide for the year 1946. The plant was closed down early in 1947 and lay idle until 1951. When a serious shortage of nickel became apparent during the Korean conflict, the plant was reopened in the interest of national security. Rehabilitation of the plant began in January, 1951 and four furnaces were put into operation in December. The average recovery of nickel for the period July, 1952 to December, 1953 was 76.5 percent [52]. This recovery was better than the average of 70.31 for the 1945-1946 period of operation. The plant reported net sales of $11,964,444 for the period July 1, 1952 to June 30, 1953. Total costs, including amortization were $12,213,624. Later expansion programs and increases in the price of nickel have probably pushed the operation into a profitable position. Contributions of the Nicaro plant to the theory and practice of hydrometallurgy are not measureable in terms of dollars and cents. This pioneer plant will be a source of technical information for the planning of many future ore processing plants.

An electric furnace plant, operated by the M. A. Hanna Company is now recovering nickel from a deposit located about 5 miles northwest of Riddle, Douglas County, in southwestern Oregon. The final product from this operation is ferronickel. Future process improvements may result in recovery of other products in the future. According to a 1956 report [53], the plant produced 6,500,000 pounds of nickel in 1955. A fourth furnace was placed in operation in 1956.

The International Nickel Company has pioneered

(52) McMillan, W.D. and H.W. Davis:Nickel-Cobalt Resources of Cuba, U.S. Bur. Mines Rept. of Inv. 5099, Feb. 1955, 86 pp.
(53) Anon:Wall Street Journal, April 4, 1956, p 24.

a process for recovery of high-grade iron ore and
nickel from nickeliferous pyrrhotite ore.   Laboratory and pilot plant investigations of the
process began in 1947 with resulting commercial
operations beginning in 1956.   The new plant rep-
resented an investment of approximately 16 million
dollars and had an initial capacity of 1000 tons
of ore per day [54].   The pyrrhotite concentrate
used in pilot operations ranged from 2 to 10 percent on 200 mesh and contained 57% Fe, 37% S, 0.04
- 0.07% Cu, 0.70 - 0.90% Ni, 1 - 3% SiO_2 and 0.002
oz. per ton precious metals [55].   The process includes the following steps:

> a)production of pyrrhotite concentrate.
> b)roasting of pyrrhotite for removal of
>   sulphur.
> c)reduction of calcine;iron content con-
>   verted to magnetite;nickel, cobalt
>   and copper to elemental state.
> d)leaching of calcine with ammoniacal
>   solutions.
> e)purification of leach liquors and
>   recovery of nickel values.
> f)agglomeration of high-grade iron ore.

The final iron ore product is the highest-grade
iron ore being produced in quantity in   North
America.   The pellets contain:

Fe	68.00%	MgO	0.30%
P	0.003%	S	0.01%
SiO_2	1.50%	Cu	0.01%
Mn	0.05%	Ni	0.15%
Al_2O_3	0.65%	Cr	0.03%
CaO	0.25%	TiO_2	0.10%
		L.O.I.	0.00%

(54) Anon:Iron Ore Now a By-Product from Nickel
     Mining, Inco Nickel Topics, vol 6, 1953, p4.
(55) Int. Nickel Co. Staff:Development of the
     Inco Iron Ore Recovery Process, Canadian
     Mining & Met. Bulletin, May 1956, p 337-343,
     Trans. Canadian Inst. of Mining & Metallurgy
     vol 59, 1956, p 201-207.

Miscellaneous By-Products

Current research aimed at the utilization of lateritic iron ore is, for the most part, being developed around combination pyro- and hydromet-allurgical methods. Use of these methods will encourage recovery of the large quantities of aluminum present in these ores. The U.S. Bureau of Mines and several Portland cement companies have undertaken considerable research in the development of processes for recovery of alumina (Al_2O_3) from kaolin, anorthosite, clay mixtures and laterites [56,57,58,59,60,61] . The Anaconda Company announced plans for a one million dollar pilot plant for testing a process for extraction of alumina from low-grade domestic clays in October, 1956 [62].

Minerals of interest to the ceramic industry are also present in tailings of iron ores such as those of the Adirondack district in northeastern United States. These include feldspar and sillimanite. The sillimanite content may range from 0.1 to 0.5 percent while feldspar may be present

(56) Blue, D.D.:Raw Materials for Aluminum Production, U.S. Bur. Mines Inf. Circular 7675, March, 1954.

(57) Frary, F.C.:The Alumina Problem in Peace and War, Chem. & Eng. News, vol 23, Aug. 10, 1945, p 1324-1327.

(58) Anon:Alcoa Finds Laterite Likely Alumina Source, Chemical Eng. vol 51, June 1951, p 200.

(59) Gardner, D.:Process for Beneficiation of Iron Ores and Recovery of By-Product Values, U.S. Patent 2,353,613, July 11, 1944.

(60) St. Clair, H.W. et al:The Ammonium Sulphate Process for Production of Alumina from Western Clays, AIME Trans. vol 159, 1944, p 255-266.

(61) Hayward, C.R.:Extraction of Nickel and Alumina from Cuban Iron Ores, Chemical & Met. Eng., Feb. 8, 1922, p 261-266.

(62) Anon:Anaconda to Try Out Method to Get Alumina Economically from Clay, Wall Street Journal, Midwest Edition, October 8, 1

to the extent of 30 to 45 percent in some ores.
Removal of contaminating iron to permit ceramic
use is a formidable problem worthy of further
effort.

Mica is also present in many iron ores and can
be easily recovered by simple beneficiation procedures. Some iron ores contain up to 15 percent
by weight of various mica minerals.

As increasing amounts of sulphide iron ores are
processed for recovery of iron, the element selenium may become an important by-product of iron
ore beneficiation operations. Since 1947 selenium
has become extremely important in the manufacture
of rectifiers. A small selenium rectifier used
as a voltage multiplier in radio and television
sets can deliver 200 to 500 volts D C from a 117
volt A C source. By eliminating a heavy trans-
former and a rectifier tube, a saving of about
$\frac{1}{2}$ pound of copper and $7\frac{1}{2}$ pounds of steel can be
made per television set. The only present com-
mercial source of selenium is in the anode mud of
slime produced in electrolytic refining of copper.
Selenium is closely related to sulphur and is
commonly associated with the iron and copper sulphide minerals. About 25 selenium minerals contain varying amounts of the element but none of
the species is considered a commercial source [63].
Rocks formed during the Cretaceous period have
been found to be the most highly seleniferous.
Limonitic concretions from the Cretaceous Niobrara
formation contain from 20 to over 500 p.p.m.,
whereas the surrounding shales contain only 2
p.p.m. It appears that the most likely possibility for selenium recovery from iron ores will be
those plants processing ores containing pyrite or
other iron sulphide minerals [64,65].

(63) Sargent, J.D.:Selenium, U.S. Bur. Mines Inf.
        Circular 7690, July 1954, 25 pp.
(64) Williams, K.T. and H.G. Byers:Occurrence of
        Selenium in Pyrites, Industrial & Eng. Chem.
        Anal. Edition vol 6, 1934, p 296-297.
(65) Fleischer, M.:Minor Elements in Sulphides,
        Economic Geol. vol 51, Jan. 1956, p 113-114.

ADDITIONAL REFERENCES

Arbiter, N. and H.H. Kellogg:What the Future
Holds for Hydrometallurgy, Eng. & Mining Jnl.
vol 152, July 1951, p 139-143.
Sullivan, J.D. and A.P. Towne:Agglomeration and
Leaching of Slimes and Other Finely Divided Ores,
U.S. Bur. Mines Bulletin 329, 1930.
Rankama, K.:Geochemistry, Univ. of Chicago Press,
1950, 912 pp.
Hillebrand, W.F.:The Analysis of Silicate and
Carbonate Rocks, U.S. Geol. Survey Bulletin 700,
1919.
Iler, R.K.:The Colloid Chemistry of Silica and
Silicates, Cornell Univ. Press, 1955, 324 pp.
Lenhart, W.B.:Recovering High Value By-Products
from Sand and Gravel, Rock Products vol 56, Nov.
1953, p 92,96.
Friedman, I.I.:The Solubility of Quartz in Sodium
Carbonate Solutions at High Temperature, Jnl.
Amer. Chem. Soc. vol 70, Aug. 1948, p 2649-2650.
Vail, J.G. and J.H. Wills:Soluble Silicates, Their
Properties and Uses, Vol I - Chemistry, Reinhold
Publishing Co. New York, 1952.
Ishigaki, Y.:Silica Gel from Iron Ore Tailings,
Jnl. Soc. Chem. Ind. Japan, vol 45, 1942, p 73-
78;Chem. Abs. vol 43, March 10, 1949, p 1925.
Van Arsdale, G.D.:Hydrometallurgy of Base Metals,
McGraw-Hill Book Co. New York, 1953, 370 pp.
Anon:Recovery of Iron Oxide by Sintering of Waste
Pyrite Ashes from a Sulphite Paper Mill, Eng. &
Mining Jnl. vol 156, March 1955, p 168.
Rushton, J.H. and L.H. Mahony:Fundamentals of
Mixing and Agitation With Applications to Extrac-
tive Metallurgy, Trans. AIME vol 200, 1954;Jnl.
of Metals Nov. 1954, p 1199-1206.
Talbot, H.L.:Chemical Metallurgy Solves Low-Grade
Complex Ore Problems, Eng. & Mining Jnl. vol 156,
March 1955, p 52-55, 96.
Twiehaus, H.C. and N.J. Ehlers:Caustic Purifica-
tion by Liquid-Liquid Extraction, Chemical Ind-
ustries, July and August, 1948.
Renken, H.C.:Process of Recovering Sulfur from
Pyrite, U.S. Patent 2,530,630 Nov. 21, 1950.

Murata, K.J.:The Significance of Internal Structure in Gelatinizing Silicate Minerals, U.S. Geol. Survey Bulletin 950, 1946, p 25-33.

Sullivan, J.D. and E.O. Ostrea:Factors Governing the Entry of Solutions into Ores During Leaching, U.S. Bur. Mines Technical Paper 498, 1931, 23 pp.

Shell, H.R.:Chemical Analysis of Clay, U.S. Bur. Mines Rept. of Inv. 4420, Aug. 1949, 36 pp.

Gwinn, G.R.:Domestic Mica, U.S. Bur. Mines Inf. Circular 7617, Nov. 1951, 37 pp.

Linz, A.:Uranium Oxide from Ores, Chem. Eng. Progress vol 52, May 1956, p 205-209.

Mancantelli, R.W. and J.R. Woodward:Eldorado Mining and Refining Ltd. Beaverlodge Hydrometallurgical Plant, Paper presented at AIME annual meeting Chicago, Feb. 1955.

Osborn, C.E.:Starting a New Uranium Mill, Mining Congress Jnl. vol 42, May, 1956, p 56-58.

Knoerr, A. and G. Lutjen: U_3O_8 - Formula for Profits, Eng. & Mining Jnl. vol 155, Sept. 1954, p 88-118.

Downes, K.W. and D.W. Morgan:The Utilization of Low-Grade Domestic Chromite, Dept. of Mines and Tech. Surveys, Mines Branch, Ottawa Canada, Memorandum Series No. 116, October 1951, 54 pp.

McCormack, R.H.:Continous Recovery Process for Acid and Metal from Pickling Solutions, Metal Progress vol 64, October 1953, p 134-135.

Myers, R.J. et al:The Distribution of Ferric Iron between Hydrochloric Acid and Isopropyl Ether Solutions, I. The Compound Extracted and the Extraction at Constant Acid Concentration, Jnl. of Amer. Chem. Society vol 72, Aug. 1950, p 3767-3771.

Gardam, G.E.:Production of Iron Powder by Electrodeposition, Selected Govt. Research Reports (London) (Powder Metallurgy) vol 9, 1951, p 75-84.

Anon:Wah Chang's Unique Plant for Concentrating Tungsten, Eng. & Mining Jnl. vol 145, Sept. 1944 p 64-72.

Gaudin, A.M., R. Schuhmann, and E.G. Brown:Making Tin Flotation Work - No. 1, Canutillos Ore, Eng. & Mining Jnl. vol 147, October 1946, p 54-59.

Monet, G.P.:Cost of Ion Exchange, Chem. Eng. vol 57, March 1950, p 106-107.

Baragwanath, J.G. and J.B. Chatelain:Nicaro
Nickel Project, Mining & Met. vol 26, August,
1945, p 391-394.

Dufour, M.F. and R.C. Hills:Nickel from Cuba,
Chem. Industries, October 1945, p 621-627.

Brogdon, V.H.:Recovery of Nickel and/or Cobalt
from Ores, U.S. Patent 2,400,098, May 14, 1946.

Hills, R.C.:Magnetic Separation and Settling for
Serpentine Ores, U.S. Patent 2,400,461, May 14,
1946.

Hills, R.C. and M.F. Dufour:Reduction of Ores
Containing Nickel, U.S. Patent 2,473,795, June
21, 1949.

Tafel, V.:Nickel Recovery, German Patent 693,519,
June 13, 1940.

Eustis, F.A.:Treatment of Nickel Ores, U.S. Patent 1,212,334, Jan. 16, 1917.

Eustis, F.A.:Method of Treating Iron Ores, U.S.
Patent 1,237,765, Aug. 16, 1917.

Brown, E.H. and S.J. Broderick:Treatment of Iron
Ores Containing Nickel, U.S. Patent 2,067,874,
Jan. 12, 1937.

Simpson, K.M.:Recovery of Nickel from Nickel-
Containing Iron Ores, U.S. Patent 2,212,459,
Aug. 20, 1940.

Grothe, J.D.:Treating Lateritic Ores, U.S. Patent
2,363,315, Nov. 21, 1944.

Queneau, P.E. et al:Process for the Treatment of
Nickel-Containing Ores, U.S. Patent 2,478,942,
Aug. 16, 1949.

Caron, M.H.:Separation of Nickel and Cobalt,
Trans AIME vol 188 and Jnl. of Metals Jan. 1950,
p 91-103.

Caron, M.H.:Ammonia Leaching of Nickelaand Cobalt
Ores, Trans. AIME vol 188, p 67-90.

Anon:Nicaro Resumes Production, Eng. & Mining Jnl.
vol 153, March 1952, p 88-90.

Weld, C.M.:The Residual Brown Iron Ores of Cuba,
Trans. AIME vol 40, 1910, p 299-312.

Lutjen, G.P.:Nicaro Proves Lateritic Nickel Can
be Produced Commercially, Eng. & Mining Jnl. vol
155, June 1954, p 81-89.

Cox, J.S.:The Iron Ore Deposits of the Moa District, Oriente Province, Island of Cuba, Trans.
AIME vol 42, 1912, p 73-90;other refs. p 90-169.

DeVletter, D.R.:How Cuban Nickel Ore Was Formed – A Lesson in Laterite Genesis, Eng. & Mining Jnl. vol 156, Oct. 1955, p 84-87.

Waldron, H.L.:Is the Chemico Metals Technique Tomorrow's Metallurgy? Eng. & Mining Jnl., vol 153, June 1952, p 84-87, 176.

Anon:Selby Plant Makes Liquid SO_2 From Waste Smelter Gases, Eng. & Mining Jnl. vol 150, July 1949, p 138.

Arbiter, N.:Ion Exchange – Does It Have a Role in the Mineral Industry? Eng. & Mining Jnl. vol 153, Nov. 1952, p 80-85.

Hartford, W.H.:Properties of Technically Important Hexavalent Chromium Compounds, Ind. & Eng. Chemistry vol 41, p 1993-1997.

Hart, J.J. and W.H. Wickham:A Process and Apparatus for the Elimination of Chromium and Silica from Iron Ores Containing the Same, British Patent No. 516, Jan. 8, 1907.

Foerster, C.V. and A.T. Cape:Method for Recovering Chromium Values from Ores, U.S. Patent 2,435,304, Feb. 3, 1948.

McCormack, C.P.:Beneficiation of Ores, U.S. Patent 1,575,852, March 9, 1926.

Brackelsberg, C.A.:Apparatus for Treating Ores, U.S. Patent 1,729,534, Sept. 24, 1929.

Wechter, E.J.:Method of Roasting Ores, U.S. Patent 1,832,069, Nov. 17, 1931.

Vedensky, D.:Electrolyzing of Chrome Solutions to Recover Chrome, U.S. Patent 2,504,095, Nov. 21, 1950.

Kingsbury, F.L. and F.J.Schultz:Recovery of Vanadium and Chromium, U.S. Patent 2,530,616, Nov. 21, 1950.

Rasmussen, R.T.C. and T. Kasahara:Experimental Smelting & Refining of Iron-Chromium-Nickel Ore in Japan, Genl. Hdqs. Supreme Commander for the Allied Powers (Tokyo), Natural Resources Section, Prelim. Study No. 12, 1947, 67 pp.

Anon:Bayer Process Red Mud Treated for Alumina Recovery, Chem. & Met. Eng. vol 52, Jan. 1945, p 106-107.

Archibald, F.R. and C.F. Jackson:Alumina from Clay by the Lime-Sinter Method, Trans. AIME vol 159, p 227-240.

Seyfried, W.R.:The Ammonium Sulphate Process for
the Extraction of Alumina from Clay and Its Application in a Plant at Salem, Oregon, AIME Tech.
Publication No. 2473, 1948, p 1-12.

Teague, K.H.:Sillimanite in the Soutneast, Mining
Eng. vol 187, July 1950, p 785-789.

Dean, R.S.:Manganese Extraction by Carbamate Solutions and the Chemistry of New Manganese-
Ammonia Complexes, Mining Eng. vol 4, Jan. 1952,
p 55-60.

Conley, J.E. et al:Production of Metallurgical
Alumina from Pennsylvania Nodular Diaspore Clays,
U.S. Bur. Mines Bulletin 465, 1947.

Wysor, R.J.:Potash as a By-Product from the Blast
Furnace, Trans. AIME vol 56, 1917, p 257-302.

Pratt, A.M.:The Iron Ores of the Phillipine Islands, Trans. AIME vol 53, 1916, p 90-105.

Skow, M.L. and J.E. Conley:Laboratory Tests on
Percolation Leaching of Silica from Bauxites,
U.S. Bur. Mines Rept. of Inv. 4649, Jan. 1950.

Dasher, J., A.M. Gaudin and R.D. Macdonald:Ion
Exchange in Extractive Hydrometallurgy - Especially for Uranium, Paper presented at annual
meeting of AIME, New York, Feb. 1956.

Minder, A.B. and C.F. Paulson:Where Ion Exchange
Fits in Hydrometallurgy, Eng. & Mining Jnl. vol
156, No. 3a, March 1955, p 56-62.

Kenworthy, H. and K.K. Kershner:Metallurgical
Investigations of southeastern Missouri Cobalt-
Nickel Resources, U.S. Bur. Mines Rept. of Inv.
4999, Sept. 1953, 37 pp.

F.A. Schaufelberger, and T.K. Roy:Nickel-Cobalt
Separation by Selective Reduction, Paper presented at annual AIME meeting New York, Feb. 1955.

F.A. Schaufelberger:Metal Precipitation from Salt
Solution by Hydrogen Reduction, Paper presented
at annual AIME meeting, New York, Feb. 1955.

Macdonald, R.D.:High-Temperature Hydrometallurgy,
Battelle Technical Review, vol 4, Nov. 1955,
p 143-147.

Chapter XI

AGGLOMERATION

"Undoubtedly the physical structure and chemical composition of
the manufactured ores can be
made such that the fuel consumed
in smelting them will be less
than the fuel consumed in smelting natural ores."---E.W. Davis,
Univ. of Minn. Mines Expt. Station
Bulletin No. 9, Dec. 21, 1921.

The ultimate use of perhaps 99 percent of the
iron ore produced is in the production of iron
and steel. In order to be acceptable to the iron
and steelmaking processes, these iron ores must
have certain physical characteristics. One of the
most important of these is the size distribution
of the ore particles. If the particles are too
coarse, reduction is slow; if they are too fine,
dust losses are excessive and furnace operation is
difficult. The crushing and sizing of lump
ores has not been a difficult problem in the past.
Preparation of ore fines for blast furnace use has
been accomplished by the sintering process for
many years. Now, as the iron ore industry begins
to process the taconite ores which require processing at very fine sizes, the agglomeration processes
become extremely important. Direct sintering
processes are not applicable to ore concentrates
in the 325-mesh particle range. New methods have
been developed and experimentation continues on
methods which will efficiently and at low cost
produce agglomerates of acceptable physical characteristics. The four most common methods of
agglomerating iron ore are sintering, pelletizing,
nodulizing and briquetting. All are expensive
and fairly complex processes. Iron ore agglomeration is commanding much attention. Minor process
improvements evolve regularly and the search for
entirely new processes is vigorously pressed by the

iron ore industry.

Agglomeration may be defined as a process whereby small particles are combined into larger, permanent masses in which identity of the original
particles, in many cases, is retained. The mechanisms involved in all iron-ore agglomeration
processes remain somewhat obscure. In sintering
and nodulizing the bonding action may be obtained
by incipient fusion of the ore, an added agent,
or both. Little is known regarding solid-solid
reactions, effect of pressure on fusion at temperatures below the fusion points of components,
fluxing agents and the effect of trace elements.
In fact it has been stated that sinter is a more
or less heterogeneous result of relatively incom-
plete chemical reactions. In pelletizing iron
ore the mechanisms of the bonding action taking
place in the "green" or "wet" pellet involve po-
lar attraction, surface tension, and undefined
phenomena involved in cohesive and adhesive forces. But when the pellets are fired, the bonding forces involved change to those of ceramic
bond and grain growth causing interlocking forces.
When ores are briquetted, the forces involved are
similar to those encountered in green pellets,
plus effects of high pressures. "Chemical" agglomeration methods involve most of the forces
utilized in forming green pellets plus other planned low temperature chemical reactions which produce strong chemical bonding of the particles.

Thus it appears that production of satisfactory iron-ore agglomerates relies more on art than
science at the present time. This picture may
rapidly change as more effort is applied in the
way of microscopical studies, other studies of
physical characteristics, and detailed chemical
analyses.

Sintering

Sintering is often defined as, "the formation
of a coherent cinder-like agglomerate through
incipient fusion." The sintering process as applied to iron ores is not only a means of utilizing fine-sized particles but is also a method of
upgrading carbonate ores by removal of carbon

dioxide. In addition, the process is used to remove sulphur and arsenic from iron ores. The end product of the sintering process is a porous, sponge-like cake or mass of agglomerated iron oxides.

Some of the "firsts" in iron-ore sinter plants are:

(a) First sintering of pyrite on a commercial scale by James W. Neill at Leadville, Colorado -- 1889;(updraft, intermittent operation).

(b) First U.S. plant for sintering iron oxides -- E & G Brooke Iron Co. at Birdsboro, Pa. 1911;(first downdraft, continuous operation).

(c) First Lake Superior plant -- Evergreen Mining Co. at Ironton, Minn., 1911.

(d) First Swedish plant -- 1925.

The three main steps in sintering iron ore are preparation of the feed or raw materials, ignition of the prepared layer of raw materials, and combustion of the fuel resulting in the end product-- an agglomerated mass of iron oxides. Reactions and phenomenon occurring in the latter step have led many to state that there are perhaps more variables in sinter making than in iron making. A sintering plant usually includes a tremendous installation of materials handling equipment. Successful sinter plant operation requires skilled operators and good supervision.

The versatility of the continuous sintering process as applied to the agglomeration of iron ores has not been fully explored. A sinter machine can agglomerate materials having a considerable range in physical properties. Iron ores ranging in size from $\frac{1}{4}$-inch to minus 325 mesh can be processed. The finer sized ores require special preparation before commercial operation can be successful. For example, wood shavings can be added to fine-sized ores to "open up the bed" and permit successful sintering. Also pelletizing of the ore prior to burning on a sinter machine has been utilized in both iron ore plants and in cement plants. In Europe, one sintering plant is satisfactorily producing cement clinker from fine-sized materials with good thermal efficiency[1]. The raw materials for cement manufacture are pelletized before sintering. Developments in processing wet cement slurry on a sinter machine were reported as early as 1935 in Germany. The Jones & Laughlin Steel Corporation has reported on the sintering of fine taconite concentrates in a pilot plant by pelletizing before the sintering operation[2].

Machines for Sintering

There are two basic types of iron ore sintering machines. These are the stationary hearth type (a batch operation) and the moving bed type. The stationary hearth sintering machine is a shallow, rectangular steel compartment which has air-cooled cast iron liners and an inclined, slotted hearth. A suction box with an air manifold provides downdraft. A traveling charging car loads the hearth prior to each sintering operation. A typical sintering schedule requires 15 to 30 minutes for a complete cycle of operations. One distinct characteristic of stationary hearth sintering operations is the high air suction possible. This may reach 40 to 50 inches water gauge while continuous machines often operate at only 20 to 27 inches water gauge. The difference is due to the much better air seals in stationary hearth operations. Recent developments in moving bed sinter machines indicate that new adjustable rails and use of special high-temperature grease will improve seals in these machines. There were only two stationary hearth iron ore sinter plants in the United States as of 1955. One plant, located at Tahawus, N.Y. consists of three 10 by 25-foot pans. It processes a fine-sized magnetite concentrate with good results. Pilot plant tests at this operation

(1) Pearson, B.M.:Calcining Cement Slurry on Continuous Conveyor Grate, Rock Products vol 55, October 1952, p 102-104, 138.
(2) Anon:New Process Magnetizes Low-Grade Iron Ore, Chemical Engineering vol 62, June 1955, p 128.

showed that magnetite containing up to 50 percent
of minus 200-mesh material could be sintered on
a stationary hearth machine[3].

During the early development stages of the moving bed type sintering machine, a drum type and
a horizontal round-table type machine were developed. These have, for the most part, been replaced by the straight-line type machine. The straight
line machine consists of a structural-steel frame
which supports a closed loop track and numerous
suction boxes. Grate-bottom pallets are pulled
along the track providing a continuously moving
hearth. The pallets are charged, leveled and
ignited at the feed end of the upper track;then,
with suction continuously applied, the pallets
move to the discharge end of the machine. After
discharging their load by a dumping operation,
the upside-down pallets return to the feed end of
the machine via the lower loop of the track. In
the past, the standard machine has been 72-inches
wide and about 100-feet long. Some of the more
recent installations of straight-line machines
are wider and longer than the older machines. The
modern Benson Mines, N.Y. machine which began
operation in August, 1952 is 6-feet, 6-3/4 inches
wide by 147-feet long and was, at that time, the
largest ever made for iron ore operation[4]. A
giant sintering installation was made at Blackwell
Oklahoma in 1951 for processing zinc concentrates.
This machine is 12-feet wide and 168-feet long
with a hearth area of 2016 square feet or about
3-1/3 times that of a standard six-foot machine.
As of 1955 the trend in iron ore sintering and
pellet hardening straight-line machines indicates
that 8-foot wide machines will become common.

Regardless of manufacturer, most moving bed
type sintering machines are similar. The most

(3) Stanley, A. and J.C. Mead:Sintering Charact-
    eristics of Minus Sixty-five and Twenty-Mesh
    Magnetite, Mining Eng. vol 1, June 1949,
    p 181-186.
(4) Fleck, R.G. and F.M. Hamilton:J & L's Star
    Lake Sinter Strand, Mining Eng. vol 8,
    Sept. 1956, p 901-903.

common type drive is a single sprocket arrangement. This drive wheel is usually located at the feed end of the machine. Improper alignment causes wheel, track, and pallet wear, but this is not a serious problem in most plants.

Maintenance of sintering machines is fairly expensive and most iron ore sintering plants shut down one shift per week for repairs. Those items requiring frequent replacement or repair are grate bars, mixer paddles, pallets, pallet wheel bearings and fan impellors. The two chief types of grate bars used are slotted and finger. The slotted bars usually consist of large castings measuring about 8 by 36 inches each and installed six on a pallet. These lay across the long dimension of the pallet. The finger bars are about 24-inches long and $1-\frac{1}{4}$ to $2-\frac{1}{2}$ inches wide. They are placed across the short dimension of the pallet and number up to 50 on a single 72-inch pallet. Grate bars are usually made of Mallix[5], a high manganese iron which contains 0.30 to 1.30 percent manganese. Carefully annealed cast-iron grate bars sometimes prove more economical than malleable iron in spite of their shorter life. Ductile iron has been used by the Canadian Furnace Company Ltd. at Port Colborne, Ontario with good results[6]. Plants with good maintenance schedules regularly weld up pallet ends to minimize air leakage. Replacement or repair of pug mill blades and paddle blades for tumbling barrels is a frequent item of maintenance in some plants. Hard-facing treatments and Ni-hard blades are frequently used.

Preparation of Feed

The uniformity and composition of the mixture to be sintered are very important in the production of high quality sinter at an acceptable cost. Most important of the variables in the preparation

(5) Mallix is made by National Malleable and Steel Castings Company, Cleveland Ohio
(6) Anon:Ductile Iron Makes Good in Sintering Grates, Nickel Topics vol 4, 1951, p 2.

of a mixture to be sintered are:

a) size of materials.
b) fuel content, nature of fuel and its distribution throughout the mix.
c) moisture content
d) homogeneity of mixture.
e) nature and use of return sinter.

Once the sinter mixture is prepared for burning, another variable must be considered. This is the technique used in "laying" the sinter mix on the sintering hearth. For best results, the prepared mixture should be gently placed on the hearth to give a "fluffy" but uniform bed. This promotes uniform burning of the bed at maximum speed.

As stated earlier in this chapter, ores as coarse as $\frac{1}{4}$-inch can be sintered. However, this is a waste of good blast furnace feed. It has been shown in large-scale sinter plant tests that there is a difference in sintering rate of up to 25 percent between a coarse ore(95% of particles between $\frac{1}{4}$-inch and 100 mesh) and an intermediate size concentrate containing about 40 percent minus 100 mesh. The finer ore gave the best results. Thus it is evident that sinter mix should not be too coarse or too fine. The Tennessee Copper Company sinters iron sulphide ores which contain 97 percent minus 100-mesh material (of which 49.5% is minus 400 mesh). There is no known plant which can sinter iron oxides commercially in this size range without special pretreatment such as pelletizing or addition of materials to open up the bed. When iron sulphides are sintered, the bed opens rapidly as the sulphur is removed. An ideal iron ore for sintering may range from 1/8-inch to 100 mesh in size, with perhaps not over 20 percent finer than 150 mesh.

In a survey of United States iron ore sintering plants it was found that the carbon content of the feed had the surprisingly narrow range of 4.4 to 6.7 percent[7]. Also, when comparison was

---

(7) Powers, R.E.:A Survey of Blast Furnace Sintering Practice, Paper presented before the Chicago Regional Meeting of Amer. Iron & Steel Institute, Dec. 1, 1950.

made on the basis of the heating value of the
fuel, there was a close correlation between plants
sintering sulphide ores as compared to plants processing oxide ores. The three common types of
fuel used are coke breeze, anthracite coal and
bituminous coal. When flue dust makes up part of
the charge, the fuel may be present as a very
fine powder. The choice of fuel is usually made
on the basis of economics and not because of its
properties. Coke breeze and coal often range
from minus 1/8- to minus 5/8-inch top size. Grinding of the fuel in a rod or hammer mill is
practiced at several plants. An increase in the
fuel content of a given sinter mix results in a
harder sinter. Sinter plant operators (except
possibly in Sweden) tend to operate on the high
side of fuel addition since plant operation is
then more uniform. The use of layered fuel is
one method of decreasing fuel cost in sintering
operations. At Benson Mines, N.Y. two layers of
sinter mix are used. The layer nearest the
hearth contains less fuel than the upper portion
of the bed.

When iron ores contain appreciable sulphur,
this factor should be calculated in the heat balance since proportionately less carbon additions
are required. Each percent of sulphur in a sinter mix can be calculated to produce the equivalent of about 0.6 percent carbon. Thus an ore
containing 7 to 9 percent sulphur should be nearly self sustaining as to heat requirements.

There is no single figure which can be given
to designate the optimum moisture content of a
mixture which is to be sintered. In general, the
finer sized ores require more water than the
coarser ones. If a mixture is too dry much of it
may be pulled through the grate bars;if the mixture is too wet the decrease in air flow will
slow down the sintering rate. Plant control of
moisture in sinter mixtures is very difficult because of the wide variations in the moisture contents of the raw materials and the use of sinter
returns of varying size and temperature. Most
iron ore concentrates contain about 10 percent
moisture while the moisture content of the fuel
may average 12 to 14 percent. The moisture content of sinter mixtures may range from 3 to 14

percent.

Complications arising from the strong magnetism shown by fine sized artificial magnetite has, in at least one German plant, made the sinter bed too compact for satisfactory sintering.

Thorough mixing and blending of raw materials entering a sinter mixture is extremely important. This is usually attempted by use of pug mills and tumbling barrels (either with or without paddles). Water is generally added at the mixer through nozzles, sprays or a single pipe. Tumbling barrels often cause more-or-less pelletizing of a portion of the mixed feed. Full scale trials in a stationary hearth plant in England proved conclusively that partial pelletizing of the bed was beneficial. The tests also showed that coke addition should be delayed until a late stage of the pelletizing step[8]. Laboratory tests at the same plant verified American practice in that, "the end point of sintering in a laboratory unit can be defined as the time at which the wastegas temperature reaches a maximum".

All sinter plants use returns from the discharge end of the machine as an ingredient of their raw mixtures. These returns consist of pieces of broken sinter and some unsintered material which has made at least one trip across the sinter machine. Returns larger than 1/8- to $\frac{1}{4}$-inch are of no value in promoting bed porosity and are a waste of good sinter in many cases. A few modern plants include crushing and sizing equipment in the sinter return circuit in order to accurately control the size distribution of returns used in the raw sinter mixtures. The amount of returns used in a sinter mixture may range from 15 to 65 percent. Hot returns have been found useful in plants where filter-cake and comparable materials are processed. Good quality returns are made only when good quality sinter is being produced. As a British investigator states, "It must be emphasized that return fines must be return sinter;not

---

(8) Grice,M.A.K. and W. Davis:Towards Faster Sintering of Ironstone, Jnl. of the Iron & Steel Inst. (London) vol 175 Part 2, Oct. 1953, p 155-160.

just rubbish[9]."

After a sinter mixture is carefully prepared
it must be evenly distributed to the sintering
hearth or grate. Most of the older plants cling
to the swinging spout type distributer, but newer
installations are appearing with roll feeders of
various types. The bulk density of the bed on
the sintering hearth offers a criterion for
roughly determining its permeability. Powers[10]
found bulk densities ranging from 59 to 136 pounds
per cubic foot in his survey of 15 iron ore
sintering plants.

Ignition and Burning

Ignition of iron ore sinter mixtures is accomplished by burning a wide variety of fuels in
two general types of burners; these are usually of
the arch-furnace or the torch type. Fuels used
include blast furnace gas, natural gas, fuel oil,
coke oven gas, powdered coal or various gas mixtures. The ignition burner for moving bed type
machines is placed above the pallets adjacent to
the feeding zone and ignites the sinter mixture
as it enters the suction zone of the machine.
Stationary hearth machines are ignited by a
traveling burner or ignition car. The arch-
furnace type burner is characterized by a refractory arch which deflects the hot products of combustion uniformly across the surface of the charge.
Torch burners consist of a row of nozzles extending across the bed. The latter gives an intense
concentrated flame of short duration on the bed
while the arch furnace gives a relatively long
exposure. Exposure time for torch burners may
range from 3 to 25 seconds while arch furnaces
allow 15 seconds to one minute. Some operators
claim that iron sulphide charges are more easily
ignited than iron oxides. Early in the history of
sintering, a strong, penetrating ignition was
stressed. This is now less fashionable and most

---

(9) Elliot, G.D. and N.D. Macdonald:Sinter Making
      at Appleby-Frodingham, Jnl. of the Iron &
      Steel Inst. (London) March 1951, p 261-272.
(10)Powers, R.E. op cit.

operators believe that it is only necessary to
ignite the fuel particles in the surface layer of
the sinter mix. An over-ignited mixture may show
evidence of surface slagging which will offer
resistance to air flow.

As Klugh so aptly stated in 1912 [11], "the
Dwight and Lloyd sintering machine is a piece of
chemical apparatus in which to carry out the
reaction between the oxygen of the continuous supply of air and the solid combustible material of
the charge." "It logically follows that the capacity of the machine is limited by the weight of
carbon burned per unit of time." It is also
logical that the volume of air passing through the
charge is an important factor. In addition, the
relationship between time and temperature throughout the burning process is very important.

All the care in preparing the feed for the sinter machine pays dividends in the burning operation. The burning step involves a multitude of phy-
sico-chemical reactions, some of which still re-
tain important secrets. When more knowledge of
these reactions is developed, further increases
in the efficiency of the sintering process will
be possible. Figure 1 illustrates the various
zones prevailing in a sinter bed about 3 minutes
after ignition of the charge.

The speed of travel of the combustion zone
through the charge is influenced by all the variables discussed under "Preparation of Feed", plus
exo- and endothermic heat reactions, variations
in air flow, slagging zones and others. The end
product may range from almost all hematite to almost all magnetite, depending primarily upon the
amount of fuel used. American practice favors
production of a "hard burned" sinter which, on
the average, contains only 10 to 30 percent hematite with the balance of the iron present as
magnetite. Sinter practice in the Scandinavian
countries favors production of more highly oxidized sinter with some plants reporting as high as

(11)Klugh, B.G.:The Sintering of Fine Iron-
      Bearing Materials by the Dwight and Lloyd
      Process, Trans. AIME vol 43, 1912, p 364-
      375.

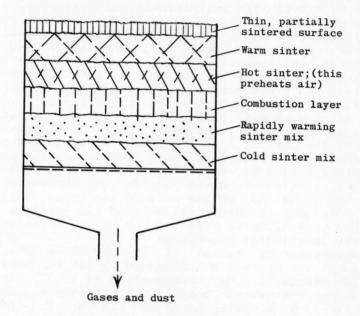

Thin, partially
sintered surface

Warm sinter

Hot sinter;(this
preheats air)

Combustion layer

Rapidly warming
sinter mix

Cold sinter mix

Gases and dust

Figure 1.   Various Zones in a Sintering
            Bed of Iron Ore

98 percent of the iron present as hematite. In any study of fusion phenomena taking place in the sintering operation, the melting points of the raw materials becomes important. Table I is a compilation of various published data giving the melting points of various ores and minerals. In order to effectively cause binding or sintering of iron ore particles, it is unnecessary to produce temperatures as high as the melting points of the constituents. Laneuville[12], in checking the sintering and melting points of iron ores from Canada concluded, "The difference between the sintering and the melting points varies from 200 to 400 degrees Centigrade, depending on the ore." The sintering points of the 12 ores tested showed a range from 1137 to 1235 degrees Centigrade.

Sinter Cooling

Two methods used in the cooling of iron ore sinter are water cooling and air cooling. Water cooling involves a severe quenching of sinter piles in the ore yard or curtain sprays in railroad shipping cars. The sprays are usually neccessary to prevent burning of the sides of the car. All experiences with water cooling of sinter leave no doubt that this method of cooling not only breaks some of the sinter into fine fragments, but also weakens the internal structure of the larger pieces. While European practice has always favored air cooling of sinter, only the more recent American plants are making provision for this type of cooling. A 46-foot diameter rotary cooling table was developed for air cooling sinter at the Fontana, California plant of the Kaiser Steel Company. This cooling mechanism has walls 8-feet high with enough storage capacity to hold the sinter for about 2 hours before discharge. As the table rotates at a rate of 400 feet per hour, the cool sinter is plowed from the bottom of the table while hot sinter is

---

(12) Laneuville, J.:Sintering and Melting Points of Iron Ores from New Quebec, Dept. of Mines Prov. of Quebec, P.R. No. 265, 1952, 11 pp.

TABLE I

Melting Points of Iron Ores and Minerals

Material	Melting Point -- Degrees C.				
	(a)	(b)	(c)	(d)	(e)
Lake Superior Ore (56% Fe)	1513				
Cuyuna Range Ore	1496				
Southern U.S. Ore	1238				
Magnetite	1535	1532	1538	1597	1580
Magnetite East. U.S.	1560				
Mixture of 50% magnetite and 50% silica				1455	
Magnetic taconite ores		1200 to 1582			
Fayalite 2 FeO.SiO$_2$			1336		
Silica	1700				
Conversion of alpha to beta quartz	573				

(a) Howard:Blast Furn. & Steel Plant, vol 33, 1945,
        p 971-972.
(b) Knoerr:Eng. & Mining Jnl. vol 147, Nov. 1946,
        p 66-69.
(c) Firth:Proc. Blast Furn. & Raw Matls. Committee,
        AIME, 1944, p 46-69.
(d) Darken:Jnl. Amer. Chem. Soc. vol 71, 1949, p 1114.
        Also June, 1948 of same journal.
(e) Sosman:Jnl. Washington Acad. Science, vol 7, 1917,
        p 55-72.

fed to the top of the table. Sinter reaches the
table at 200 to 260 degrees Centigrade and is discharged at about 95 degrees. Some cooling is done
on the last five windboxes of the sinter machine.
Other installations of rotary cooling tables have
since been made. In some cases coolers have been
installed without regard to the advantage of natural prevailing winds and drafts. Location of any
cooler which depends on radiation cooling is quite important and should be placed to take advantage of prevailing winds and drafts. The modern
sintering plant at Benson Mines, N.Y. uses the
last five windboxes (35 feet) of one machine for
sinter cooling. An added feature is the use of
cooler air from outside the building in this cooling zone. The result is production of high quality sinter.

British reports[13,14] on sinter cooling tests
showed that, "Lump sinter can be water quenched
from 300 degrees Centigrade with little breakdown in size and only a small reduction in strength." Recommendation is made that sinter should
be broken into pieces not greater than 6 to 8
inches before being cooled;also as much as possible of the circulating load should be removed be
fore cooling. One English plant reported cooling
of sinter on the sinter machine to an average final temperature of less than 350 degrees Centigrade in order to prevent failure of concrete
storage walls.

Sinter in the Blast Furnace

The properties of sinter commonly considered
important for use as blast furnace feed are the
same properties considered important when non-
agglomerated iron ores are used. These include,
size, strength, porosity and reducibility. It is

(13) Voice, E.W. et al:Factors Controlling the
     Rate of Sinter Production, Jnl. of the Iron
     & Steel Inst. (London) vol 175, Part 2, Oct.
     1953, p 97-152.
(14) Jennings, R.F. et al:Sinter Plant Assessment
     Trials at Dagenham and at Cleveland, Jnl.
     of the Iron & Steel Inst. vol 175, Part 3,
     Nov. 1953, p 267-277.

generally conceded, both here and abroad, that
iron ore sinters generally show poorer reducibility than the iron ores from which they were made.
Swedish blast furnace operators have long favored
the use of high percentages of sinter in blast
furnace burdens. More recently the British have
taken a similar view.

In America, much discussion took place before
sinter was accepted as an excellent furnace raw
material. The reports of Agnew[15] and Whiting[16]
in 1938 showed good results with high sinter
burdens. In 1940 Shallock[17] gave results for a
number of furnaces which showed steadily increasing iron production and decreasing coke rate with
increased sinter up to a figure of 70 percent in
the burden. In 1943 Williams and Stubblefield[18]
reported that the advantage in the use of sinter
began with 10 to 20 percent in the charge and increased up to about 35 to 45 percent sinter. After
that, the advantage did not increase directly with
the increase in sinter. At 30 percent sinter, the
improvement in production was 6 to 8 percent and
the decrease in coke consumption was about 13 percent. Practically none of the reports state
clearly what types of ores were replaced by the
sinters. Likewise, control tests on sinter quality were lacking. Powers[19] concludes in a 1951
report, "These experiences when studied together
seem to indicate that sinter, as commonly produced

(15) Agnew, C.E.:Benefits from Use of High-Iron
      Concentrates in a Blast Furnace, Trans.
      AIME vol 131, 1938, p 116-126.
(16) Whiting, J.T.:Microscopic and Petrographic
      Studies of Blast Furnace Materials, Yearbook
      Amer. Iron & Steel Inst. 1938, p 58-96.
(17) Shallock, E.W.:Thirty Years of Iron Sinter-
      ing, Blast Furnace & Steel Plant vol 28,
      1940, p 71-75, 169-170.
(18) Williams, G.T. and B.M. Stubblefield:Increa-
      sed Blast Furnace Capacity and How Accomp-
      lished, Yearbook Amer. Iron & Steel Inst.
      1943, p 95-108.
(19) Powers, R.E.:Improving Current Practice in
      Blast Furnace Sintering, Paper given at N.Y.
      meeting of A.I.S.I. May, 1951, 27 pp.

and used at present, acts very much like   ore of
similar chemical analysis." More recent reports
indicate that at least some of the American operators are   falling in   line with European belief
that sinter burdens are decidedly beneficial   in
almost all cases. Most American furnaces in 1951
were using from 18 to 65 percent sinter in their
burdens.

A 1953 British report[20] on high-sinter burdens
was decidedly optimistic. The Appleby-Frodingham
plant has   used sinter   since   1934 and for   many
years their blast   furnace practice was based on
about 33 percent sinter in the burden. In   1952
the plant was forced to accept burdens containing
about 63 percent sinter. In   the course of testing the new high-sinter burdens,   some runs were
made with the burden approaching 100 percent. The
results were   so good   that two 25-foot   furnaces
were put on a burden containing   an average of 93
percent sinter. In conclusion the authors state,
"The operators are convinced that the future will
see   an increasing   use of wholly sinter burdens.
It is suggested   that the   practice has much   to
commend it for both lean and rich ore working."

Some Swedish furnaces have used 100   percent
sinter burdens since 1934[21]. The   smallest
blast furnace making pig iron in the United States
has been operating on 100 percent   sinter burdens
since 1939[22]. Holowaty[23] explains   the   high
sinter burdens in Swedish practice by the   fact
that, "Swedish Government regulations specify that
only iron ores containing   less   than 38 percent

(20) Elliot, G.D., J.A. Bond, and T.E. Mitchell:
     Ironmaking from High-Sinter Burdens,   Jnl.
     of the Iron & Steel Inst. (London) vol 175,
     Part 3, Nov. 1953, p 241-247.
(21) Tigerschold, M.:Reducing Coke Consumption in
     Iron and Steel Production, The   Iron Age,
     July 1949, p 84-91.
(22) Anon:Tennessee Blast Furnace Produces Pig
     Iron from Sinter, Industrial Heating, Aug.
     1951, p 1420.
(23) Holowaty, M.O.:History of Iron Ore Sintering
     Recalls Variety of Experimentation, Jnl. of
     Metals, vol 7, Jan. 1955, p 19-23.

iron can be used for domestic steel production."
Stationary hearth sintering machines are almost
exclusively used in Sweden. By careful control
a sinter containing up to 98 percent hematite
(Fe_2O_3) is made from magnetite concentrates. The
sinter has poor physical characteristics (especially resistance to crushing and physical strength).
However this weaker sinter is satisfactory for
use in the smaller blast furnaces used in Europe.

Johnson[24] states that Japanese furnace practice includes about 20 percent sinter in the burden under normal conditions. Late in World War
II as much as 60 percent sinter was used when
imported lump ores became scarce.

Rice[25], in his report on use of sinter in domestic furnaces states, "Operating statistics
applying to over 100 blast furnaces in the U.S.
show that about 635 pounds of sinter were charged
in 1950 per net ton of pig." Rice also included
some approximate conversion costs, including fuel,
which are reproduced here:

Cost of Producing Sinter - 1950

Plant	Tons sinter produced/yr.	Type plant	Total Cost N.T. Sinter	Provis. for dep.
A	1,760,000	pallet	$0.95	$0.07
B	710,000	pan	1.45	0.17
C	50,000	pallet	1.65	0.30
D	800,000	pallet	1.95	0.50

For similar sinter machine installations, some
idea of whether it is a high or a low cost operation can be gained from production rates. A
generally accepted method of expressing production rates is to give net tons produced per
square foot of effective grate area per 24 hours.
This may range from 1.1 to over 4 net tons.

(24) Johnson, T.L.:Sponge Iron in Japan, U.S. Bur.
     Mines Inf. Circular 7440, Mar. 1948, 12 pp.
(25) Rice, O.R.:Potential Sources of Iron Ore
     Bolster Conservation Program, Steel vol 129
     Oct. 1, 1951, p 88, 91.

Some sinter is used to replace open hearth charge ore, but little published information is available on the subject. Hill[26] described the use of special open hearth sinter at the Steubenville, Ohio plant of the Wheeling Steel Corporation. At this plant sinter has replaced most of the charge ore used in the open hearths. Sinter can be used for the entire charge ore but usually some lump ore is charged with the sinter.

Pelletizing

Pelletizing is a method of agglomeration in which fine-sized ore minerals are rolled to form small spheres by a snow-balling technique. These spheres are then heat-treated to bake them into hard pellets 3/8- to $1\frac{1}{2}$-inches in diameter.

The best known iron ore pelletizing process is the process developed at the University of Minnesota by C.V. Firth, E.W. Davis, H.H. Wade and others. A detailed history of this process was published by Davis and Wade in 1951[27]. They state that their process "grew out of a study of the Grondal briquetting process". Work on the Minnesota process for pelletizing iron ores began prior to 1920. Studies were made independently in Sweden by A.G. Anderson in 1911. This work culminated in Swedish Patent No. 35124 in 1912[28].

C.A. Brackelsberg developed a pelletizing process in Germany in which sodium silicate was used as a binder. A pilot plant was built at Rheinhausen in 1935;a Dwight-Lloyd sintering machine

(26) Hill, E.G.:Sinter for Open Hearth Charge,
     Industrial Heating vol 21, Aug. 1954,
     p 1556-1566, 1598.
(27) Davis, E.W. and H.H. Wade:Agglomeration of
     Iron Ores by the Pelletizing Process, Univ.
     of Minn. Mines Expt. Station Inf. Circular
     No. 6, Jan. 17, 1951, 20 pp.
(28) Tigerschiold, M. and P.A. Ilmoni:Fundamental
     Factors Influencing the Strength of Green
     and Burned Pellets Made from Fine Magnetite
     Ore Concentrates, AIME Blast Furnace & Raw
     Materials Proceedings, 1950, p 18-53.

was used to harden the pellets. Various ores were
tested, including Swedish concentrates, but all
tests were unsuccessful and the pilot plant
discontinued operation.

H.J. Stehli of the Dwight-Lloyd Company and
J.E. Greenawalt experimented in the early 1920's
with pellet formation by the drum rolling method.
In 1936 a patent was issued to R.S. Dean of the
U.S. Bureau of Mines on the subject of pelletiz-
ing (U.S. Patent 2,131,006).

By 1943 the University of Minnesota pelletizing experiments had proceeded to a point where a
public demonstration was made for interested iron
ore producers. The reaction from this demonstration and attendant publicity stimulated interest
in the pelletizing process. In 1948 the Aurora,
Minnesota magnetic taconite iron ore pilot plant
of Erie Mining Company began operations. Pelletizing was the agglomeration method used at this
plant. At the same time, pilot pelletizing furnaces were undergoing test runs at Ashland,
Kentucky (Reserve Mining Co.) and at Lebanon, Pa.
(Bethlehem Steel Co.). The Ashland pilot plant
was located on the Armco Steel Corporation property where blast furnaces and several open hearths
were available for smelting tests with the pellets.
Since large tonnages of taconite concentrates
were not available, magnetite concentrates were
purchased from the Benson Mines operation in
New York and ground to the desired size range[29].
Little information was released regarding the
Lebanon and Ashland pelletizing operations but
later commitments in large commercial plants by
both companies indicated that these pilot operations were successful.

The iron ore pelletizing process consists of
two basic steps. The first is formation of
green or "wet" pellets and the second is the firing step which consists of burning the green
pellets to the desired hardness. Generalizations
regarding the behavior of a specific iron ore
during the "balling" or firing steps are unwise

---

(29) Anon:Ashland, Kentucky Pilot Plant to Make
        Iron Pellets, Eng. & Mining Jnl. vol 149,
        Oct. 1949, p 108.

since a multitude of variables are involved in
each step of the process. Cooke and Ban[30] list
the important factors influencing balling as
follows:

a) the specific surface of the ore or concentrate as indicated by the size distribution of the particles.
b) the nature and quantity of the additives
   which are incorporated prior to balling.
c) the mineralogical composition of the ore.

These same factors are also important in the
subsequent firing process as well as the firing
temperature and the composition of the atmosphere
in which the pellets are fired. Precise control
of expulsion of combined and absorbed water
during the firing step is important. In firing
tests with "limonite" and magnetite pellets, Cooke
and Ban found that 73 percent of the water originally contained in limonite balls was evolved between 300 and 400 degrees Centigrade. When
the magnetite balls were fired, 31 percent of the
water was evolved between 300 and 600 degrees. It
was noted that between these same temperature
limits a marked decrease in strength occurred.
    Davis and Wade[31] found that magnetic taconite
concentrates must be practically all finer than
65 mesh and 60 percent or more must pass a 325-
mesh screen to effect satisfactory ball formation.
Rowen[32] makes the observation that "most earthy
materials pelletize rather readily with the simple addition of moisture." In other words, the
specific surface of a material must be high before balling will take place.
    Much work has been done on the effect of addi-
tives on the balling step and their influence
on the properties of the fired pellets. Some of
the materials which have been investigated are

(30) Cooke,S.R.B. and T.E. Ban:Agglomerating Iron
     Ore Concentrates, Chemical Eng. Progress
     vol 51, Aug. 1955, p 364-368.
(31) Davis, E.W. and H.H. Wade:op cit.
(32) Rowen, H.E.:Some Aspects of Pelletizing in
     Drum Pelletizers to be Considered in Design-
     ing, Paper given at A.I.Ch.E. meeting, 1954.

bentonite, slaked lime, limestone, iron ore slimes, starch, sodium silicate, lignin, petroleum products, magnesia and borax. Most of the organic additives are used only for their effect during the balling step and burn out during firing. Additives such as borax, bentonite, lime and magnesia may influence the final physical strength of the pellets to a marked degree.

The mineralogical composition of the ore affects the final pellet product in several ways. Generally speaking, optimum results have been obtained when magnetite ores are pelletized. Also some excellent results have been obtained when pyrite calcine is pelletized. When specular hematite flotation concentrates are processed some new difficulties are encountered. The use of a desliming operation prior to flotation results in a granular type material which is difficult to process by a pelletizing operation. When siderite ores are pelletized considerable shrinkage is noted in the form of cracks on the outer surfaces of the pellets[33]. The effect of various gangue minerals associated with iron ore minerals is less well known but undoubtedly affects the pelletizing process.

The first public release of the flowsheet for the pioneering Aurora, Minnesota taconite plant of Erie Mining Company was made on October 13, 1949[34]. This plant used an 8 by 24-foot balling drum to produce pellets ranging from $\frac{1}{2}$- to 1-1/2 inches in diameter. The Aurora, Ashland, and Lebanon pilot planting of the Minnesota pelletizing method paved the way to commercial acceptance of pelletizing of iron ores. All these pilot plants used shaft-type furnaces for the firing step.

Another method of heat-hardening iron ore pellets was announced at Duluth, Minnesota on September 18, 1950. On that date announcement was

(33) Sengfelder, G:Pelletizing of Dogger Ore Concentrate and of Spathic Ore Fines, Stahl & Eisen vol 70, 1950 p 765-767.

(34) Anon:Taconite Flowsheet at Aurora is Disclosed, Eng. & Mining Jnl. vol 150, Nov. 1949, p 110.

made of preliminary results of work by an
Allis-Chalmers and A.G. McKee Company team which
had investigated the traveling-grate type pellet
hardening machine. Dr. Lellop, of Lepol kiln
fame, aided the Allis Chalmers team in addition
of fuel economy steps to the process. Further details of the process as practiced at a Carrolville,
Wisconsin pilot plant were given by Stowasser[35].
Figure 2 is a flowsheet which was prepared from
details given in Stowasser's paper. Pilot plant
successes led to use of this method of pelletizing in the Silver Bay taconite plant of Reserve
Mining Company in Minnesota. All sections of the
plant were placed in operation by 1956 and the
plant had a design capacity of 3,750,000 tons of
iron ore pellets per year.

As soon as pilot operations showed that the
pelletizing method of agglomeration would be successful on a commercial scale in America, foreign
iron ore producers began to re-evaluate the process. Some detailed pelletizing tests on German
iron ores were described by Sengfelder in 1950[36].
These tests differed considerably from U.S. work
in that the ore concentrates were very low grade.
The Dogger ores which were pelletized contained
only 40 to 41 percent iron. Spathic(siderite)
concentrates containing only 32-33 percent iron
were also agglomerated. Blast furnace gases were
used as external fuel. The hardest pellets were
obtained at a firing temperature of 1100 degrees
Centigrade. Pellets made at 1100 degrees still
contained 14.8 percent of ferrous iron out of a
total of 46 percent iron. Pellets made at 1020
degrees contained only 0.6 percent ferrous iron
out of a total of 44.9 percent iron.

Tigerschiold reported that Sweden sent experts
to the United States after results of the Minnesota pelletizing method were published [37]. He

(35) Stowasser, W.F.:An Agglomeration Process for
     Iron Ore Concentrates, Mining Eng. vol 7,
     May, 1955, p 473-475.
(36) Sengfelder, G. op cit.
(37) Tigerschiold, M.:Aspects on Pelletizing of
     Iron Ore Concentrates, Jnl of the Iron &
     Steel Inst.(London) vol 177, May 1954, p 13.

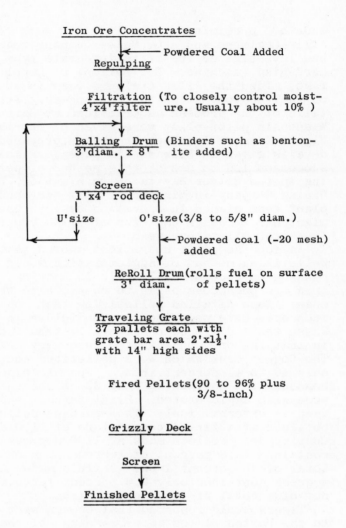

Iron Ore Concentrates

Powdered Coal Added

Repulping

Filtration (To closely control moist-
4'x4' filter   ure. Usually about 10%)

Balling Drum (Binders such as benton-
3'diam. x 8'   ite added)

Screen
1'x4' rod deck

U'size   O'size(3/8 to 5/8" diam.)

Powdered coal (-20 mesh)
added

ReRoll Drum(rolls fuel on surface
3' diam.   of pellets)

Traveling Grate
37 pallets each with
grate bar area 2'x1½'
with 14" high sides

Fired Pellets(90 to 96% plus
3/8-inch)

Grizzly Deck

Screen

Finished Pellets

Figure 2.   Pilot plant flowsheet for Allis-
Chalmers - A.G. McKee Pelletizing
Process

also gave some information regarding the Bodas
plant where 1¼-inch pellets were made in a 4-foot
diameter balling drum. Production was about 120
metric tons per day in 1954. Swedish practice
recommended drums with a length 2.3 to 3 times
the diameter and with peripheral speeds of 70 to
120 feet per minute. When 7/8-inch diameter balls
were made, drum speed was increased to 270 feet
per minute. Swedish practice favored 1¼-inch pellets whereas early U.S. plants preferred 7/8-inch
diameter pellets. Tigerschiold also mentioned
Swedish work on the "flying saucer" pelletizing
disc. The first tests were made at Malmberget
with a 12-foot diameter table, "with a cylindrical edge." He states that this table was originally developed in Czechoslovakia for the Portland
cement industry. Disc-type pelletizers are growing in popularity and were used both in cement and
iron ore plants before introduction to America.
Figure 3 is a photograph of a disc pelletizer. An
Australian cement plant refers to the disc pelletizer as a "pan-type nodulizer."[38]   In this cement
plant the pelletizer is located directly above the
shaft furnace for easy supervision by the furnace
operator. An early installation of a commercial
pelletizing disc in America was made by the International Nickel Company in 1955 for pelletizing
high-grade iron ore[39]. This was a 16-foot Lurgi
disc which had been successfully used in Europe.
Figure 4 is a sketch comparing balling in drums
with balling on a disc.
Wright[40] gave a summary of the state of the
pelletizing art late in 1956. He mentions that
bentonite is the most popular binder and is added
in the proportion of about 10 to 16 pounds per ton
of concentrate. The net result of U.S. and
Swedish studies is agreement that pellets
should be fired at 2300 to 2400 degrees Fahrenheit.

(38) Gottlieb, S.:Cement Can be Made Efficiently
        in a Shaft Kiln, Rock Products vol 58,
        Aug. 1955, p 122-130, 174-176.
(39) Anon:Spinning Disc Pelletizes Iron Ore,
        Chemical Eng. vol 62, Aug. 1955, p 236.
(40) Wright, E.C.:Magnetite Concentrates Supple-
        ment High-Grade Iron Ore, Metal Progress,
        vol 70, Sept. 1956, p 97-102.

Figure 3   Disc-type pelletizer in operation
(Photo courtesy Dwight Lloyd Division
of McDowell Company, Inc.)

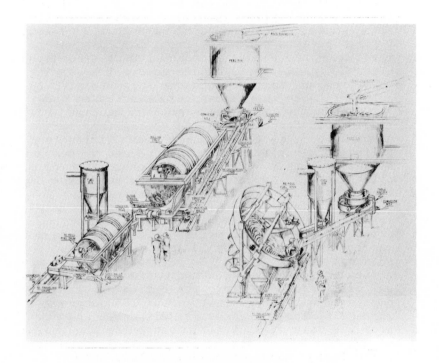

Figure 4   Comparison of drum-balling vs disc-
balling when end product desired is
a fuel-coated ball.
(Photo courtesy Dwight Lloyd Division
of McDowell Company, Inc.)

Wright gives the estimated heat requirements per
ton of pellets for two types of furnaces for pellet hardening as follows:

    Closed-top recuperative traveling
    grates (Reserve Mining)   1,300,000 Btu
    Shaft furnace   750,000 Btu

Wright describes the Silver Bay plant as follows:
"The Silver Bay plant has six recuperative traveling grates, each producing more than 2000 tons
of fired pellets per day. Each machine has a
traveling grate 6-feet wide and 170-feet long;the
pellet bed is 9- to 12-inches deep. The drying,
preheating and firing sections are completely
enclosed; there are 28 separate wind boxes under
the grates and six stacks on each machine, which
permits both downdrafting and updrafting, with
recuperation of hot gases from the firing and
cooling sections for use in drying and preheating
the wet pellets." Figure 5 is a photograph of one
of the traveling grate furnaces at the Silver Bay
plant of the Reserve Mining Company.

As the outcome of Professor Davis's and Erie
Mining Company's developments, Wright describes a
shaft-type furnace for pellet hardening: "the rectangular furnace is 6 by 14 feet in cross-section
and about 50-feet high. On both sides of the wide
section are combustion chambers from which enough
fuel oil is injected into the bottom of the shaft
to raise the temperature to about 1850 degrees
Fahrenheit. The hot gases are withdrawn and re-
enter the main shaft 6 to 8 feet below the top,
and dry the bed of wet pellets as they descend into the firing zone. Excess air blown into the
bottom cools the hot charge and then supplies oxygen for the coal in the pellets and to oxidize
the Fe_3O_4 to Fe_2O_3 (an exothermic reaction which,
by the way, supplies over 40% of the total heat
requirements). In contrast to the 3/8-inch Reserve pellets, which are mostly magnetite, the
Erie pellets are mostly hematite and are 1-inch in
diameter. The shaft furnace fires 1000 tons of
pellets per day;two of them have produced more
than 1,000,000 tons in the past seven years."

Figure 5.   Traveling grate pelletizing furnace
in operation at Silver Bay, Minn-
esota taconite plant.
(Photo courtesy Reserve Mining Co.)

The Marmora, Ontario Canada plant of Bethlehem Steel Corporation uses four shaft type
furnaces to harden magnetite pellets.[41]. Marmora
shipped its first boat load of pellets on May 12,
1955 from its Picton, Ontario port. The plant
has a capacity of 500,000 tons of pellets per
year. The pelletizing plant consists of four
similar lines, each with a disc filter, a balling
drum and an oil-fired vertical shaft furnace.
Pulverized coal is fed to a thickened pulp before
the filtration step. Bentonite is added at the
rate of $13\frac{1}{2}$ pounds per ton. The horizontal balling drums produce $\frac{1}{2}$- to 3/4-inch diameter pellets.
A baking temperature of about 2280 degrees Fahrenheit is used. The finished pellets contain from
63 to 64 percent iron after having been downgraded
from 66 percent iron by the addition of bentonite
and coal.

At Sydvaranger, Norway a taconite plant produces high-grade magnetite concentrates containing
about 60 percent minus 325-mesh particles. This
plant has adopted the pelletizing method of agglomeration after a study of all known methods.
Johanssen[42] claims that the new agglomeration
plant will process about 500,000 tons of concentrate per year, or half of the total magnetite
produced. Hydrocyclones are used to separate a
coarse magnetite fraction for export and the fine
fraction is pelletized.

Nodulizing

Nodulizing, like sintering, is an agglomeration
method which uses partial fusion to convert finely
divided particles into larger pieces. Sintering
is a static method in which there is little relative movement between the charge and processing

(41) Mamen, C.:Marmora's Iron Goes to Market,
     Canadian Mining Jnl. vol 8, Aug. 1955,p43-48
(42) Johanssen, J.K.:The Ore Dressing Plants of
     Sydvaranger A.S. Norway, The Mining & Dress-
     ing of Low-Grade Ores in Europe, The Organ-
     ization for European Economic Co-operation,
     (O.E.E.C. Mission Washington D.C.)
     June 1955, p 281-286.

equipment. Nodulizing requires continuous relative movement between the charge and the processing equipment and is usually carried out in a rotary kiln. With kiln temperatures of 2300 to 2500 degrees Fahrenheit, nearly spherical bodies of varying diameters are formed from fine particles. A surfacial liquid phase is first formed and then the mixture is allowed to snowball into spheres before the temperature drops. A cooling step then allows almost complete solidification of the liquid phase before the nodules leave the kiln. The size of nodules can be controlled but a wide range of size is acceptable when iron ores are processed. The main advantages of nodulizing over other agglomeration processes are that nodulizing is almost unaffected by moisture variations, carbon content of the feed, and particle size of the raw materials. Table II compares size analyses for iron, manganese, and phosphate ore nodules. From these data it is evident that the nodulizing process is capable of producing iron ore agglomerates of suitable size.

Vogel, at a 1912 AIME symposium on iron ore agglomeration, stated that the nodulizing process is the oldest agglomeration method used in the United States[43]. Mention is made of kilns 80- to 120-feet long and use of 200 to 300 pounds of coal per ton of nodules. According to Seil[44] two of the first U.S. iron ore nodulizing installations were made in 1904 at the South Chicago plant of the Illinois Steel Company and at a Pennsylvania Steel Company (Bethlehem Steel) plant. These kilns were about 6-feet in diameter and 60-feet long. Lee[45], in 1914, reported on the use of iron ore nodules in the blast furnace. One Lebanon, Pennsylvania furnace of the Pennsylvania Steel Company was burdened exclusively with nodules.

(43) Vogel, F.A.: Sintering and Briquetting of Flue Dust, Trans. AIME vol 43, 1912, p 381-387.
(44) Seil, G.E.: Nodulizing Iron Ore, The Iron Age, April 27, 1944, p 39-46
(45) Lee, R.H.: The Use of Nodulized Ore in the Blast Furnace, Trans. AIME vol 47, 1914, p 344-356.

TABLE II

Size Analyses of Nodulized Ores

| | | Cumulative | Percent | Weight | |
Nodule Size	Iron ore sludge	Iron ore (Minn.)	U.S. Mn ore	Cuban manganese ore	Phosphate ore
Plus 2"	-	2-3		4.77	6.2
Plus 1½"	-	35-45			
Plus 1"	8			28.63	40.7
Plus ½"	54		14		72.5
Plus 3/8"	74			73.13	
Plus 4 mesh	88		53		91.6
Plus 8 mesh	96				
Plus 10 mesh		92-95	89	94.23	
Kiln feed	flue dust sludge 4.9% SiO$_2$	taconite concts. 80% minus 200 mesh 7.33% SiO$_2$		Flot. concts. 8.3-11% SiO$_2$	phosphate ore fines

Data Sources:

Seil, G.E.:Nodulizing Iron Ore, The Iron Age, April 27, 1944, p 39-46.

Bennet, R.L., R.E. Hagen and M.V. Mielke:Nodulizing Iron Ores and Concentrates at Extaca Plant, Mining Eng. vol 6, Jan. 1954, p 32-38.

Norcross, F.S.:Development of the Low-Grade Manganese Ores of Cuba, Trans. AIME vol 153, 1943, p 97-110

Stout, E.L.:Agglomeration of Phosphate Fine for Furnace Use, T.V.A. Chemical Eng. Report No. 4, 1950, U.S. Govt. Printing Office, 124 pp.

Nodulizing of iron ores has been practiced on a continuous basis in Germany since 1914. The nodulizing kiln is a preferred method of agglomeration when large percentages of flue dust are processed[46]. Ring formation is reported to be a serious problem and boring bars are used in all kilns. The cost of nodulizing, excluding the cost of raw material, was said to be higher than sintering. Modern Lurgi sinter plants in Germany handle up to 20 percent of flue dust in the feed.

A shortage of open hearth charge ore in the U.S. during World War II induced steel producers to encourage some nodulizing tests in idle cement kilns. Reports on these tests were given by A.A. Oesterle of the Federal Portland Cement Company and E.F. Brownstead of the Alpha Portland Cement Company at the 1949 Chicago meeting of the Blast Furnace, Coke Oven and Raw Materials Committee of the AIME. Both investigators told of difficulties due to ring formation. Many observers concluded that the design of cement kilns was not optimum for iron ore nodulizing. Brownstead reported that an 8- by 100-foot kiln would produce 250 tons of nodules per day at a fuel rate of 6000 cubic feet of 500 Btu coke oven gas per ton. The temperature in the burning zone was about 2350 degrees Fahrenheit. Good nodules for open hearth charge should weigh about 130 pounds per cubic foot and this weight is attainable by the nodulizing process. A total of about $1\frac{1}{4}$ million tons of iron ore nodules were made in the two plants described by Oesterle and Brownstead.

Simons[47] described a British nodulizing kiln which produced 3000 tons of iron ore nodules per week by processing in a 200-foot long kiln. The feed was usually 35 percent flue dust plus fine ore and pyrite. The kiln rotated at 1 to 2 RPM,

(46) Members of British Intelligence Objectives Subcommittee: Iron Ore Preparation in Germany, B.I.O.S. Trip Report No. 1234, Nov. 1945, (London)

(47) Simons, W.E.: The Smidth Agglomerating Kiln, Plant and Practice at East Moors Works, Blast Furnace & Steel Plant vol 39, Oct. 1951, p 1216-1223.

was installed at a 4 degree angle and was driven by a 110 hp motor. In comparing the operation with a sinter plant, Simons pointed out that advantages of nodulizing included: 100 percent flue dust can be charged, no coke breeze is required, a bigger variation in particle size of raw materials is permissible, fine crushers are eliminated and there are no returns as in sintering. Analyses of nodules from the plant showed 62.91 percent FeO and 12.7 percent Fe_2O_3.

The most recent large-scale testing of the nodulizing process for iron ores was undertaken by the U.S. Steel Corporation at its Extaca plant near Virginia, Minnesota. Bennett[48] and co-workers gave a detailed report of the operation in 1953. The Extaca kiln was designed for a capacity of 1000 tons of nodules per day. It is 350-feet long and has a $10\frac{1}{2}$-foot inside diameter. The size of the kiln and general process design were based on theoretical relationships developed by the Allis-Chalmers Manufacturing company[49]. This is an early example of an operations research technique being applied to a pyrometallurgical problem. The plant was designed for operation by a minimum plant staff. The plant is equipped with excellent control and recording instruments. Some pertinent operating statistics for test runs with hematite and magnetite ores are given in Table III. The nodules from the Extaca plant are primarily used as open hearth charge ore.

Nodulizing of manganese ores is similar in many respects to nodulizing of iron ores. Manganese carbonate(rhodochrosite) flotation concentrates have been successfully nodulized on a commercial scale since 1941 at a Montana plant by

(48) Bennett, R.L., R.E. Hagen, and M.V. Mielke: Nodulizing Iron Ores and Concentrates at Extaca Plant, Mining Eng. vol 6, Jan. 1954, p 32-38.

(49) Matzke, W.J.:A Rotary Kiln Design Formula, An engineering development division report, Allis-Chalmers Mfg. Co., August 1, 1945.

TABLE III

Operating Statistics - Extaca Nodulizing Plant*

Optimum nodulizing temperature	2300-2380 °F. high silica ore(over 8%) 2450-2500 °F. low silica ore(under 4%) 2300-2350 °F. magnetite
Secondary air temp.	about 1400 °F.
Kiln exit gas temp.	530-580 °F.
Temp. nodules discharged from cooler	70-300 °F.
Kiln hood pressure	-0.03" WG.
Oxygen in kiln exit gas	1-2% (hematite ore) 2-3.5% (magnetite ore)
Kiln speed - rev. per hour	67

Average ore feed rate,

(LT/hr.- dry)	44.1	(hematite)
(LT/day - dry)	1058	"
(LT/hr.- dry)	47.4	(magnetite)
(LT/day - dry)	1137	"

Percent limestone in feed (dry)	4.06	(hematite)
	4.00	(magnetite)

Average nodule production rate,

(LT/hr. - dry basis)	42.4	(hematite)
(LT/day - dry basis)	1018	"
(LT/hr. - dry basis)	45.8	(magnetite)
(LT/day - dry basis)	1098	"

Coal consumption per LT nodules	175.66 lbs.	(hematite)
	133.92 lbs.	(magnetite)
Heat value of coal Btu/lb.	13666	(hematite)
	13782	(magnetite)
Fuel consumption Btu/ton nodules	2,400,532	(hematite)
	1,846,000	(magnetite)
Kwh per ton of nodules, (average)	16.2	

*Bennett, R.L., R.E. Hagen and M.V. Mielke:Noduliz-
ing Iron Ores and Concentrates at Extaca Plant,
Mining Eng. vol 6, Jan. 1954, p 32-38.

the Anaconda Company[50,51]. The kiln at this plant is 270-feet long and varies in diameter from 10 feet 8 inches in the drying section to 15-feet in the control zone. The section in which nodule formation takes place is 11 feet 5-inches in diameter and 19-feet long. The kiln design is similar to an earlier kiln used in the plant of the Cuban-American Manganese Company in Cuba. The Anaconda kiln shell is made from 13/16-inch plate in the cooler sections and with 1-inch plate in the hotter zones. The kiln is driven by a 125 hp motor and consumes about $2\frac{1}{2}$ million cubic feet of gas fuel per 24-hour day. The kiln feed is a slurry containing 65 percent solids. A large boring bar is used to remove rings as they form.

A more recent manganese ore agglomeration plant is the Nevada plant of Manganese Inc. which nodulizes manganese oxide flotation concentrates. A 10-foot by 150-foot nodulizing kiln and an 8-foot by 98-foot rotary cooler are used. The kiln measures $11\frac{1}{2}$ by 20-feet in the hot zone. It has been reported that 10 to 12 percent insoluble content is desirable for the formation of good nodules at this plant[52]. Operation of the earlier Cuban installation for nodulizing manganese oxide flotation concentrates was described by Norcross[53]. The Cuban plant used a 9-foot by 213-foot kiln. Both the Cuban and the Nevada kilns used a water-cooled boring bar for ring removal. Norcross reported that when the manganese concentrates contained less than 8.3 to 11.0% SiO_2 nodulizing became more difficult.

The present state of development of the

(50) Anon:Concentrating and Nodulizing "Pink" Manganese at Anaconda, Mining World vol 5, Jan. 1943, p 2-8.

(51) Huttl, J.B.:Domestic Manganese from Butte Helps in Emergency, Eng. & Mining Jnl. vol 143, Jan. 1942, p 56-58.

(52) McCarroll, S.J.:Upgrading Manganese Ore, Mining Eng. vol 6, March 1954, p 289-293.

(53) Norcross, F.S.:Development of the Low-grade Manganese Ores of Cuba, Trans, AIME vol 153 1943, p 97-110.

nodulizing process for agglomeration of iron ores
seems to indicate that the method is finding use
only in special cases where a high-density end
product is desired or where unusual raw materials
are processed. Also the type of fuel available
may encourage use of nodulizing kilns.

Briquetting

Briquetting of iron ores has never attained
large-scale use and in recent years only one
American plant used the process. Briquetting is
a process for binding or agglomerating fine-sized
particles into compact masses by application of
pressure and often includes addition of a binder.
These masses may be tablets, balls, pillow-like
shapes, barrel shapes, egg shapes, rods or double-
pyramidal shapes. According to Landis[54], the
briquetting of peat and lignite waste at Paris,
France was probably the earliest example of agglomeration of fine materials into larger masses.
Hence the word "briquette" comes from the French
"la brique" due to similarity in shape to a
building brick.
The most common machine used for briquetting
is a double-roll machine in which the rolls are
provided with appropriately shaped pockets. The
extreme pressures involved require massive construction in briquetting machines. Briquetting
is a popular agglomeration method in the chemical
industry and is widely used in agglomeration of
coal fines. The U.S. production of fuel briquettes in 1950 totaled 2,770,020 net tons[55]. The
more common binders used in fuel briquettes are
starch, Portland cement, lignin products, sodium
silicate, lime and asphalt. Other binders of
less importance are molasses, iron filings, iron
sulphate, magnesium chloride, sodium chloride and
spent pickling liquor. Because of the necessity
of using low-grade brown coals in Europe, briquetting has had more rapid development there.

(54) Landis, W.S.:Agglomeration of Fine Materials,
        Trans. AIME vol 43, 1912, p 375-381.
(55) Mineral Market Report M.M.S. No. 1972, May
        1951, U.S. Bureau of Mines.

In 1950 there were 110 coal briquetting plants in
Germany alone.
Loiseau[56] reported, in 1878, on a briquetting
plant which was built by the Anthracite Fuel
Company at Fort Ewen, near Rondout, New York.
This installation processed anthracite coal dust
into useable fuel briquettes. Schorr[57] later
described this same plant and another located
at Port Richmond, Pa. These plants had an annual
capacity of about 150,000 tons of anthracite briquettes per year. About 8% of bituminous coal
and 10% of hard-pitch binder were used. Schorr
also stated that Edison used a number of small
"intermittent-acting" presses at his magnetic iron
separation works in New Jersey.
Vogel and Tweedy, in 1914, reported on the
Schumacher briquetting process which was used on
flue dust at a Lackawanna, N.Y. steel plant[58].
Large rectangular briquettes, 7.75-by 6-by 3.25-
inches were formed at a rate of 18 to 22 units
per minute. The various binders tested were
calcium chloride, magnesium chloride, iron sulphate and pickling liquor.
A recent report[59] on the Russian-Jarcho method of iron ore briquetting was outlined by Radzwicki in 1951. The Jarcho method utilizes corr-
osive binders such as sulphuric acid, hydrochloric acid, magnesium chloride, sodium chloride,
ferrous sulphate and spent pickling liquors. The
method is based on the utilization of "corrosion"
phenomena which bind the ore particles together.
The briquettes are made in a brickmaking machine,

(56) Loiseau, E.F.:On the Manufacture of Artifi-
     cial Fuel at Port Richmond, Philadelphia,
     Trans. AIME vol 6, 1879, p 214-220.
(57) Schorr, R.:Fuel and Mineral Briquetting,
     Trans. AIME vol 35, 1905, p 82-116.
(58) Vogel, F.A. and A.M. Tweedy:The Briquetting
     of Flue Dust in the United States by the
     Schumacher Process, Trans. AIME vol 47,
     1914, p 338-343.
(59) Radzwicki, K., W. Madej, and W. Stronczwak:
     Briquetting of Ore Fines for Steel Plants,
     Jnl. of Iron & Steel Inst. (London), Jan.
     1952, p 63.

weigh 13 to 16 pounds each and measure 9.8-by 5.1-
by 2.6-inches. Russian practice requires a comp-
ression strength of 50 kg/sq. cm., porosity not
over 5 - 10%, good adherence when briquettes are
kept at 1500 degrees C. for 3 minutes, and generation of not over 10% fines(below 5 mm.) when a
briquette is dropped twice on a steel plate from
a height of 2 meters.

A British report[60] on German iron ore briquetting practice gives considerable detail regarding a plant at Rheinhausen. This 1945 report
states that iron ore briquetting has been carried
out at Rheinhausen for over 25 years. Three
brick-type presses have a capacity of 350 tons
per day per machine. The mixture for briquetting
was reported as 3% cast iron borings or cut turn-
ings, 8-10% coke breeze (minus $\frac{1}{2}$-inch), and 3-5%
of calcium or magnesium chloride added as a solution. The newly made briquettes are weak but
after 48 hours ageing are very strong. Temperature control is important; the liquid is added
while nearly at its boiling point so that briquetting is carried out at temperatures approaching
100 degrees Centigrade. Briquetting pressure is
4,300 lbs. per square inch. The cost of briquetting, excluding the raw material, was reported to
be identical with the cost of sintering at the
same works.

The Woodward Iron Company at Woodward, Alabama
has successfully briquetted iron ores for many
years. A fossiliferrous red hematite containing
34.75% Fe, 14.65% SiO_2, 3.25% Al_2O_3 and 16.45% CaO
is briquetted with Portland cement used as the
binder. Two Komareck-Greaves briquetting machines,
which utilize pressures of 3250 psi., produce 1200
gross tons of briquettes per day. Mold life is
approximately 150,000 tons and costs were reported at about 50 cents per gross ton[61]. It has been
reported that the "earthy" nature of this ore
gives it some lubricative properties which helps

(60) Report by British Intelligence Objectives
      Subcommittee, op cit.
(61) Byrns, H.A.:Briquetting Practice on Fine Ores
      at Woodward, Alabama, Blast Furnace, Coke
      Oven & Raw Matls. Comm. AIME, Chicago, 1949.

extend mold life considerably.

The briquetting process can be classed as a special method of agglomeration which is competitive only when certain types of iron ores are processed. These ores will generally contain a minimum of abrasive particles and require only small amounts of low-cost binders.

"Blocked" Iron Ore

A shortage of open hearth charge ore(high-density ore which will sink through the slag) has encouraged the development of a process known as the "blocked iron process". An announcement in the technical press[62] in 1951 stated, "The first Ohio blocked iron ore plant is now in production in Cleveland. The process is simple. Ore dust is mixed with salt, cement, chemical binder, and water, pressed in a cylindrical mold and then kilned for 12 hours. The 25-pound blocks that are produced supplement the charge ore for the open hearth furnaces. Developed by Blocked Iron Corp., the process is being operated in Cleveland by Concrete Pipe Co. of Ohio. Present production of the $150,000 plant is approximately 150 tons per shift. Six other plants, two in the Pittsburgh area and four in the Gary area, are now in operation." A directory of research laboratories in New York state[63] listed the Blocked Iron Corporation research laboratories at Montrose, New York in 1954. Golden and Warren[64] reported that blocked iron is made in both six and eight-inch diameter cylinders. Also they note that in one test blocked iron was superior to charge ore, both from the standpoint of production rates and ore requirements. Little information is available regarding costs of producing blocked iron.

(62) Anon:Ohio Agglomerator, Chem. & Eng. News vol 29, Aug. 6, 1951, p 3142.
(63) State of New York, Dept. of Commerce:Directory of Industrial Research Laboratories in New York State, 1954, 126 pp.
(64) Golden, J.J. and H.E. Warren:Openhearth Charge Ores, Paper presented at the May, 1951 meeting of Amer. Iron & Steel Inst.

Due to the relatively small scale of operations
to date, it appears that costs would be over two
dollars per ton. In 1956 the construction of a
larger plant was announced[65]. This plant was to
be located near the Pennsylvania Railroad's new
$12,000,000 ore pier near Philadelphia, Pa. The
initial unit of the new plant was to cost more
than $1,000,000.

A distinct advantage of the blocked iron process over nodulizing or sintering is that it is
carried out at low temperature. Further advancement of this and similar low-temperature agglomeration processes may open up a new field of iron
ore agglomeration which could be termed "chemical
agglomeration".

(65) Anon:News Item, "Iron Ore Plant", Mining
      Congress Jnl. vol 42, July 1956, p 80-81.

ADDITIONAL REFERENCES

Harrison, P.G.:Sintering Limonitic Iron Ores at
Ironton, Minnesota, Trans. AIME vol 90, 1930,
p 346-357.
McClurkin, R.:Sinter in Blast-Furnace Burdens,
Trans. AIME vol 100, 1932, p 47-56.
Harrison, P.G.:Sintering Economics, Trans. AIME
vol 100, 1932, p 57-63
Schwartz, G.M.:Iron-ore Sinter, Trans. AIME vol
84, 1929, p 39-67.
Joseph, T.L.:Porosity, Reducibility and Size Pre-
paration of Iron Ores, Trans. AIME vol 120, 1936,
p 72-98.
Klugh, B.G.:The Microstructure of Sintered Iron-
Bearing Materials, Trans. AIME vol 45, 1914,
p 330-345.
Saunders, H.L. and H.J. Tress:Sinters and Sinter-
ing, Blast Furnace & Steel Plant, Nov. 1945, p
1385-1390.
Anon:Sinters Economize Blast Furnace Operation,
The Iron Age, Nov. 29, 1945, p 62-63.
Colclough, T.P.:Considerations on Blast Furnace
Practice, Blast Furnace & Steel Plant, Oct. 1945,
p 1253-1261, 1277.
Anon:How Republic Concentrates Adirondack Iron
Ores, Eng. & Mining Jnl. vol 146, July 1945,
p 90-93.
Nilsen, A.A. and R. Yingling:Remote Control a
Feature of Ore-Conditioning Plant, Eng. & Mining
Jnl. vol 148, April 1947, p 74-79.
Davison, L.M.P. and C.M. Spencer:Igniter Cuts
Fuel Costs, Eng. & Mining Jnl. vol 148, Sept.
1947, p 75-76.
Najarian, H.K. et al:Sintering Practice At Joseph-
town Smelter, Trans. AIME vol 191, p 116-119,
1045.
Morgan, M.F.:Methods of Agglomeration and the
Problem of Agglomerating Fine Taconite Concen-
trates, Univ. of Minn. Mines Expt. Station Inf.
Circular No. 5, Sept. 1945, p 34-40.
Anon:Sintering to Raise Iron Ore Output, Eng. &
Mining Jnl. vol 150, June 1949, p 59.

Howat, D.D.:Britain Gets Half Its Iron From Its
Lean Ores, Eng. & Mining Jnl. vol 150, June 1949,
p 66-69.

Webb, W.R. and R.G. Fleck:Sintering Adirondack
Magnetites, Mining Eng. vol 187, June 1950,
p 671-672.

Hamilton, F.M. and H.F.Ameen:Laboratory Studies
on Iron Ore Sintering and Testing, Mining Eng.
vol 187, Dec. 1950, p 1275-1282.

Hamilton, F.M.:Physical Tests and Results on Some
Agglomerated Iron Ores, AIME Blast Furnace, Coke
Oven & Raw Materials Conf. April 2-4, 1951,
Cleveland, Ohio.

Hill, E.G. and R.E. Powers:Testing of Sinter,
Paper given at General Meeting of American Iron
& Steel Inst. New York, May 1951.

Burrow, W.R.:Continuous Updraft Sintering Process
Recovers More SO_2 for Smelter, Eng. & Mining Jnl.
vol 153, Nov. 1952, p 90-94.

Bartholomew, F.J.:Chemico's New Pickle Liquor
Process, Chem. Eng. vol 57, Aug. 1950, p 118-120.

Anon:Agglomeration, Chem. Eng. vol 58, October,
1951, p 161-174.

Stehli, H.J.:Sintering Zinc Ores, Trans, AIME vol
121, 1936, p 374-386.

Oldright, G.L. et al:Some Experiments on Sintering Lead Sulphate Products, Trans. AIME vol 159,
1944, p 81-93.

Somiya, T. and A. Tominaga:The Use of Hokkaido
Bog Iron Ores Containing Arsenic, Paper given
before 12th Intnl. Congress of Pure & Applied
Chemistry, New York, Sept. 1951.

Counselman, T.B.:Concentration of Iron Ores in
the United States, AIME Tech. Paper 1629, 1943.

Dobscha, H.F.:Effect of Size and Sintered Mesabi
Iron Ores On Blast Furnace Performance, Steel,
April 26, 1948, p 125.

Hay, R. and J.M. McLeod:The Principles Underlying
the Sintering of Iron Ores, West of Scotland
Iron & Steel Inst. Jnl. vol 52, part 6, p 108-121.

Gillings, D.W.:High Quality Sinter From Lean Iron
Ores,Blast Furnace & Steel Plant vol 40, June
1952, p 663-671.

Klemantaski, S.:Action of Inhibitors of Carbon
Deposition in Iron Ore Reduction, Jnl. of Iron &
Steel Inst.(London) vol 171, June 1952, p 176-182.

Anon:New York Iron Mines Expanding, Iron Age, vol 171, Jan. 8, 1953, No. 2, p 43.

Cockburn, K.O.:Production of Iron Sinter at Helen Mine, Canadian Mining & Met. Bulletin, vol 44, Nov. 1951, p 745-754.

Nichols, P.R.:Features of the Sintering Plant at Wisconsin Steel Works, Blast Furnace, Coke Oven & Raw Materials Comm. AIME, 1948 Proceedings, p 83-86.

Cromwell, D.P.:Operations and Practice, Campbell Sintering Plant, ibid, p 86-89.

Wehr, G.:Sintering Plant and Practice at Steubenville, ibid, p 89-94.

Saussaman, J.D.:Sintering Practice at Fontana, Calif. ibid, p 95-106.

Fosdick, A.H.:Operating Features and Practices at the Bethlehem Sintering Plant, ibid, p 106-118.

Betz, C.P.:Operating Features at the Zug Island Sintering Plant, ibid, p 118-126.

LeVisuer, K.G.:Use of Magnetite Ores From New York State, Blast Furnace & Steel Plant vol 39, Feb. 1951, p 200-202, 222.

Cover, M.L.:Sinter Production Tied to Plant Design, The Iron Age vol 169, June 5,1952,p 145-149.

Bond, W.R.:Beneficiation of East Texas Iron Ores, Blast Furnace, Coke Oven & Raw Materials Comm. AIME, Proceedings vol 12, 1953, p 6-17.

Kalling B.:New Manufacturing Processes for High-Grade Steel in Sweden, Metal Progress vol 65, Jan. 1954, p 108-111, 200, 202.

Wild, R.:The Chemical Constitution of Sinters, Jnl. of Iron & Steel Inst.(London) vol 174, June 1953, p 131-135.

Voice, E.W. et al:The Permeability of Sinter Beds, ibid, p 136-139.

Hamilton, F.M. and H.F. Ameen:Production and Properties of Experimental Pellet-sinter, Blast Furnace, Coke Oven & Raw Materials Conference, AIME, Philadelphia, Pa. April, 1955.

Dean, S.K. et al:A Method of Automatic Control for Sinter-Plant Feeder Tables Jnl. of Iron & Steel Inst. (London) vol 177 Part 2, June 1954, p 220-223.

Baldwin, B.G.:The Formation and Decomposition of Fayalite($2FeO.SiO_2$), ibid, vol 177 Part 3, July 1954, p 312-316.

McBriar, E.M. et al:The Nature of Ironstone
Sinter, Jnl. of Iron & Steel Inst. (London) vol
177, Part 3, July 1954, p 316-323.
Macdonald, N.D.:Sinter-Plant Operation at Appleby-
Frodingham, ibid, vol 178 Part 1, Sept. 1954,
p 51-60.
Agnew, C.E.:Correlating Blast Furnace Operating
Concepts, Part 6, Steel vol 135, No. 26, Dec.
27, 1954, p 68-71.
Strassburger, J.H.:Weirton's New Sintering Plant,
Jnl. Metals vol 8, 1956, p 840-842.
Anon:Largest Iron Ore Sintering Plants Being Ins-
stalled, Industrial Heating vol 23, Sept. 1956,
p 1874.
Sullivan, J.D. and A.P.Towne:Agglomeration and
Leaching of Slimes and Other Finely Divided Ores,
U.S. Bur. Mines Bulletin 329, 1930.
Zetterstrom, J.D.:Oxidation of Magnetite Concen-
trates, U.S. Bur. Mines Rept. of Inv. 4728, Sept.
1950, 8 pp.
Klinefelter, T.A.:Evaluation of Some Binders for
Use In Pelletizing Slimes, U.S. Bur. Mines Rept.
of Inv. 3846, Jan. 1946, 13 pp.
Hunner, G.B.:Operating Practices at the Ports-
mouth Sinter Plant, Blast Furnace & Raw Matls.
Comm. AIME 1950 Proceedings, p 236-245.
Robinson, A.W.:Swedish Sintering Practice, ibid,
p 246-267.
Riddle, E.H.:Use of Adirondack Sinter in Blast
Furnaces, ibid, p 268-279.
deBruyne, N.A.:Some Investigations Into the Fund-
amentals and Applications of Synthetic Adhesives,
a paper in book - Plastics Progress, Iliffe &
Sons, Ltd. London, 1951, p 137-152.
Lund, W.:Agglomeration of Taconite Concentrate,
Jnl. of Iron & Steel Inst. (London), May 1949,
p 1-3.
Hay, R. and J.M.McLeod,:Some Aspects of Sintering Iron Ores. Jnl. of the West Scotland Iron &
Steel Inst. vol 50, Session 1942-43, p 55-64.
Voice, E.W., C. Lang, and P.K. Gledhill:Invest-
igation of the Effects of Controlled Variables
on Sinter Quality, Part I Development of Exptl.
Sinter Plant and Preliminary Results Using Nor-
thants Ore, Jnl. of Iron & Steel Inst. (London)
vol 167, Part 4, April 1951, p 393-399.

Cohen, E.:Radiographic Studies of the Process of Sintering Iron Ore, Jnl. of Iron & Steel Inst. (London) vol 175, Part 2, October, 1953, p 160-166.

Danielsson, C.:Sintering Practice at Domnarfvet, Sweden, ibid, p 152-154.

Jennings, R.F.:The Rating of Sinter Plants for Economic Output, Jnl. of Iron & Steel Inst. (London) vol 175, Part 3, Nov. 1953, p 248-256.

Gledhill, P.K., G.C. Carter, and C.F. Ely:Effect of Mineral Additions and Moisture Control on the Sintering of Sierra Leone Concentrates, ibid, p 277-279.

Wendeborn, H.B.:Sintering as a Physical Process, ibid, p 280-288.

Firth, C.V.:Agglomeration of Fine Iron Ore, Blast Furnace & Raw Materials Proceedings 1944, p 46-69.

Smith, R.C.:Sintering, Its Nature and Cause, Jnl. Chem. Soc. London, vol 123, 1923, p 2088-2094.

Caine, J.B.:A Study of the Thermal Stability of Materials Used in Sintering Machine Pallets, Blast Furnace & Steel Plant vol 43, March, 1955, p 315-319.

Greenawalt, J.E.:The Sintering Process and Some Recent Developments, AIME Tech. Pub. 963, 1938.

Fournier, E.J.:Sintering Conserves Our Iron Ores, Compressed Air Magazine, vol 39, Feb. 1935, p 4345-4347.

Duby, C.J.:Design and Operation of Modern Sintering Plants, Iron and Steel Eng. vol 22, May 1945, p 39, 44, 61.

Morgan, M.F.:Design and Operation of a Modern Sintering Plant, Iron and Steel Eng. vol 19, April 1942, p 103-113.

Davis, E.W.:Agglomeration by the Pelletizing Process, Paper given at the 11th Annual Mining Symposium, Center for Continuation Study, Univ. of Minn. Jan. 1950, 4 pp.

Anon:Plan Pilot Taconite Plant, Mining Eng. vol 4, May 1952, p 450.

Woody, G.V.:Heat Hardening of Pellets Made From Taconite Concentrates, Blast Furnace & Steel Plant vol 41, March 1953, p 314-317.

Cooke, S.R.B. and T.E. Ban:Microstructures in Iron Ore Pellets, Mining Eng. vol 4, Nov. 1952, p 1053.

Cooke, S.R.B. and W.F. Stowasser:The Effect of
Heat Treatment and Certain Additives on the
Strength of Fired Magnetite Pellets, Mining Eng.
vol 4, Dec. 1952, p 1223-1230.

Cooke, S.R.B. and R.E. Brandt:Solid State Bonding
in Iron Ore Pellets, Paper given at 1954 annual
meeting AIME, New York.

Anon:Dravo-Lurgi Iron Ore Pelletizing Equipment
Ordered for International Nickel Plant, Eng. &
Mining Jnl. vol 155, Nov. 1954, p 160.

Stirling, A.:The Pelletizing of Northampton Sand
Ironstones by Vacuum Extrusion, Jnl. of Iron &
Steel Inst. (London), vol 177, Part 1, May 1954,
p 25-42.

Ridgion, J.M., E. Cohen and C. Lang:The Development of a Pelletizing Process for Fine Iron Ores,
ibid, p 43-63.

Henderson, A.S. et al:Filtration and Control of
Moisture Content on Taconite Concentrates, Paper
given at 1956 annual meeting AIME, New York.

Doak, S.E.:Rotary Kilns for Desulphurization and
Agglomeration, Trans. AIME vol 53, 1916, p 144-
149.

Addicks, L.:Nodulizing Blast-Furnace Flue Dust,
Trans. AIME vol 49, 1915, p 500-506.

Kenworthy, H.:Nodulization and Pelletization of
Fluorite Flotation Concentrates, U.S. Bur. Mines
Rept. of Inv. 4829, Dec. 1951, 13 pp.

Anon:Nodulizing Phosphate in Kilns, Denver Equip.
Company Bulletin No. M4-B20.

Stout, E.L.:Agglomeration of Phosphate Fines for
Furnace Use, T.V.A. Chemical Eng. Report No. 4,
1950, U.S. Govt. Printing Office, 124 p.

Anon:Weirton Tests Agglomerates, Steel vol 125,
Sept. 12, 1949.

DeVaney, F.D.:Nodulizing Process & Apparatus,
U.S. Patent 2,590,090, March 25, 1952.

Newhouse, R.C.:Method and Apparatus for Noduliz-
ation of Iron Ore, U.S. Patent No. 2,584,808.

DeVaney, F.D.and D. Beggs:Induration Furnace,
U.S. Patent 2,676,095, May 13, 1954.

DeVaney, F.D.:Iron Ore Concentrate Pellets, U.S.
Patent 2,596,132, May 13, 1952.

Royster, P.H.:Heat-Hardening of Magnetite Pellets
U.S. Patent 2,608,481, Aug. 26, 1952.

Rowen, H.E.:Solid Fuels and the Dwight-Lloyd
Sintering Process, Mining Eng. vol 8, April
1956, p 396-398.
Argall, Jr., G.O.:Eagle Mills Pellet Plant Opens
New Era For Michigan Hematite, Mining World, vol
18, Dec. 1956, p 42-46.
DeVaney, F.D.:Pelletizing in Shaft Furnaces,
Paper presented at the Annual Meeting AIME,
New Orleans, Feb. 1957.
Mitchell, E.A., J.F. Melvin and R. Bainbridge:
Conminco's New Sinter Plant, Jnl. of Metals,
March 1957, p 361-370.

Chapter XII

RESEARCH

"The greatest gamble a company
can make is to have no research
program at all."--James C. Zeder,
Director of Engineering and
Research, Chrysler Corporation.

Research, whether in the mineral industry or
any other industry, is sometimes referred to as
educated gambling. The success ratio in research
speculation has risen to a point where no industrial venture can afford to overlook the use of
a research program in some form or another.

Research expenditures in 1955 reached a total
of $ 4.1 billion, up $350 million from 1954. For
the past quarter century, expenditures on research
have been increasing faster than the gross nat-
tional product, or total production of goods and
services [1]. In the past five years, research
has averaged about one per cent of the nation's
total economic activity and the ratio has gradually increased. In a 1949 speech before the
Industrial Research Institute, Robert E. Wilson
of Standard Oil Company expressed thoughts on the
attitude of management toward research [2]. The
increasing difficulty of planning and prosecuting
successful research programs is recognized by top
management. Wilson stated,"There is some question
in management's mind as to whether the law of diminishing returns may not be starting to take
hold. Research costs can not continue to go up
forever as they have in the past. The costs have
been justified to date--have been more than

(1) Williams, C.E.:Research in 1956, Battelle
      Technical Review, vol 5, Feb., 1956, p 12.
 (2) Wilson, R.E.:The Attitude of Management To-
      ward Research, Chem. & Eng. News vol 27,
      Jan. 31, 1949, p 274-277.

justified. But some time we are going to reach
a place where we can not afford to go further in
expanding our research organizations, because
the rest of the operations will not be able to
carry the load. Some day there will not be enough
yield for each dollar expended in research." One
suggestion given by Wilson is to encourage cooperation between laboratories in a given region
in the matter of use of specialized, expensive
equipment. "Research has long done a fine job
in studying the costs of operations of all sorts,
but the time has come when it must give some
attention to cutting its own costs." Exactly
this is now taking place through the application
of operations research techniques.

The high cost of modern research programs often forces cooperative ventures when the planned
investment in research effort is large. A good
example of this in the minerals industry is a
long-range research program sponsored by eleven
iron ore companies at Battelle Memorial Institute
during the years 1942 through 1952. This program was directed toward the development of beneficiation processes for Lake Superior District
taconite ores.

History of Minerals Beneficiation Research

The history of organized research in the field
of minerals beneficiation in America covers only
a short span of time. Professor Robert H.
Richards described his new metallurgical laboratory at the Massachusetts Institute of Technology to AIME members in 1873 [3]. Richards mentioned the excellent mining schools of Prussia
which were owned and controlled by the government as were most of the mines and metallurgical
establishments. Fundamental knowledge which provided the foundation of many gravity concentration
principles was developed in early European ore
dressing laboratories. The success of Richard's
early laboratory encouraged adoption of similar

(3) Richards, R.H.:The Mining and Metallurgical
     Laboratories of the Massachusetts Institute
     of Technology, Trans AIME vol 1, 1873
     p 400-406.

facilities by other educational institutions and
mining companies.

"The United States Bureau of Mines was established in the public interest to conduct inquir-
ies and scientific and technologic investigations
concerning mining and the preparation, treatment,
and utilization of mineral substances; to promote
health and safety in the mineral industries; to
conserve mineral resources and prevent their
waste; to further economic development and to increase efficiency in the mining, metallurgical,
quarrying, and other mineral industries; and to
inquire into the economic conditions affecting
these industries. The organic act of the Bureau,
as amended by Congress and approved February 25,
1913, made it the province and duty of the Bureau
to disseminate information concerning these subjects in such manner as will best carry out the
purpose of this Act," [4]. The continuing effort
of the Bureau of Mines in the area of minerals
beneficiation research has been felt in most of
the minerals processing plants of the world.
The dissemination of technical information
through free or nominally priced bulletins has
been thorough and is gratefully accepted by all
minerals engineers.

Early private laboratories such as A.D.Little
and non-profit foundations such as Mellon Institute
offered some services in the field of minerals
beneficiation but it was not until the founding
of Battelle Memorial Institute in 1929 that a
large integrated facility was made available to
the mineral industry. This institution has had
a part in many of the largest mineral beneficiation research programs undertaken during the past
quarter century.

Iron Ore Research

The impact of the taconite beneficiation problem on the iron ore producing companies resulted

---

(4) Stratton, H.J. and M.E. Winslow:List of Pub-
    lications of the Bureau of Mines, July 1,
    1910 - Jan. 1, 1949, U. S. Govt. Printing
    Office, 1950, 460 pp.

in establishment of several privately owned ore
research laboratories. These were initially
designed for both fundamental and applied research on iron ores. As the value of a well-
planned ore research program became apparent to
some of the steel firms which sponsored these
laboratories, work was initiated on other mineral
products which are used in the production of iron
and steel. These included limestone, chromium
ores, nickel ores, solid mineral fuels and minerals used in refractories.

As iron ore beneficiation methods increase in
complexity and demands of the iron and steel
furnaces become more exacting, expansion of iron
ore research facilities will be required.

ADDITIONAL REFERENCES

Hersam, E.A.:The Status of Research in Ore Dressing, U.S. Bur. Mines Rept. of Inv. 2669R, 1925, 48 pp.

Dietrich, W.F. et al:Ore Dressing Tests and Their Significance, U.S. Bur. Mines Rept. of Inv. 3328, 1937, 161 pp.

Doerner, H.A.:Centrifugal Concentration, Its Theory, Mechanical Development and Experimental Results, U.S. Bur. Mines Technical Paper 457, 1929, 39 pp.

Hillebrand, W.F.:The Analysis of Silicate and Carbonate Rocks, U.S. Geol. Survey Bulletin 700, 1919.

Egleston, T.:Analysis of Rocks, Trans. AIME vol 3, May 1874 to Feb. 1875, p 94-98.

del Giudice, G.R.M.:Microscopy in Flotation Research, Trans. AIME vol 112, 1934, p 424-448.

Roberts, E.J.:Colloidal Chemistry of Pulp Thickening, ibid, p 178-188.

Maxson, W.L., F. Cadena and F.C. Bond:Grindability of Various Ores, ibid, p 130-145.

Bond, F.C.and W.L. Maxson:Crushing and Grinding Characteristics as Determined from Screen Analyses, ibid, p 146-160.

Schuhmann, R.:Cleanliness Achieved in New Crushing Laboratory, Eng. Mining Jnl. vol 143, Sept. 1942, p 59-61.

DeRycker, H. and M. Rey:The Haultain Superpanner Improved, Eng. & Mining Jnl., vol 141, Dec. 1940, p 47.

Clemmer, J.B. and B.H. Clemmons:An Improved Flotation Test Cell, Eng. & Mining Jnl. vol 144, March 1943, p 72-73.

Black, M.:A Jones Riffle for Sampling Wet Pulps, Eng. & Mining Jnl. vol 145, May 1944, p 88.

Fahrenwald, A.W.:Batch Flotation Test--When and How to Use It, Eng. & Mining Jnl. vol 146, Jan. 1945, p 74-76.

Hanley, H.R.:Experimental Sintering Pot Perfected for Ore Tests, Eng. & Mining Jnl. vol 146, April 1945, p 111.

Wiser, O.:A Safe, Effective Roaster for Sulphide
Ore Tests, Eng. & Mining Jnl. vol 147, July 1946
p 65.

Anon:Radioactive Tracers--How They Can Be Used in
Flotation Research, Eng. & Mining Jnl. vol 149,
March 1948, p 53-55.

Gaudin, A.M.:Improving Flotation of Non-Sulphide
Minerals, Eng. & Mining Jnl. vol 146, Dec. 1945,
p 91-95.

Kiser, J.E.:Drill Cores Logged by Color Photography, Eng. & Mining Jnl. vol 146, Sept. 1946,
p 82-84.

Dobbel, C.A.:Photography for Improved Drill-Core
Records, Eng. & Mining Jnl. vol 145, May 1944,
p 86-87.

Chief of the Air Corps:Basic Photography, War
Dept. Technical Manual No. 1-219, July 1, 1941,
Washington, D.C.

Anon:Photography, Vol. I and Vol. II, Navy Train-
ing Courses Edition of 1947, Navy Dept. Washington, D.C.

Tuttle, H.B.:Color Movies for the Beginner, Ziff-
Davis Publishing Co., New York, 1941.

Anon:Kodak Reference Handbook, Eastman Kodak Co.,
Rochester, N.Y.

Roe, L.A.:Photographing Extinguisher Sprays, Natl.
Fire Protection Association Quarterly, vol 46,
October, 1952, p 136-138.

Anon:An Aerosol Camera, Research for Industry,
vol 5, No. 5, July, 1953, p 4-6, 8.

Waddell, J.H.and J.W. Waddell:Photographic Motion Analysis--Underwater Photography, Industrial Laboratories vol 5, Nov. 1954, p 101-108;
Flow of Solids, Liquids and Gases, ibid, Jan.
1955, p 43-50.

Faugust, W.D.:Photomicrography Simplified, Industrial Laboratories, vol 7, April 1956, p 122-125.

Broadston, J.A.:Measuring and Designating Surface
Finish, The Iron Age, Oct. 26, 1944, p 76-81.

Bennett, A.H. et al:Phase Microscopy, Trans. of
the American Microscopical Society, vol 65,
April 1946, p 99-131.

Bates, T.F.:The Electron Microscope Applied to
Geological Research, Trans. of The N.Y. Acad.
Sciences, Ser. II, vol 11, No. 4, Feb. 1949,
p 100-107.

Dayton, R. W.:Theory and Use of the Metallurgical
Polarization Microscope, AIME Tech. Publication
593, 1935, 32 pp.

Wright:Examination of Ores and Metals in Polari-
zed Light, Proc. Amer. Phil. Soc. vol 58, 1919,
p 401.

Faust, G.T.:A Polarizing Comparison-Microscope
For Use In Petrographic Measurements, U.S. Bur.
Mines Rept. of Inv. 3503, April 1940,   7 pp.

Munson, G.A. and E.P. Barrett:Quantitative Esti-
mation of Potash and Soda Feldspars In Pegmatite Rock by Means of Chemical Coloration, U.S.
Bur. Mines Inf. Circular 7412, July 1947, 5 pp.

Gibbs, H.L. and L.G. Evans:Improvements in Methods
for Preparing Thin Sections of Rock, U.S. Bur.
Mines Rept. of Inv. 4711, June 1950, 6 pp.

Stone, D.E. et al:Investigation of a Photoelec-
tric Device for the Determination of Low Concen-
trations of Dust, U.S. Bur. Mines Rept. of Inv.
4782, March 1951, 6 pp.

Jenkins, J.E., D. R. Buchele and R.A. Long:A Spec-
ially Constructed Metallograph for Use At Elevated Temperatures, Natl. Advisory Committee for
Aeronautics Research Memorandum E51G12, Sept. 11,
1951, Washington D.C.

Rogers, A.F. and P.F. Kerr:Optical Mineralogy,
McGraw-Hill Book Co. N.Y. 1942, 390 pp.

Winchell, A.N.:Elements of Optical Mineralogy,
Part I. Principles and Methods, 262 pp; Part II
Descriptions of Minerals, 459 pp; Part III De-
terminative Tables, 231 pp., John Wiley & Sons,
Inc. N.Y. 1937.

Dallavalle, J.M.:Micromeritics (Second Edition),
Pitman Publishing Corp. N.Y. 1948.

Bond, F.C.:Standard Grindability Tests Tabulated,
Trans. AIME vol 183, 1949, p 313-329.

Norman, T.E. and C.M. Loeb:Wear Tests on Grinding
Balls, Trans. AIME vol 183, 1949, p 330-360.

Spedden, H.R. and W.S. Hannan:Attachment of Mineral Particles to Air Bubbles in Flotation,
Trans. AIME vol 183, 1949, p 208-213.

Arbiter, N:Flotation Rates and Flotation Efficiency, Mining Eng. vol 190, Sept. 1951, p 791-796.

Gaudin, A.M.:Flotation, McGraw-Hill Book Co.,
N.Y., 1932, 552 pp.

Morris, T.M.:Measurement and Evaluation of the
Rate of Flotation as a Function of Particle
Size, Mining Eng. vol 4, Aug. 1952, p 794-798.

Schellinger, A.K.:Solid Surface Energy and Calorimetric Determinations of Surface-Energy Relationships for Some Common Minerals, Mining Eng.
vol 4, April 1952, p 369-374.

Moyd, L.:Determination of the Coefficient of Lin-
ear Thermal Expansion of Rock Speciments by Means
of Resistance Wire (SR-4) Strain Gauges, Mining
Eng. vol 187, June 1950, p 683-684.

Spohn, Dr. E.J.:High Temperature Laboratory Furnaces, Rock Products vol 52, Nov. 1949, p 58-
59, 86.

Hamilton, F.M. and H.F. Ameen:Laboratory Studies
on Iron Ore Sintering and Testing, Mining Eng.
vol 187, Dec. 1950, p 1275-1282.

Schellinger, A.K.:A Calorimetric Method for Studying Grinding in a Tumbling Medium, Mining Eng.
vol 190, June 1951, p 518-522.

Anon:For Long Range Iron Ore Research, Eng. &
Mining Jnl. vol 149, May 1948, p 101.

Bush, G.P.:Bibliography on Research Administra-
tion, The Univ. Press of Washington D.C., 146 pp.

Turner, H.S.:How Much Should a Company Spend on
Research, Harvard Business Review, May-June,
1954, p 101-112.

Bureau of Labor Statistics, U.S. Dept. of Labor:
Scientific Research and Development in American
Industry--A Study of Manpower and Costs, U.S.
Govt. Printing Office, 1953, 106 pp.

Research-A National Resource. Part I - Relation
of The Federal Government to Research (1938);
Part II - Industrial Research, (1941) Report
of the National Research Council to The National
Resources Planning Board.

Bush, V.:Science--The Endless Frontier, A report
to the President on a program for postwar scientific research, July 1945, 184 pp.

INDEX

A

C